THE
GLASGOW REGION

A General Survey

Edited by

RONALD MILLER AND JOY TIVY

*Prepared for the meeting of the British
Association, held from the 27th of
August to the 3rd of September in*

GLASGOW

1958

PRINTED IN GREAT BRITAIN

Set in Monotype Bembo 12 *point by*
T. & A. CONSTABLE LTD., Edinburgh

LOCAL EXECUTIVE COMMITTEE

Chairman
THE RT. HON. THE LORD PROVOST OF GLASGOW

Vice-Chairman
SIR HECTOR HETHERINGTON, K.B.E., D.L.,
Principal of the University of Glasgow

Local Honorary Secretaries
ROBERT T. HUTCHESON, O.B.E., J.P.,
Registrar and Secretary of Court, University of Glasgow

T. WEIR, M.B.E., D.L.,
The Lord Provost's Secretary

Local Honorary Treasurer
LESLIE G. WATT
Assistant Secretary of Court, University of Glasgow

ACKNOWLEDGEMENTS

THE Editors acknowledge with gratitude the assistance of the following:

Mr Ian Kinniburgh, of the Department of Geography, the University of Glasgow, for most of the cartography;

The Editors and authors of The Third Statistical Account of Glasgow, and other counties in the West of Scotland, for access to unpublished material;

The Controller of H.M. Stationery Office for permission to publish maps and diagrams based on Ordnance and Geological Survey Maps and other publications;

T. & A. Constable Ltd., Edinburgh (printers), and Hislop & Day Ltd., Edinburgh (blockmakers), for their friendly co-operation and advice;

Miss Catherine B. Smith, of the Department of Geography, University of Glasgow, for her valuable clerical and editorial work.

CONTENTS

ix

LIST OF PLATES

LIST OF FIGURES

LIST OF TABLES

FOREWORD

THE Editors are well aware that at an annual meeting in a centre as populous as Glasgow only half of the members will be visitors, the others will be local people; the Handbook must therefore serve a double purpose. It must not only introduce the region to the visitor but also give the local reader food for thought. Our visitors are likely to know little of us: Glasgow does not rank as a tourist attraction; the Glorious Twelfth takes them to the North, the Royal and Ancient to the East and the Festival to Another Place. Local people, on the other hand, will soon have available The Third Statistical Account of Glasgow with its exhaustive detail and comprehensive cover.

The Editors do not imagine that either visitors or natives will read this Handbook from cover to cover—rather will it be dipped into at a point corresponding to the reader's special interest. Thus while the volume as a whole is designed to give a balanced general picture of the region, the individual essays, at the cost of a little overlap, are also entities and within reason can be read in any order.

THE GEOGRAPHY OF THE GLASGOW REGION

Ronald Miller

Professor of Geography, University of Glasgow

Sir Halford Mackinder, a founder of modern Geography and sometime Member for the Camlachie Division of Glasgow, said when asked his opinion on the future of Glasgow: 'It seems to me that on this subject there is only one thing which can be said with certainty and it is that the geographical circumstances which in the past have conduced to the growth of the city would not in this twentieth century suffice to create anew in this locality a great centre of activity, if for any reason, whether of military defeat or economic strife Glasgow were now to cease to flourish.' He linked Glasgow with London and Manchester as examples of cities which owe their greatness to momentum from the past. We can, of course, trace many geographical influences shaping the development of the city and region, but the enormous Clydeside conurbation of today has in many ways transformed its physical environment and it is to a great extent an illustration of the parable of the talents: unto him that hath shall be given. Wealth, hands and brains have won, extracted and created more wealth—nothing succeeds like success.

The prevalent street-canyons and smoky atmosphere of Glasgow rarely reveal the remarkable siting of the city. It lies on the floor of what would be called in east Scotland a Howe—a hollow place—ringed around by bleak plateaus. Though traversed from south-east to north-west by the Clyde, this Howe is more than simply the valley flats of the river: it is a true intermontane basin. For example, it expands north-eastwards to a degree quite disproportionate to the size of the tributary—the Kelvin—draining this embayment of the Howe: again, unlike a normal valley, it does not open out downstream, but on the contrary is almost closed at Bowling, where the modest height of the Erskine plateau on the left bank faces the formidable escarpment of the Kilpatrick Hills on the right. It is indeed very firmly encircled except on the east and has in fact only four rather narrow outlets at altitudes under 400 feet. We must remember, too, that the 'Lowlands' of Scotland are all too seldom low, that bleak high ground is only too common, and therefore a low and sheltered basin such as this must have been attractive to man at quite an early date. Floored by glacial sands, gravels and clays, soils were generally of considerable potential. Some of the glacial deposits take the form of drumlins, of which there is a swarm in the lower part of the Howe (Fig. 1), and these little hills provide better natural drainage. The finest-grained soils are on the flats flanking the river, but drainage there was difficult.

With its mild moist climate, the Howe would in primitive times be well wooded: the surrounding plateaus, however, subject to the rapid diminution of temperatures with height in the oceanic climate, would then, as now, carry only peaty moorland and therefore be open country. The earliest settlement thus would not be in the Howe, and

A

1

it is significant that the ancient capital of Strathclyde was not within it but on the rock-fortress of Dumbarton. As man evolved from hunting to agriculture, so he would progressively colonise the Howe, felling the woods and tilling the soil.

Within the well-favoured Howe, the first settlements would no doubt be nucleated in relation to the available routeways. Of these, the most important was probably that from Clydesdale to the estuary and so on to the Highlands. This route from the south bifurcates downstream of Lanark, one route holding to the left bank and debouching on the Howe at the ancient burgh of Rutherglen. The right bank road, probably used by the Romans, crosses the Howe to Dumbarton, which commands the north-west exit. It is perhaps significant that Glasgow is centrally placed on it. The routes entering from the south-west, the major by Lochwinnoch and the minor by Lugton Water, meet at Paisley. From there, making directly for the north, the Clyde would be crossed at the ancient royal burgh of Renfrew. For a ford usable at all times of tide, and for the lowest bridging point on the river, the route had however to go up to Glasgow. The antiquities of Govan Old Church, set in its circular yard, suggest an early and important crossing, or head of navigation. These were the five ancient centres then: Rutherglen, Paisley, Renfrew, Govan and Glasgow; scarcely even villages, for they were but simple foci in the rural Howe. One of them, Glasgow, was at the lowest bridging-point of the river, and thus exercised a function which has been reason enough for many a town to flourish. It may be that we need look no further in seeking to explain why Glasgow out-grew its neighbours. But Glasgow had yet another function, one which set it clearly ahead of its rivals. Govan might go back to earliest times; Rutherglen might be the senior burgh; the King's eldest son might take his baronial title from Renfrew; Paisley might have its Abbey; Glasgow, however, had a Cathedral.

It is impossible to say with certainty what considerations located the Cathedral in Glasgow. The region must have been populous enough to justify the presence of a Bishop. It may be that St Mungo and later the Church and King simply recognised the focal value of Glasgow and founded accordingly. When we examine the building itself, however, we find that it is on a most curious and awkward site. The long axis is on ground plunging from west to east so that the eastern half of the edifice is two-storeyed, and indeed three-storeyed if the chapter house and crypt chapels are included. The Blackadder chapel, too, representing a south transept, is one storey below the nave. These complications are necessary in order to bring the high altar of the medieval church over the tomb of the Celtic saint, Mungo, and we may therefore suppose that the site, to justify all this inconvenience, was one of outstanding sanctity. Tradition indeed connects with it also the burial of St Fergus and residence by St Ninian and St Columba, the two founders of Christianity in Scotland. It is possible, therefore, that the very special sanctity of the site attracted the Cathedral and so set Glasgow above its neighbours. Even if the influence of the saint was not so great and more practical con-siderations account for the pre-eminence of Glasgow, it would seem at least to be responsible for the precise location of the Cathedral and thus for its unique form. The choice of symbols of the St Mungo legends for the city's coat of arms suggests, however, that the cult was of real significance. The great importance of the Cathedral to Glasgow lay, of course, not only in the presence of the Bishop and Chapter, but in the existence of a market and fair. In this respect, Glasgow is in a class with Chartres, Paris, Amiens, Aachen and other 'Bishop's Towns'.

2

FIG. 1. The Site of Glasgow.

OVER 300 FEET

200–300 FEET

OVER 100 FEET

LIMIT OF
LOWER TERRACE

LIMIT OF
HIGH TERRACE

GLASGOW IN 1778

N

ONE MILE

FIG. 1

THE SITE OF
GLASGOW

CLYDE

KELVIN

CART

3

The charter of King William the Lion of 1176 decrees 'Know ye all that I have given and granted my absolute protection to all those who shall come to the markets of Glasgow, which I have granted (in 1174) to God and St Kentigern (St Mungo) and the burgh of Glasgow, in coming there, standing there and returning thence, provided they behave themselves according to the laws and customs of my burghs and Kingdom.' It is difficult to exaggerate the importance of an established market: it attracts both buyers and sellers, for each wishes to find the optimum trading conditions. The annual July Glasgow Fair was added in 1190 and must have been of enormous significance in the region for it still flourishes vigorously in the form of a 'Trades holiday' period. To these regular markets we may confidently attribute the origins of the commercial development of Glasgow with its strong Merchants' House and the accumulation of capital which has multiplied to such good purpose over the centuries.

The status of 'city' was of great economic value, for the influence of the bishops—lords of Glasgow—who were often also high officials at court—Chancellors, Treasurers and the like—saw to it that the city was protected from claims of superiority in trade by its neighbouring royal burghs and that its status was in practice second to none. But the Church enriched Glasgow in another respect: it procured the founding of the University. While the event may have been merely the outcome of a jealous desire of the Bishop to be even with his brother of St Andrews, who had recently been granted a University, we may note that the Papal Bull of 1450 recognises Glasgow as 'a place well suited and adapted to that purpose on account of the healthiness of the climate and the plenty of victuals and of everything necessary for the use of man'. While the early college did not perhaps distinguish itself greatly and had to await the dissolution of the old Church for its re-erection, it has not only served sound learning but made some outstanding contributions to the economic and industrial life of the city. Adam Smith, Watt, Kelvin—and our President this year, Sir Alexander Fleck—all prominent in economic life, are of the University; and it was another Professor, Anderson, who, in his zeal for popular education and the practical application of science, founded the institution which has contributed so much in this respect and grown so notably into the Royal College of Science and Technology.

But although the diocese of Glasgow extended as far as the Tweed Valley and became an archbishopric, all this did not make Glasgow more than a very small provincial town of under 3,000 souls, and at no time did it ever come near to rivalling certain eastern towns as capital of Scotland. It was far west, and until the discovery and opening up of America this meant it was on the outer fringe of Europe. Trade flourished in the North Sea, not the Atlantic, and so it was eastern Scotland that owned the ships, traded with the Staple and was familiar with the Low Countries. Politically, England was by far the most important neighbour both in war and peace. Routes over the Border, by which armies and raiders moved so often, led primarily into the east, as did especially the easiest route, the coast route, by which the heavily armoured English invaders could be supplied by sea. Figure 2 shows how these routes focus on Edinburgh, which thereby becomes the obvious base for the civil power. Glasgow is nearly twice as far from the Border and stands aside from the main stream of affairs of this period. The troubled and bloody history of Scotland was worked out on a scene that rarely included Glasgow. Stirling, Perth, Falkirk and Edinburgh witness the strife of Kings and Nobles, and it is no accident that the two great battles in Scottish history, Bannock-

4

burn and Flodden, are in the east. Border churches and abbeys were destroyed by the English, never Glasgow or Paisley. It is only in relation to the Norse power in the Hebrides that the region occupied a frontier rôle, and this phase was quickly ended with the defeat of Haakon at Largs in 1263. Though there are tombstones in Govan Old

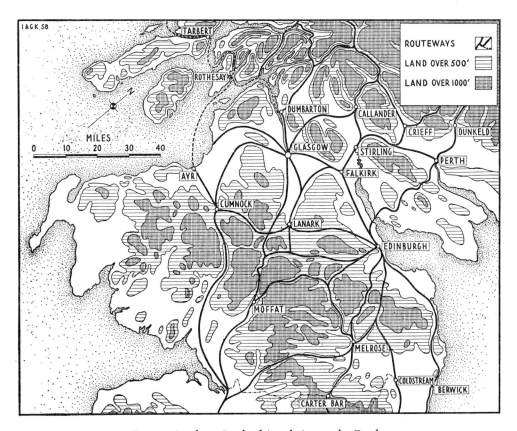

FIG. 2. Southern Scotland in relation to the Border.

Church which are of Norse type, the Clyde of the time apparently did not permit of Norse raids as far as Glasgow.

It was no loss to stand aside from Scottish history: the relative peace and tranquillity of the town may well have contributed substantially to the firm establishment of commercial and industrial skill and experience as well as permitting the accumulation of capital. Glasgow avoided power politics on more than one occasion and profited accordingly. It is significant that on the contrary one of Glasgow's least prosperous periods was when she became heavily involved in the religious strife of the seventeenth century.

Early Glasgow was on a simple plan—a cross of Lorraine extending north-east from the ford (Fig. 3), with the Molendinar burn flanking it closely on the east. The Cathedral and Bishop's Castle and the manses of the clergy were on the high ground at the head of the main High Street axis, and the top bar of the double cross was represented

5

by Rottenrow and Drygate, a portion of the Lanark-Dumbarton trunk route parallel to the river. This is the 'Townheid', the cathedral close in the large sense (Pl. II). This area, however, grew only very slowly and was quite outpaced by the lower bar of the cross, the Tron Gait and Gallow Gait, where the lay city had its focus. No doubt in early times

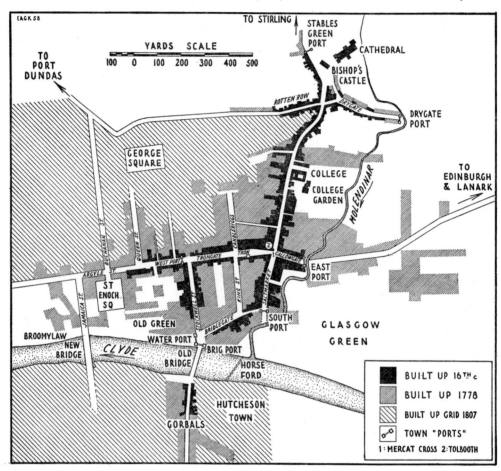

FIG. 3. The first three major stages in the growth of Glasgow : 1. Medieval ; 2. slow growth to the end of the eighteenth century ; 3. first phase of modern rapid growth—the gridded town.

the flat ground near the river was marshy and wooded, and the trunk route therefore avoided it and also responded to the attraction of the Cathedral. With the progressive clearing and improvement of the site, however, ease of movement on the lower ground and the proximity of the river drew traffic and business and commercial Glasgow came to be centred on the Mercat Cross with the Tolbooth (Town Hall) and Tron (public weighbridge) nearby. The deferred junction of the Molendinar burn with the Clyde may have been responsible for the siting of the first bridge not on but *downstream* of the prolongation of the High Street-Saltmarket axis, or it may be that the bridge was intended to supplement, not supersede, the ford. Whatever the reason, the bridge was offset and the Brig Gait (now Bridgegate) was created to link it to the main street. The

6

direct line from the bridge to the Tron Gait created Stockwell Street and completed the basic plan that was to serve Glasgow for centuries (Pl. Ia). The swift little Molendinar served to turn the town mills, but not reliably, for water often was lacking in summer. The Clyde was wide, sandy-bottomed and shallow, only some fifteen inches deep at low water, but liable on occasions to disastrous floods, and was of more use at first for water supply and salmon fishing than for navigation. Indeed, Glasgow records are punctuated by ineffectual efforts to deepen or maintain the channel. Commissioner Tucker, reporting to his master, Cromwell, wrote in 1656: 'The situation of this towne in a plentifull land, and the mercantile genius of the people, are strong signes of her increase and groweth, were she not checqued and kept under by the shallownesse of her river, every day more and more increasing and filling up, soe that noe vessells of any burden can come neerer up than within fourteene miles, where they must unlade, and send up theyr timber and Norway trade in rafts or floats and all other comodityes by three or four tonnes of goods at a time, in small cobbles or boates of three, four, five, and none of above six tons a boate.' Irvine, on the Ayrshire coast, was Glasgow's seaport, and communication was maintained by pack-horse. Irvine's estuary harbour, however, had a continual struggle with sand and there can have been little temptation to Glasgow merchants to invest heavily in it or to move there. Glasgow's offer to make Dumbarton its outport was snubbed by the magistrates, who felt that the town was better off without mariners.

The Clyde and its estuary, however, led into what we now know as the Clyde Sea Area, a suite of veritable fiords running back into the Argyllshire highland plateau in such a way as to render a large area tributary to the Firth. Rothesay and Tarbert (Loch Fyne), on the through route to the Isles, had royal castles. These waters form a favoured marine habitat teeming, until modern times, with herring. The humble herring is so commonplace that its importance can easily be overlooked. Originally with oatmeal, and later with potatoes, it formed a very wholesome and cheap diet and was until quite recently the staple food of the people. Salt herring are indeed still to be had in Glasgow shops. The abundance of good-quality herring in the Firth—'Loch Fyne' is synonymous with 'high quality'—contributed in no small measure to the prosperity of the region. Gibson notes in 1777 its importance after porridge and barley broth: 'three pounds of these (potatoes) boiled with a couple of salted herrings do not exceed in value one penny half-penny and are a sufficient dinner for any labouring man whatever; add to this, that the healthfulness of this food cannot possibly be called in question, for there is no set of people in the world more healthy than the mechanics in Glasgow, and yet potatoes and herrings are daily made use of, by a very great number of them, for a considerable time of the year'. When salted, herring keep indefinitely and are easily transported. They are thus an obvious item of commerce, and we do in fact find Glasgow sending great quantities of them abroad, particularly to southern lands. In return, came salt, barrel staves and hoops, wine and exotic dried fruits. This was no mean contribution to the commerce of the region, and in addition the catching of and traffic in herring bred a stock of seamen and boat-builders. The fishing also forms, perhaps, Glasgow's initial contact with the Highlands, a contact that has linked Argyll firmly into the region. (Glasgow is now the most convenient centre for that County's Council meetings.) Indeed, the herring has more right to appear on the arms of Glasgow city than the salmon!

The geographical factors so far considered account only for a small, but active, town of merchants subjoined to a Cathedral whose Bishop was soon to flee before the Reformers. But nearly seventy years before this latter event, the discovery of America profoundly changed Glasgow's situation. From being on the extreme westerly flank of the civilised world she now faced a new and economically interesting continent and was in a position to be middleman between Old and New Worlds. After slow, and even false starts—the South Sea Bubble of the Darien disaster cost Glasgow dear—the city cornered the nascent chemical industry (soap), the sale of sugar for the greater part of Scotland, and the distilling of rum. It had some, mostly illicit, trading contacts in the New World and at home had developed its own private outport at Port Glasgow. When the Act of Union of 1707 brought free access to the English Colonies, Glasgow was therefore ready and able to exploit her favourable situation. Gibson writes in 1777, 'we may from this era date the prosperity of the city of Glasgow; whatever efforts the inhabitants had made, for the introduction and extension of commerce prior to this time, they were but trifling and unimportant; by the Union, the trade to America was laid open, the inhabitants were sensible of their advantageous situation on the west coast, and they began almost immediately to prosecute this commerce'. Apart from geographical situation, the region had a special reason for an early interest in the American tobacco trade—many of the settlers already there had come from the south-west of Scotland, having been transported to the Plantations for their part in the religious disturbances. Their Glasgow trading compatriots were devout Presbyterians also, who attributed much of their success, in competition with the English, to their frugality and sober attention to business.

To freight the tobacco ships on their outward voyages, manufactures developed: some assorted goods including ironmongery, suitable for pioneers, but above all textiles, beginning with the traditional flax and wool and changing and expanding later into a strong emphasis on cotton. Glasgow flourished as never before: some of her merchants became fabulously wealthy and the 'Tobacco Lords' set the pace in building, in style and in enterprise. Gibson records 'how streets have been laid out, and houses built with a taste and elegance unknown in former times . . . the manner of living is far better in general, and a cleanliness and neatness in dress and in furniture are now almost universal'. These advances were, of course, not confined to Glasgow. Greenock, a new foundation conveniently situated at the lowest sheltered anchorage on the estuary, participated most briskly in the trade and indeed was the main centre of shipping.

The cotton industry, begun in the cottages of the region, gradually became concentrated as machinery and water power were introduced. Roads were being built and 'for the conveniency of their trade to the eastern side of the island' an Act was obtained in 1767 for a canal from the Clyde to the Forth, and with a branch to Glasgow. Owing to the co-operation of financiers in Edinburgh and elsewhere, this was projected on a greater scale than might otherwise have been the case. In 1771 another Act followed, authorising a canal 'from the coalleries in the parishes of Old and New Monkland, to the city of Glasgow'. The branch canal to Glasgow took off at quite a high level, presumably for the convenience of traffic with the Forth, and therefore entered the northern outskirts of the town at Hamilton Hill, now Port Dundas. This may imply that no high hopes were then entertained of deepening the river to any great extent.

But this new-found prosperity received a sharp shock with the American revolt

Pl. Ia.   GLASGOW, 1768, from the south-west (McUre's *History* 2nd Ed.)

Cathedral on edge of drumlins in background; merchants' town on river flats below. Broomielaw left, with boats; glassworks, (conical kiln smoking), Old Glasgow Green with trees; Ramshorn and Tron Kirks behind. To the right of the Cathedral the spires are University, Blackfriars, Tolbooth, Merchants' House and St Andrew's on right. The village of Gorbals in right foreground conceals Glasgow Bridge. See Figure 3.

Pl. Ib.   UNIVERSITY OF GLASGOW, INNER COURT

Fine Art Exhibition by the Foulis' Academy of Fine Art on the occasion of the Coronation of George III in 1761. The smoke is from a bonfire in the High Street. Reproduced from Macgeorge, *Old Glasgow*, Blackie, 1880.

Pl. II.
GLASGOW
CATHEDRAL,
from the south-east.
Molendinar valley
across foreground:
Firhill bottom right.
Townhead left
centre with High
Street coming in on
left, Drygate from
bottom left, Rotten-
row from top left.
Open space centre
was site of Bishop's
Castle. Royal Infir-
mary behind Cathe-
dral. Port Dundas
top right. See Figure
3.

D. L. Stewart, Giffnock

PL. III.
THE CLYDE, downstream from main docks

Left bank: immediate foreground, graving docks; centre and foreground, Harland and Wolff ship-building and fitting-out basin with Govan Cross and Govan Old Church beyond. Fairfield shipbuilding yard with big cranes and Alexander Stephen's shipbuilding yard top left. *Right bank:* Yorkhill Quay in foreground; Kelvin River, centre, with Inglis' shipyard (small ships). Vacant ground beyond resulting from pre-war extinction by rationalisation of a shipyard. Meadowside Quay and Granary in near distance, Merklands Quay (Irish cattle) beyond; Barclay Curle's shipyard in distance. Top right, Partick and Scotstoun with Jordanhill in corner.

Aero-Pictorial Ltd.

Pl. IV. GLASGOW: THE INNER HARBOUR, looking east

Broomielaw, Anderston and Lancefield Quays on left; Kingston Dock and General Terminus Quay on right (equipped in 1957 with ore-handling installation). The nearest bridge is the newest, George V Bridge, flanked by railway bridge (leading to Central Station on left) which conceals the principal bridge, Glasgow Bridge. Beyond, Victoria Bridge on the site of the earliest bridge, then a railway bridge (leading to St Enoch Station, end-on beyond Central Station) and lastly the modern Albert Bridge on the site of the old ford. Glasgow Green forms open space beyond and in right distance industrial plants of the Dalmarnock area. Right centre, Gorbals; left centre, east half of Argyle Street.

in 1775 which terminated Britain's legal monopoly of trade with the Colonies. Many merchants were ruined, but the region had developed sufficient momentum and capital to carry it forward in face of this check. Trade and industry had become soundly based and the exploitation of natural resources of coal and iron was beginning to be significant. It was just at this crucial period, also, that another important alteration of the physical scene took place, a veritable transformation of the geographical setting. After initial failures with the problem of deepening the Clyde to Glasgow, the English expert Golborne was eventually called in. Presumably he discovered that the Clyde ran not over a solid bed but on sand, marls and clays. If the Clyde bed had been solid, nothing could have been done to deepen it with the resources of the period, but, as it was, Golborne's simple scheme proved most effective. He built jetties to confine the wide, shallow, and in places branching Clyde, and by raking the bed assisted the now swifter current to scour out the loose material and carry it down into the Firth. He contracted, in 1773, to achieve a depth of six feet ten inches: by 1775, the very year of the American revolt, the constricted river had dug a seven-foot-eight-inch channel on the hitherto intransigent Dumbuck Ford near Dumbarton. Originally there had been, at low water, only two feet of water and even less at the Broomielaw. An immediate result of this work was that a vessel with a draught of six feet could reach the city on the tide, and it is little wonder that a jubilant Town Council gave him a handsome cash bonus and a silver cup. He should have had a gold cup six years later, for the depth was then fourteen feet! This transformed the situation, of course, and by bringing ocean-going ships right into the centre of the Howe, opened up far more possibilities than if they had been restricted to Greenock or Port Glasgow, both somewhat peripheral and sharply restricted as to site by the Renfrew plateaus which rise so sharply above their cramped raised-beach sites. (See Plates IV and X.)

Golborne's achievement had far-reaching consequences. He had shown that the river *could* be deepened and the work was steadily pressed forward until, after some difficulty with rock at Elderslie, the present virtual ship-canal was achieved. Further, instead of low, shelving, insubstantial, sandy banks, the eventual linking by a training wall of Golborne's jetties and the infilling of the spaces between them gave a firm, substantial and roomy platform for industrial and commercial development convenient to sea transport. It was, in effect, an advance example of the kind of thing that we regard as a feature of our modern industrial estates—the provision of facilities *before* industry moves in. Moreover, the deepening works had a perhaps unforeseen but enormously beneficial effect; they lowered the level of the river at the Broomielaw by some eight feet, and the river which in its unregenerate days used to cause devastating floods on the river flats (see Fig. 1), inundating the lower parts of the town, was now safely confined within its banks. So much of the bottom of the Howe is on the lower river flat and so much of this now carries industrial and commercial installations that it is difficult to envisage the economic value of this new-found freedom from flooding. Lastly, this lowering of the river at the Broomielaw gave the section above the adjacent weir at Glasgow Green a considerable 'head' and thus enabled the east side of Glasgow to draw on it by leets for water for use in industry. Probably this is the main reason why Glasgow's fraction of the textile industry was concentrated on this side of the town (see Fig. 38 and Pl. XV).

All this development took time, labour and capital, and its full achievement is relatively recent. Only 140 years ago, there was still as much quay space (and depth of water) at Port Dundas as at the Broomielaw, and the Custom House at the latter place is only 120 years old. But it must have been a great stimulus to effort and must have contributed to the buoyancy of thought and economic effort in the region. The environment had been transformed by man's effort: 'Glasgow made the Clyde': progress was inevitable: all was for the best in the best of all possible worlds and in this vigorous and stimulating economic climate it only remained for 'the Clyde to make Glasgow'.

Truly, 'unto him that hath shall be given'. The flourishing cotton industry stimulated the development of new methods of processing and so the region gave birth to a great chemical industry. The need for water for processing caused the Vale of Leven, where the pure waters flowing from Loch Lomond were so convenient, to become a subsidiary conurbation. The mechanisation of industry brought forth developments in the steam engine in which James Watt of the University was so prominent. Trade required ships and the building of wooden sailing ships in the estuary expanded in response. The new steam engines required much iron: it was there in great quantity in the blackband ores. When Mushet discovered their possibilities and Neilson's hot blast in 1828 made it possible to exploit them effectively, the accumulated skill of the local coal-mining and iron industries, which had been working quietly through the previous century, was able to achieve a spectacular expansion. For the first time, local natural resources became prominent in the economy and mark yet another milestone in the evolution of the region. These vast quantities of cheap iron became available at precisely the right moment. Machines, especially steam engines, were developing fast. The latter were being applied to propulsion both on land and sea. This stimulated the production of rails, bridges, rolling stock and, above all, locomotives. It was only a step for the region to export the same commodities to the rest of the world, which was in most cases at least one phase behind in both invention and mass production of these commodities. The vast trade needed new ships, and since the trade was with the other side of the world, huge ships. Iron, then steel and the new steam power were applied to them. Clydeside raced ahead of the rest of the world in this type of shipbuilding, and from furnishing its own shipping lines—no small order—it passed on to building the world's big ships. Steam power had already made possible the deepening of the Elderslie barrier and had powered the tugs which brought the ships to the heart of the Howe and so the *Port* of Glasgow also grew to major stature (Pl. III).

There was no holding the expansion: financial crises of the mid-nineteenth century were overcome, and when the American Civil War almost completely ruined the cotton industry—the life-blood of the economy for so long—developments in other directions filled the breach. Success bred success; the great transatlantic liners became first floating hotels and then veritable small towns, with demands in every direction outside engineering, for furniture, carpets, bedding, cutlery and the like, and industries providing these auxiliaries came into being. It is no coincidence that the Coronation carpet was made in Glasgow: the scale and quality required were comparable rather to the public rooms of a great liner than of a private house.

But in spite of a proliferation of auxiliary industries, the accent remained strongly on heavy industry—on industry using great quantities of steel in proportion to the labour involved: large ships, railway installations, pipe-lines, bridges and other heavy constructional work are all Clydeside specialties. There would no doubt have been, as elsewhere in Britain, an evolution away from this, but the two world wars with their enormous expenditure of ships, guns, shells, railways and the like confirmed Clydeside in these specialties. But the blackband is now exhausted and the local coal nearly so, and instead of the exploitation of local resources there is a costly import of ore, scrap, pig-iron and coke. The most recent development in the port of Glasgow is the erection of extensive equipment for the mass import of ore, on the very site from which coal was formerly exported. It is well known that the location of a steelworks is a matter of a delicate balance of factors of ore, fuel and labour supply and of access to markets. In the case of Clydeside, the local demand for great quantities of steel is an over-riding factor. But the commodities produced by heavy industry are capital goods and it is notorious that the demand for these is more sensitive to fluctuations in world economy than are consumer goods. The heavy engineering industries—and iron and steel in train—are running, then, under their own momentum. If they were severely checked by a world recession, they might never recover. They were saved on the last occasion by war: another recession might not so conveniently be overcome—wars of the future do not appear to require vast tonnages of battleship and shells. Since the last emergency, too, shipbuilding has greatly expanded in Japan, Germany and elsewhere, so that it is not impossible that Glasgow may yet have to write off shipbuilding and some other heavy industry in the same ledger as contains cotton, chemicals and tobacco.

The effervescent upsurge of commerce and industry in the nineteenth century required, of course, ever-increasing numbers of workpeople. By good fortune these were to hand in immigrants from Ireland and from the Scottish Highlands. In both places population was outgrowing natural resources and hunger drove the surplus out. In Ireland, Rebellion and Famine and in the Highlands of Scotland the Clearances, were especially responsible for large-scale migrations of people. In the Lowlands of Scotland, also, the reorganisation of agriculture involved the displacement of many workers who either migrated to the industrial centres or turned to home industries for which cotton offered ample scope. Thousands of immigrants, however, pressed into Glasgow and other existing centres, filling them beyond capacity, and also created entirely new settlements, many of which were later absorbed by expanding Glasgow. One-third of Scotland's population was in the region—three times as great a fraction as London is of England—but it was, and still is, not typically Scottish. The dominance of commerce and industry: the vast spread of crowded city streets and their consequent way of life: the large leavening of English, Irish (many Catholic) and, later, Italians and Indians: a metropolitan preference for their city above all other habitats distinguishes the region from the rest of Scotland.

Building to house the multitudes proceeded at a feverish pace and for all classes in the community. The ancient city—in 1723 'the beautifullest little city'—forgot its grace and elegance and became a new town, a boom town, a Victorian town. At first conditions were fantastically bad and would not be allowed in a farmyard today, but gradually the solution was found in the tenement (Pl. XVII), solid stone buildings normally of four storeys and with a continuous frontage to the streets, which are usually quite reasonably wide. The tenements contain some eight to thirteen one- and two-room houses opening off a common staircase. Most houses had a sink with running water and there was a water-closet to each landing, sometimes less. These were the urban equivalent, or often superior, of the cottages from which the immigrants had come. They were no doubt warmer and drier than anything they had known before and were a most economical method of housing large numbers. But they had one irredeemable fault—they concentrated people at a density up to 700 to the acre (almost the same as in a graveyard), which could only be endured by those trained to such highly urban conditions. Centuries of experience permit close urban living in the ancient towns and cities of the Mediterranean and of the Low Countries, but the immigrants to the new towns of Glasgow and the West were mostly from the outer fringe of Atlantic Britain and had no such experience. They had been up-rooted from their own culture, there was a preponderance of males, they were in a sense foreigners, for many spoke a different language and were of another religion. At the best, they made a poor show of urban living, and in bad times, when unemployment brought poverty, it would scarcely be an exaggeration to say that civilisation as we know it collapsed. In the worst depression, that of the nineteen-thirties, gang warfare, blackmail, razor-slashing and the rest were only too common, and the slums of Glasgow became notorious throughout Europe. Similar low housing standards, however, were to be found in parts of many of the other settlements of the region, even in quite small mining villages.

Most of the immigrants, naturally, were unskilled and therefore could command only low wages: inevitably therefore they were liable to undercut the skilled work-people. The latter were generally local people whose skills had evolved with the region and who held themselves aloof from, and were even antagonistic to, the incomers. There is actually a periodic ceremonial re-affirmation of this cleavage in the body politic when, in order to clarify the issue, one faction is regarded as Catholic and Irish, the other as Protestant and Scottish, and the active elements on either side hurl abuse, bottles and worse at each other. This ritual accompanies the Celtic-Rangers football match.

The skilled workers also occupied tenements, but with houses of a somewhat better standard, and with more experience of city life, could contrive a tolerable existence. The density of population was still, however, unhealthily high, and as property aged, or when depression brought poverty, there was always the risk of a slump in standards. It is quite mistaken, nevertheless, to regard all houses which are 'sub-standard' on the national scale as being automatically slums. Given the will, the equipment and above all the ability to live in tenements, there is no reason why they should be less satisfactory than the flats of Genoa or Oslo. Modern building in the conurbation, however, has, under national direction, turned away from the tenement and has sprawled out to occupy practically every available part of the Howe. There are still open spaces, of course, but all too few of them are green. Most are spoil-heaps: almost within half a mile of the City Chambers, even, there occurs the desolation of evil-coloured waste from the St Rollox chemical works, and because virtually the whole city is underlain by coal which has been sporadically and unsystematically worked, large areas are liable to subsidence and are thus not available for building. Since the climate of the region, though mild and sheltered at the bottom of the Howe, rapidly deteriorates with altitude, housing cannot simply climb up on the surrounding heights but must move away to favourable sites elsewhere. This is Glasgow's 'overspill' problem, which is vastly more serious than that of London or indeed any other British town. This housing need is being met by the creation of new towns at East Kilbride and Cumbernauld, but if the

12

centre were thinned out to officially approved densities, then even these satellites would be quite inadequate, for the calculated overspill is nearly half the total population. The Corporation of Glasgow, for example, is about to demolish some 111 acres of the most notorious slums and substitute modern flats. It is estimated to cost £13m. and will house only about 10,000 of the present 26,000 inhabitants. It will thus create a housing problem 1·6 times as great as it solves and is a measure of the desperation of the situation.

As Glasgow flourished and expanded in the late eighteenth century, its centre began to move west. A new bridge 500 yards downstream from the old created a new north-south axis, Jamaica Street, and the area (Pl. XIX) was laid off in a square grid. This grid was no doubt a reasonable arrangement and it has some merits, but it ignored the site, on one of the larger of the many drumlins, from which remarkable views over the Howe might have been contrived by suitably planned contour roads such as were made on the later-developed and smaller Park drumlin. The grid-town was at first a pleasant residential area with Blythswood Square as its focus, but, as in other British industrial towns, the city continued to expand westwards and residences gave way to business premises, sometimes literally, so that massive banks, insurance offices and other temples of business replaced the modest dwelling-houses on the same street plan. This created a modern traffic density which the profusion of right-angle crossings of streets of equal width throws into a fine confusion. Since, in addition to this, traffic using the main Clyde bridges must pass through this district, the congestion and delay are intensified and this part of Glasgow has the sad distinction of even slower-moving traffic than London.

As speedy passenger trains and steamers developed, fashionable Glasgow moved ever further out. Suburban railway transport made possible some really excellent villa-development, mostly in the solid Scottish style but occasionally with *nouveau-riche* exuberance, particularly on the south and also on the north-west, both within and beyond the city boundary. Two main railways terminate at Central Station and St Enoch's respectively on the river side, and their approach lines therefore must cross the river flats on embankments and viaducts, blocking many of the cross-streets. The other two, having entered from the north-east, from the lower plateau surface, are unable to make the steep descent into the city proper and must stop on its northern side. The older and higher is Buchanan Street Station, which with its clap-boarded buildings must surely be the most rustic city railway terminus in Britain. The other, Queen Street, pays dearly for its lower altitude with a steep tunnel, which makes it the dirtiest, slowest and most dangerous approach to the city centre. Elsewhere the topography of the site has exerted considerable influence on railway layout, and thus on building activity. Railway lines either make wide sweeps round drumlins or tunnel through them. Characteristically, therefore, each drumlin carried a more or less self-contained community (many such quarters carry names with the suffix 'hill') based on the local railway station for transport to the city centre. Such commutors, especially the pioneers, were well-to-do and therefore demanded good sites: their type of housing thus did not spread steadily out of the town but leap-frogged from hilltop to hilltop, often into quite rural surroundings. Later and less expensive housing often occupied the lower slopes of the drumlins and now looks down into the dismal maze of mineral sidings and other untidy industrial installations in the valleys among the drumlins. Because of this nucleated type of expansion, different classes of housing are often in close proximity,

13

especially among the drumlins. It is mainly on the South side, where hills are fewer, that large expanses of one type of housing are to be found.

On certain routes, the impossibility or undesirability of avoiding the drumlins accounts for the large number of tunnels on suburban lines and above all for those two supreme atrocities of the age of steam and coal, the Low Level stations at Queen Street and Central. It is a testimony to the toughness and discipline of Glasgow citizens that they have endured underground coal-burning railways for so long. The metropolitan character of Glasgow is attested by its Underground—electric-driven and not to be confused with the above. It circles the inner town and serves particularly the traffic between home and shipyard. Fast railway transport also leads right out of the Howe and permits those who can and so desire to enjoy the amenities of coast and mountain. Helensburgh, for example, is a relatively modern town which has grown almost entirely as a dormitory for Glasgow, but being of sufficient size and apart from other settlements is also a community in its own right. On these more distant lines, however, the topography also exerts a powerful influence. Beyond Helensburgh, for example, where the Highlands begin, steep gradients immediately slow up the line and make commuting impossible. The Renfrew plateaus permit no passage by rail, and therefore railways and settlements are confined to the margins. On the north, the railway serves not only the industrial towns of Port Glasgow and Greenock, whose worst nineteenth-century tenements are almost in the Glasgow class, but also the steamer terminals of Gourock and Wemyss Bay. To the south, railways use the Lochwinnoch gap and serve the ports of Saltcoats and Ardrossan, the residential areas north of them and the Clyde steamer piers of Fairlie and Largs (Fig. 4). Commuting, however, did not stop at the water's edge. No doubt from the earliest times there was a brisk coming and going on the Firth. With the first European application of steam to marine propulsion in the *Comet,* the first Clyde steamer, it is not surprising that it quickly followed in other Clyde passenger ships and the cut-throat competition and keen racing of the Clyde steamers did much to develop marine engines. The world's first turbine passenger steamer was on the Campbeltown run.

With cheap, fast and plentiful steamer transport, the Firth was utilised to the full. Wealthy Glaswegians built their Victorian castles on the estuary, usually in some degree of glorious isolation. Slightly less remote stretches of coast were occupied by large villas, and the more accessible places such as Rothesay and Dunoon were the choice of the people on holiday. Commuting steamers connected with fast railways from Helensburgh, Gourock, Wemyss Bay and Fairlie, but the more leisurely holiday-maker savoured his voyage—and German band—to the full by embarking at the Broomielaw. Arran was served from Ardrossan and there was even commuting from thus far. Strangely enough, however, the whole structure has decayed. Trains and steamers are slower and fewer than formerly and many of the small commuter centres are now occupied only by retired people or by week-enders who travel by car, and many piers are in decay. Similarly the yachts are fewer and smaller, and the glory has in considerable degree departed from the great regattas. Crowds still holiday 'doon the watter', but they are liable to be from the north of England, while the Clydesiders now enjoy Aberdeen, Blackpool or the Continent.

On the south, Ayrshire is reached by the Lugton as well as the Lochwinnoch gap and modern roads over high bleak moorlands also link the Howe of Glasgow to Ayr-

14

shire. (Fig. 4). The Irvine Valley, with Kilmarnock as its node, carries a minor conurbation. Ayr is the ancient capital of one of Scotland's richest agricultural provinces, which also has important mineral workings and industry. In its day Ayr was a greater port than Glasgow, but it was too peripheral and lacking in other respects to maintain

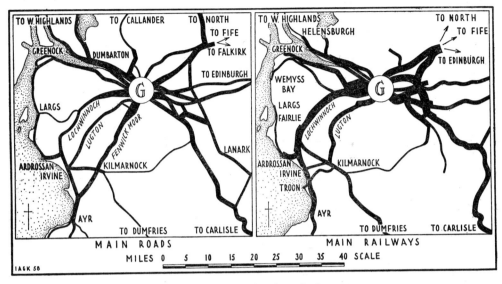

Fig. 4. Major road- and rail-traffic frequencies.
Generalised from the *Clyde Valley Regional Plan*.

its lead (Fig. 2). The Lanarkshire moors again preclude railway penetration, but there is a multiplicity of lines in the Clyde Valley and on the low plateau to the east of Glasgow. It was here indeed that railways in the region began and where the heaviest hauls of minerals and metal still persist. The low plateau carries two lines to Edinburgh, but the fastest route, after climbing out of the Howe, virtually contours to Edinburgh and so achieves a faster run in spite of its greater length. The Kilsyth gap carries the line to Stirling and the North and to Glasgow's North Sea 'outport', Grangemouth. The Campsies and Kilpatricks seal the outlets to the North except for the gap between them which leads to the Trossachs and on to Callander and the entry to a routeway into the Highlands.

No other major city in Europe, except perhaps Milan, can have such superb hill and water scenery within an hour of the city centre. It is to be feared, however, that this may not have been altogether an unmixed blessing. While those who preferred to, or could afford no better, were obliged to remain in tenement Glasgow, many of those whose wealth might have given them the leisure to engage in public affairs fled the city and were thus unlikely to concern themselves much with its physical appearance or to participate in its cultural or social life. In spite of this, however, there was a remarkable degree of interest in the visual arts, though we may reasonably suspect that some of the art collectors were also investors motivated by the kind of shrewdness which led to the remark at a recent New York sale that 'since 1909 General Motors has done a little better than Cézanne but not so well as Renoir'. However this may be,

15

the inexperience of urban civilisation was not confined to tenement dwellers and the face of Glasgow therefore suffered a neglect which would be incomprehensible to a citizen of an older town. Having virtually displaced the rural inhabitants of the Howe, there is little real country on the lowland sides of Glasgow, and the city and Howe now present an example of concentrated dirt and drabness rarely equalled in Britain. Since its enormous and rapid expansion was followed by depression and the stunning blow of an unemployment rate in the 30-40 per cent range and then by 'Special Area' status, there is a conspicuous lack of new capital equipment. Re-building in the central business district is rare and the city is saddled with certain sadly out-of-date equipment, notably most of its trams, street surfaces and ferries. It has been unable also to afford modern capital equipment demanded by changed conditions in road transport. The city which bridged the Forth, Tay and Thames cannot afford to bridge the Clyde and has to await government assistance to tunnel under the river at Whiteinch. The powers which created twelve miles of thirty-foot deep ship-canal cannot now provide a graving dock big enough to accommodate the largest ships it builds. In comparison with, say, the rehabilitation of war-devastated Rotterdam, Glasgow appears bankrupt.

It has been said that geography is concerned not only with the laws of nature but with men's decisions in the face of them. Glasgow is an excellent illustration of this: we have seen how the environment sometimes has guided man and has sometimes been defied by him. For example, it offered bounty in the form of blackband: this ore exhausted, Glasgow men brought alternatives from the ends of the earth. Several cycles of prosperity have worked themselves out, often in periods of bitterest depression: sometimes the new prosperity has been based on few special geographical advantages, and indeed it could be argued that on occasions sheer luck was a factor. A cold rationalisation of Glasgow's economic position, taking account only of geographical assets, could result in a recommendation to voluntary liquidation, but the same situation has existed more than once in the past and Glasgow men have refused to accept it. Glasgow is a going concern and the momentum of her going must be maintained as in the past by the sheer will of her people—by enterprise, energy, brains, skilled hands and capital. The superb fighting qualities of her citizens—their thrawn individualism—must be turned against her competitors and not against each other. The world does not owe her a living; she must compel her own fate, and if her citizens, masters or men, ignore this, they do so at their peril.

THE GEOLOGY AND GEOMORPHOLOGY OF
THE GLASGOW DISTRICT

T. Neville George
Professor of Geology, University of Glasgow

Geologically Glasgow lies in the western part of the Midland Valley of Scotland, a down-faulted rift of large dimensions that has had a profound influence on the Scottish landscape and that has conditioned the manner of human settlement and the growth of a Scottish industrial civilisation. The Midland Valley is sharply separated from the Highlands to the north by the Highland Boundary fault—a fracture that is a natural geological boundary no less obvious in its effects on the topography than on the rocks broken along its face. The comparable Southern Uplands fault that separates the Midland Valley from the ground to the south is only to a degree less important as a fracture and less impressive as a divide between two major topographical and cultural regions.

The rift, however, is an elongate structure several hundred miles long. It can be identified in Ireland, where the depression of Belfast Lough is the drowned line of the Southern Uplands fault; and it may be inferred to continue north-eastwards beyond Fife and the Lothians under the North Sea. The Glasgow district thus has no convenient geological boundaries to east and west. Nor, as it happens, are there in these directions obvious physical features that help to contain it or reflect significant elements of the underlying geology. The geographical boundaries of the district might conveniently be defined by the limits of the Clyde drainage basin—a basin that, especially in the lower ground from Lanark to Glasgow, and along the drowned estuary to Greenock, is no less a unitary region in its pattern of settlement and industry. The Clyde, however, is a river flowing indifferently over many kinds of rocks and a variety of rock structures: it behaves effectively as though it had been superimposed on the geological foundation. The details of the superimposition have yet to be made out, but, whatever the precise cause, in result the drainage basin is not a close reflection of the underlying rock structure. This incongruence (itself the product of a complex history) between topography and geology hinders the recognition of a natural region centred about Glasgow that happily combines all aspects of physique, rock formations, fauna and flora in a self-evident association.

For this account the regional limits are thus quite arbitrarily set at distances of about twenty-five miles about Glasgow. To the west, the waters of the Firth of Clyde exclude Bute and Arran; to the north the Highland Boundary fault, to the south the Southern Uplands fault, are for parts of their courses framing structures of the region; to the east a thoroughly unnatural limit runs from near Stirling southwards through the Central coalfield to cut the Southern Uplands fault near Abington and to reach Leadhills (see Fig. 5).

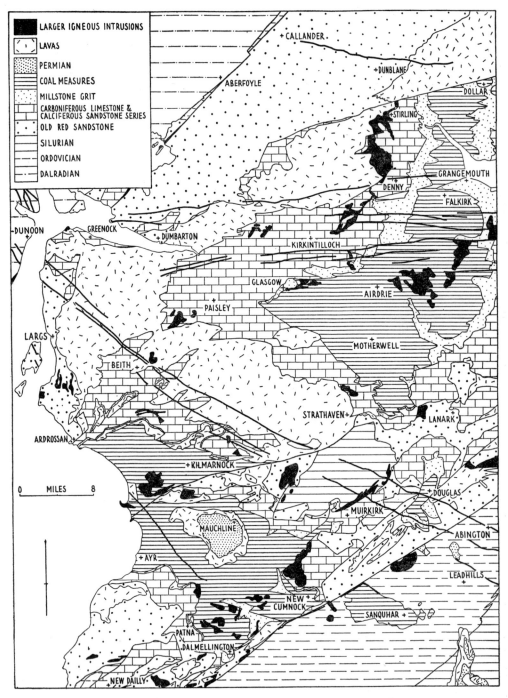

LARGER IGNEOUS INTRUSIONS
LAVAS
PERMIAN
COAL MEASURES
MILLSTONE GRIT
CARBONIFEROUS LIMESTONE &
CALCIFEROUS SANDSTONE SERIES
OLD RED SANDSTONE
SILURIAN
ORDOVICIAN
DALRADIAN

FIG. 5. Outline map of the solid geology of the Glasgow district.

After the maps of the Geological Survey.

The rocks of the region span a great part of geological time from the later Pre-Cambrian metamorphic schists of the Highland border to the unconsolidated Glacial moraines and post-Glacial alluvial sands and muds of the present-day valley floors. Broadly the geological history falls into a few major periods of sedimentation and volcanic activity separated by episodes of crustal movement and mountain building.

The oldest rocks, formed about 500 million years ago, are the Dalradian slates, quartzites and schists north of the Highland Boundary fault. They are mostly altered sediments so intensely deformed and folded that they are generally regarded as of Pre-Cambrian age; but it is possible that they are younger and may belong to the group of Lower Palaeozoic rocks, of which a narrow outcrop is preserved in the fractured zone along the Highland border. The Lower Palaeozoic rocks, 500-300 million years old, mainly of Ordovician and Silurian age, are widely exposed in the Southern Uplands, but within the Midland Valley they come to the surface only in comparatively small outcrops as the Highland Border Series, and, emerging in inliers through the wide-spread cover of younger rocks, as the marine grits and shales of the Nutberry and Hagshaw Hills in Lanarkshire.

The succeeding Old Red Sandstone, the first member of the group of Upper Palaeozoic rocks, is of non-marine origin and rests on the rocks beneath usually with great unconformity. It is a group including not only great thicknesses of lacustrine sediments but also some volcanic lavas and associated igneous intrusions, notably in the Tinto Hills. The distribution of the Old Red Sandstone is clearly related to the bounding frame of the major rift faults, which came into existence towards the close of Lower Palaeozoic times and were renewed during later periods.

Though the overlying Carboniferous rocks, formed 250-200 million years ago, were not separated from the Old Red Sandstone by a long time-interval or by great changes in the frame of the physical environment in which they accumulated, they offer sharp contrasts in their nature to the beds beneath in being mostly fossiliferous rocks, some marine, others estuarine and lagoonal in origin, containing the economically valuable coal seams and ironstones upon which industrial Clydeside has grown. They also include thick piles of volcanic rocks (the Clyde lavas) that exercise a marked control on the local landscape in forming the cores of many of the higher hills around Glasgow.

A reversion to 'continental' conditions even more extreme than those of Old Red Sandstone times is indicated by the Permian consolidated wind-blown dunes of the New Red Sandstone of the Mauchline basin, rather less than 200 million years old. Lava flows, emitted from vents and fissures, for a time interrupted sandstone formation. The Permian sandstones are the last members of the Upper Palaeozoic group of rocks. Towards the close of their formation powerful earth movements imposed upon the rift of the Midland Valley the frame of geological structure it now possesses, the rocks being folded into basins and swells and broken by many fractures.

The long interval between Permian times and the geologically recent Glacial period (which terminated in Scotland perhaps no more than 10,000 years ago) is unrepresented in the Glasgow district by sedimentary rocks—though Jurassic and Cretaceous sands and limestones and immense thicknesses of Tertiary lavas are known elsewhere in western Scotland—and the geological history of the area for nearly 200 million years, which must have been a history mainly of erosion, can only be surmised. The only evidence of rock formation during the interval is provided by narrow elongate dykes of Tertiary age, that cut through all the older rocks as continuous, more or less vertical walls of igneous rock running from the western Highlands for several hundred miles south-eastwards into England.

The former widespread drowning of much of the post-Permian land surface of Scotland by Mesozoic and Tertiary seas is perhaps to be discerned in the form of the peneplaned landscape that was incised and trimmed by subaerial erosion in later Tertiary times. A hypothesis of a Chalk cover and of its progressive removal to expose the underlying Palaeozoic foundation is commonly invoked to explain the discrepancies between river systems and geological structure that are illustrated in the superimposed appearance of the Clyde Valley. On such grounds the etching of the minor features of the present landscape and their adjustment to underlying rock formations are then the product of erosive work mainly by rivers after the cover was removed. The latest touches of ice sculpture were no more than incidental to landforms moulded in all essentials before the Glacial period, though river diversion controlled by ice movement may sometimes be spectacular. Morainic glacial deposits form a veneer over much of the low ground in the Midland Valley: in places they are several hundred feet thick, and locally have choked pre-Glacial valley beds and caused diversions of the drainage. They are associated with or overlain by raised beaches that point to changes in sea-level ranging over nearly 300 feet.

A generalised summary of the geological history is provided in Figure 6.

DALRADIAN ROCKS

Beyond the Highland Boundary fault, Dalradian rocks occur as a complex association of sandstones, grits, and shales that have been more or less intensely metamorphosed to form schists, quartzites, slates and phyllites. They were deposited as water-borne sands and muds, with some pebble beds and limestones, presumably in a shallow sea under conditions not unlike those in which some of the Lower Palaeozoic rocks accumulated elsewhere in Scotland and Wales. In original succession they belong to the upper part of the Dalradian assemblage, the arenaceous beds (the Upper Psammitic Group of the full sequence) being younger than the argillaceous (Upper Pelitic Group). At Callander, a few miles outside the limits of the district, calcareous beds (the Leny Limestone) found in shales intercalated in the Upper Psammitic Group have yielded trilobites indicating a high horizon in the Lower Cambrian stage, and presumably some of the underlying Dalradian rocks, perhaps all of them, must also belong to the Cambrian formation.

The Dalradian sediments are not only altered by metamorphic changes—the signs of intense pressures—but are also greatly deformed by folding on both large and small scale. They lie in part of the Iltay nappe of Bailey, a group of recumbent folds forming an upper structural unit in the succession of slide sheets that compose the geological foundation of the Grampian Highlands. The major structures along the Highland Boundary fault have in their turn been acutely compressed into subsidiary folds of which a main feature is displayed in the occurrence of outcrops of Pelitic Group flanked on north and south by outcrops of Psammitic Group. The relations are generally interpreted to suggest a sharp anticline having a normal outcrop of older rock in its core, an anticline with very steep dips sometimes overturned to north, sometimes to south,

20

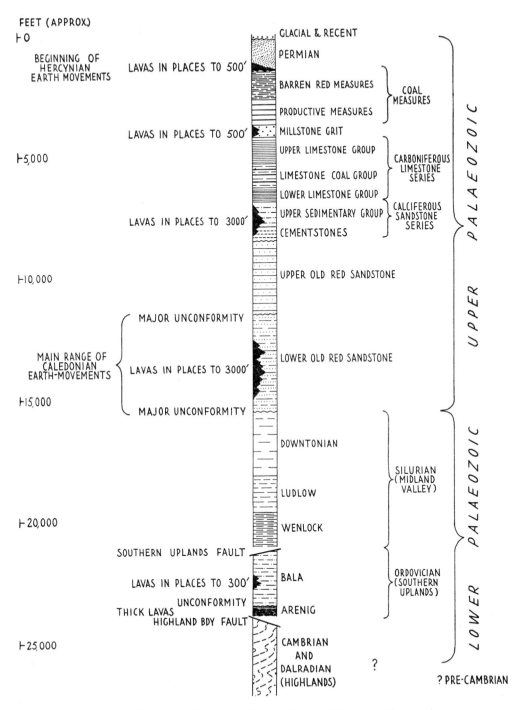

FEET (APPROX.)
⊢ 0

BEGINNING OF
HERCYNIAN
EARTH MOVEMENTS

LAVAS IN PLACES TO 500'

GLACIAL & RECENT

PERMIAN

BARREN RED MEASURES

PRODUCTIVE MEASURES
COAL
MEASURES

LAVAS IN PLACES TO 500'

MILLSTONE GRIT

⊢ 5,000

UPPER LIMESTONE GROUP

LIMESTONE COAL GROUP
CARBONIFEROUS
LIMESTONE
SERIES

LOWER LIMESTONE GROUP

LAVAS IN PLACES TO 3000'

UPPER SEDIMENTARY GROUP
CALCIFEROUS
SANDSTONE
SERIES

CEMENTSTONES

⊢ 10,000

UPPER OLD RED SANDSTONE

MAJOR UNCONFORMITY

MAIN RANGE OF
CALEDONIAN
EARTH-MOVEMENTS

LAVAS IN PLACES TO 3000'

LOWER OLD RED SANDSTONE

⊢ 15,000

MAJOR UNCONFORMITY

DOWNTONIAN

SILURIAN
(MIDLAND
VALLEY)

LUDLOW

⊢ 20,000

WENLOCK

SOUTHERN UPLANDS FAULT

LAVAS IN PLACES TO 300'

BALA

ORDOVICIAN
(SOUTHERN
UPLANDS)

UNCONFORMITY

THICK LAVAS

ARENIG

HIGHLAND BDY FAULT

⊢ 25,000

CAMBRIAN
AND
DALRADIAN
(HIGHLANDS)

?

? PRE-CAMBRIAN

UPPER PALAEOZOIC

LOWER PALAEOZOIC

FIG. 6. Generalised vertical column of the rock succession in the Glasgow district.

21

traceable from the Aberfoyle country south-westwards by Lomondside to Bute, perhaps to Arran. The convergence of dips on the flanking limbs, however, may indicate an even more complex structure, the 'core' of older slates closing downwards as a synform, a plunging nose of a recumbent anticline (part of the Cowal anticline in the west) whose outcrops are deceptive in the apparent simplicity of their suggesting a normal fold (see Fig. 7). On a yet smaller scale, the Pelitic Group, as the Luss Slates of Lomondside

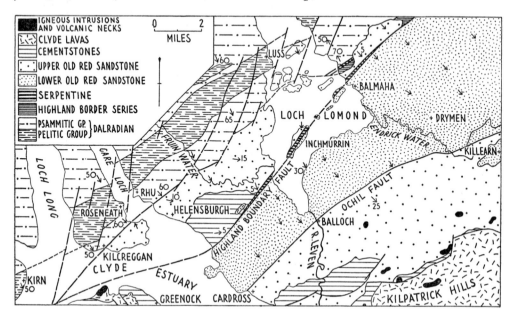

FIG. 7. Map of the geology along the Highland border between Balmaha and Kilcreggan.

and the Dunoon Phyllites of Argyll, show intricate multiple folding that is a measure of the high distortion imposed on relatively incompetent beds caught between more massive sheets of rock under conditions of extreme compression, and that is not easily resolved either mechanically or dynamically.

LOWER PALAEOZOIC ROCKS

The Dalradian rocks were laid down in a basin that, before the Highland Boundary fault came into being, continued unbroken southwards across the area of the Midland Valley to the Southern Uplands and beyond. Evidence of Cambrian rocks is nowhere to be seen in this ground, less perhaps because they are absent than because they lie at depth, Ordovician rocks being the oldest exposed. Fossiliferous shales and grits of 'Cambro-Ordovician' age (the Highland Border Series) are caught up in the Highland Boundary fault zone and suggest such continuity: it may be significant, however, that they are much less metamorphosed than the Dalradian schists and quartzites of the Highlands, even where, as can be seen near Balmaha (Fig. 7), the two rock types are directly in contact along the fault plane.

To the south, Ordovician rocks are nowhere exposed within the rift, and come to

22

outcrop only across the Southern Uplands fault in the Abington-Leadhills-Sanquhar country. They are sharply folded, the older members, of Arenig age, being found only in the cores of isoclinal anticlines emerging as small inliers in a regional development of upper Ordovician rocks. The Arenig sequence is like that of the better-known outcrop found along the coast south of Girvan. The oldest rocks are spilitic pillow-lavas, presumably the local representatives of the Ballantrae series, and, as at Ballantrae, are associated with cherts. The lavas are overlain, in places with unconformity, by a group of sediments containing beds of coarse grit and greywacke in which carbonaceous shales with graptolites are thin and comparatively rare: the age of these sediments is Bala, and the unconformity, marked by conglomerates with boulders up to two feet in diameter, reflects a long interval of mid-Ordovician time when the Southern Uplands area was above the level of the Lower Palaeozoic sea.

Presumably of Ordovician age, and associated with the Ordovician rocks of the Highland Border Series, are sill-like intrusions of gabbroid igneous rocks. Some of the intrusions, appearing as serpentine in linear outcrops in the Highland Boundary fault zone, have been exploited as sources of talc; but the shattering the rocks have suffered and the discontinuous lenticular forms assumed by the masses of talc are factors disadvantageous to systematic working of the veins.

Silurian rocks are found within the Midland Valley in two anticlines south and south-west of Lesmahagow. In neither has the level of erosion descended far into the Silurian succession, and Salopian sediments are alone exposed belonging to the Ludlow and part of the Wenlock stages. The Wenlock rocks are poorly fossiliferous, and their dating is uncertain. They consist of coarse grits and greywackes with thin bands of shale and are not greatly different from rocks of the much more extensive outcrops of the Southern Uplands. Their isolation and limited outcrops make it difficult to use them in any attempted reconstruction of Silurian geography. The Ludlow rocks, the upper group of the Silurian succession, follow the Wenlock without break and similarly consist of a mixed suite of shales, mudstones, sandstones and greywackes, with, however, a greater proportion of finer-grained sediments some of which are highly fossiliferous and provide indications of the environments of deposition. In addition to molluscs and a few brachiopods, the fossils include, abundantly in some layers, various kinds of arthropods, including the large predatory water-scorpions of which the genera *Eurypterus*, *Pterygotus*, and *Slimonia*, some of them a score of feet in length, are the most spectacular. (See Fig. 8.)

As a whole, the Lower Palaeozoic rocks, despite their limited outcrops in the Midland Valley, support an inference that the Glasgow district was submerged beneath an extensive and more or less uniform sea until the later part of Silurian times. Southwards it is certain the sea extended over the area of the present Southern Uplands, and beyond to the Lake District, the English Midlands, and South Wales. The thickness of sediment that accumulated in the Lower Palaeozoic sea was of the order of thousands of feet— nearly 3,000 feet of Wenlock and Ludlow sediments alone in the Lesmahagow inlier— and implies a crustal sagging that persisted for the greater part of 200 million years. This downfold, a geosyncline of vast dimensions, may well have continued northwards if the Dalradian rocks of the Highlands are truly referred to the Lower Palaeozoic systems, when its northernmost limits may be seen in the Cambrian and Ordovician rocks of Sutherland and Ross.

23

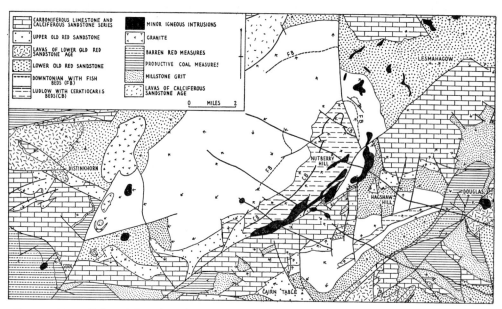

FIG. 8. Map of the solid geology between Sorn and Lesmahagow, to illustrate the outcrops of the Silurian rocks of the Nutberry and Hagshaw Hills, and the Carboniferous rocks of the Douglas coalfield. *After the maps of the Geological Survey.*

THE MIDLAND VALLEY RIFT

So far as the fragmentary evidence indicates, the Lower Palaeozoic rocks of southern Scotland were subjected to only gentle warping during the long period of their formation; and although at times they may have been elevated above sea-level and then subjected to erosion, they give no signs of crustal movements that caused significant changes in the regional geography. In particular, the faults that were to delineate the rift of the Midland Valley appear not to have come into being or to have influenced sedimentation before late Silurian times.

The succeeding strata, the Old Red Sandstone, on the other hand, are in marked contrast to the Lower Palaeozoic rocks not only in their lithological nature but also in their distribution, in the degree to which they are deformed, and in the physical environment in which it may be inferred they accumulated. Near Lesmahagow, it is true, there is a steady transition from the marine Ludlow rocks to the non-marine sandstones and mudstones of the lower part of the Old Red Sandstone, and there it is clear no great changes in geography took place; but elsewhere in the Midland Valley, and to a still greater extent in the Southern Uplands and in the Great Glen, the Old Red Sandstone rests with gross unconformity on older rocks of whatever age—older rocks that were metamorphosed, sharply folded and intensely eroded before the younger were laid down. The contrasts in lithology between the two groups of rocks are thus not contrasts merely of differing constituents or different processes of sedimentation, but reflect a radical change in the physique of the environment in which they accumulated.

The widely extended geosyncline ceased to exist either as a great sagging of the crust or as a major sea area where thick marine sediments were being formed. It became

24

the site of crustal deformation by the building of ranges of folded mountains of high and varied relief, a continental tract where erosion was dominant and in which sedimentation was limited to comparatively small and self-contained troughs between the main mountain belts. In particular, two of the principal mountain belts that were initiated during this period of powerful crustal movement—now called the Caledonian period because of the representative character of its expression in Scotland—were the Grampian Highlands and the Southern Uplands; and in the geography of Old Red Sandstone times can be discerned the first signs of a structural framework that is recognisably the fundamental framework of present-day Scotland, a framework that was modified, even mutilated, by later earth movements but which retained its essential form throughout all subsequent geological history.

The uplifted mountain masses were separated by the rift, the graben, of the Midland Valley, a segment of crust let down along the major fracture belts that still define its margins. The rift became the main site of accumulation of the Old Red Sandstone in southern Scotland, and contained the formation almost wholly within its fault walls: where along its margins younger members of the formation occasionally overstep onto the Highland quartzites to the north, they give complete evidence of the existence of the Highland Boundary fault as a barrier against which the underlying older members were banked to a thickness (implying relative movement along the fracture) of the order of several thousand feet. The Southern Uplands fault furnishes proof almost as firm, in being an abrupt limit along most of its length to all earlier, but being overstepped (in Lauderdale and along the East Lothian coast) by the later members of the Old Red Sandstone.

THE OLD RED SANDSTONE

The rugged topography brought into being by the Caledonian earth-movements in a climate characterised by heavy (though probably seasonal or intermittent) rainfall resulted in coarse erosion of the mountain masses by powerful fast-flowing streams. They carried detritus into the neighbouring low ground of the rift where, their flow rapidly checked, they deposited delta fans as spreads of conglomerate near the rift margins, and finer alluvial sands and muds in the central areas. Some of the sediments have the appearance of lacustrine marls, and the floor of the rift may have been occupied by extensive lakes much as the African rift is at the present day.

On the other hand, the Old Red Sandstone carries few evidences of truly arid conditions, and is without salt beds like those of the New Red Sandstone of England. Thin calcareous cornstones are the principal types of chemical deposits suggesting strong evaporation and perhaps desiccation, and occasional lenticles of clay containing abundant and sometimes closely packed fossil fishes present the appearance of petrified graveyards preserved in dried-up pools. But it may be that for much of the time the water in the 'lakes' was more or less fresh and that there were outflows carrying water and fine sediment beyond the present confines of the Midland Valley.

In such a comparatively humid environment the persistent red colour of the sediments is not easily attributed to desert oxidation of constituent iron compounds. On the other hand, land plants appear scarcely to have evolved beyond the stage of moss-like psilophytalian and lycopodialian forms; and there was probably no considerable cover of vegetation either to protect the exposed rocks from subaerial rotting and fragmentation or to provide a source of reducing humic acids to attack the iron compounds. Some of the red rocks have the appearance of laterite, and may further indicate tropical or subtropical temperatures.

The Old Red Sandstone is divisible into a thick Lower and a thin Upper group. The distinction is the result of discontinuous sedimentation, the interval between the two having been a time of earth-movement of no great violence but sufficient to give rise to markedly unconformable junctions with strong overstep. In consequence, Middle Old Red Sandstone, well developed around the Moray Firth, is unknown in the Midland Valley. In the Glasgow district volcanoes were active during Lower, but had died out by Upper Old Red Sandstone times.

The Lower Old Red Sandstone forms a wide outcrop along the northern flank of the Midland Valley from the islands of the Firth of Clyde to the southern shores of Loch Lomond and beyond. Its older members, truncated against the boundary fault, are coarse conglomerates and grits containing large pebbles and boulders of Highland metamorphic rocks. They are followed by dark-brown and chocolate-brown sandstones with layers of pebbles many of which are of andesite probably derived from contemporary lava flows like those of the Ochil Hills to the east—though no lavas are known in place to the north of Glasgow. The full sequence must reach a thickness of several thousand feet.

In the south of the district between Lesmahagow and Muirkirk (Fig. 8) red and brown rocks of Old Red Sandstone type follow the Ludlow rocks conformably. They have usually been regarded as of Downtonian age, but it is possible that they are more properly referred to the Ludlow stage since they contain common eurypterids of genera like those of the rocks beneath. They also contain a few feet of brown shale in which fish remains are not uncommon, including species of *Thelodus*, *Birkenia*, *Lanarkia* and *Lasanius*.

The normal Lower Old Red Sandstone that follows is defined at its base by a greywacke conglomerate with pebbles derived from the south—in significant contrast to the sandstones along the Highland border, and a sign of the conditions of sedimentation. It consists of several thousand feet of brown sandstones, felspathic and micaceous, with recurrent layers of pebbles that sometimes form thick conglomerates traceable for considerable distances and giving rise to small escarpments. Layers of marl and mudstone are common, but usually only as thin partings. Fossils are usually very rare, but cephalaspids (proving the age) have been found in the southern outcrops. Some of the beds are ashy or tuffaceous, and contain the finer volcanic detritus of contemporary explosive eruptions. As the rocks are traced towards the Southern Uplands an unconformity develops at their base, and a few miles beyond the Glasgow district the Old Red Sandstone rests discordantly on an Ordovician foundation, with the basal conglomerate, 500 feet thick, containing pebbles of chert, jaspers and acid igneous rocks of origin in the Southern Uplands. The unconformity is a sign of the local importance of the Caledonian earth-movements, and its intensification southwards implies an active rise of the major anticline of the Southern Uplands before the Old Red Sandstone began to be deposited.

Upper Palaeozoic times in the Midland Valley were marked by prolonged and widespread volcanic activity. The centres and fissures from which the lavas and ashes were emitted were neither constant in position nor uniform in intensity, and while some waxed

26

to a climatic outburst, others were declining or dormant or moribund, or were continuously fed by lavas welling gently as widespread sheets over the neighbouring land.

Igneous action was particularly powerful during Lower Old Red Sandstone times, the accumulated flows in places reaching several thousand feet in thickness. The most imposing piles are to be seen in the Ochil and Sidlaw Hills to the east of the Glasgow district; but thick accumulations also occur in southern Ayrshire and Lanarkshire. The volcanic rocks include comparatively few layers of fragmental ashes and tuffs. They are mostly basaltic flows, commonly containing large phenocrysts of olivine, augite and plagioclase felspars. Andesites are only less common, and rhyolitic lavas are found near Tinto.

Many of the rocks are vesicular, their gas-cavities filled with secondary minerals of which chalcedonic silica is the most usual. The matrix being comparatively easily eroded, the weathered rock breaks down to yield the amygdales as 'pebbles' in stream beds and on beaches—'Scotch Pebbles' that have acquired some value as semi-precious stones, the concentrically banded agate structure in many of them being beautifully revealed when the pebbles are polished. The chalcedonic amygdales are particularly common in the lavas of Dunure. Elsewhere the cavities may be lined with well-formed crystals of a variety of minerals including calcite and quartz.

Some of the lavas were poured out on land, and occasionally the fresh rock of an overlying flow can be seen to rest on the rotted top-surface of the flow underlying. In other cases the individual flows are separated from one another by thin layers of detrital sands and muds, and presumably poured out or flowed under water or at water level. In the Carrick Hills near Dunure the intercalated sands and muds sometimes carry the trails of a variety of organisms, some of them possibly annelids, others arthropods (including myriapods). Some of the interbedded sediments are coarse-grained and contain pebbles of contemporaneously eroded lavas from flows nearby. Occasionally the contained fragments may be highly angular, or consist even of single crystals, and the sediment takes on the character of a fine ash of explosive origin.

Associated with the volcanic rocks of Lower Old Red Sandstone age are numbers of intrusions including sills, dykes and volcanic necks. They range from acid to basic in composition, and point to a varied assortment of differentiated parent magmas in the local province. Topographically one of the most prominent is the laccolitic sill of Tinto, of a fine-grained pink felsite that has been widely used for road-making. Distinkhorn (Fig. 8), near Lesmahagow, is a hill made up of an association of dioritic and 'granitic' rocks, older than the local Upper Old Red Sandstone but younger than neighbouring contact-metamorphosed dykes cutting through earlier Lower Old Red Sandstone.

The Upper Old Red Sandstone is sharply distinguished from the Lower by an intervening unconformity, by notable differences in colour and lithology, and by a general lack of contemporary volcanic or intrusive igneous rocks. It is generally unfossiliferous, but its age is proved by the occurrence of the fish *Bothriolepis* in strata near the Heads of Ayr. Its unconformable base is usually not so obvious in the Glasgow district as it is elsewhere in the Midland Valley; but it is most spectacularly displayed in the neighbourhood of Balmaha (Fig. 7) by the rock relations along the Highland Boundary fault. South of the fault Lower Old Red Sandstone, dipping southwards in an outcrop five miles wide and reappearing in the core of an anticline near Killearn, has a thickness of many thousands of feet, and is followed without obvious transgression by

Upper Old Red Sandstone (nearly 3,000 feet thick). It is abruptly cut by the fault, north of which it is (at present level of erosion) absent. On this same northern flank, however, an outlier of Upper Old Red Sandstone not only appears in downthrown relation to the rocks to the south, but rests directly on the steeply dipping Lower Palaeozoic Highland Border Series or the serpentine, which it transgresses northwards on to Dalradian quartzites. The structural relations prove both the effect of the fault in limiting the area of sedimentation of the Old Red Sandstone, and the activity of fault movement during the interval between Lower and Upper Old Red Sandstone times. Other evidence of unconformable relations is provided in the Carrick Hills south of Ayr, where the Upper Old Red Sandstone transgresses lavas of Lower age to come to rest on the red sandstones beneath. It is also indirectly recognisable in the manner in which minor igneous intrusions in a number of places cut through the Lower beds but do not penetrate the Upper.

The sediments of the Upper Old Red Sandstone are usually much brighter-red in colour than those of the Lower. They are often irregularly bedded, showing signs of rapid changes of water velocity and direction as they were transported into the area. They contain pebble-beds, lenses of purple, green and mottled marls, layers of clay galls, and other signs of variable conditions of sedimentation. A feature that tends to distinguish them from the Lower Old Red Sandstone is the common occurrence of calcareous cornstones—impure sandy concretionary limestones that may be the product of chemical precipitation from shallow dried-up lakes, or that may be analogous to the kankar, a calcareous terrestrial subsoil forming at the present day in parts of the semi-arid tropics. Some of the sediments are rich in sub-spherical 'millet-seed' sand grains, wind-rounded and transported though perhaps deposited in water; occasional wind-polished pebbles are found in layers; and some bedding planes show sun cracks or marl breccias resulting from extreme desiccation. These characteristics of desert regions could well have been produced, however, on exposed lake floors—exposed either through periodic climatic changes or through slight elevation—unprotected by a cover of vegetation, without the incidence of truly arid conditions.

CARBONIFEROUS ROCKS

Though Carboniferous rocks are found in small outliers as far north as Mull and northern Argyll, and form a relatively extensive outcrop in the Machrihanish coalfield, they are confined in the Midland Valley almost wholly within the limits of the rift, and the frame of their basin of sedimentation was much like that of Old Red Sandstone times. In many localities, however, they rest with obvious unconformity on the Old Red Sandstone, and may even rest (as near Lesmahagow and New Cumnock) directly on Lower Palaeozoic rocks. The unconformity is a sign of notable though not violent earth-movement between Old Red Sandstone and Carboniferous times, and of an interval of non-deposition when much, perhaps all, of the area was above sea-level.

There is generally a sharp contrast in kind and colour of sediment between the Carboniferous rocks and the beds beneath. Red sands and marls like those of the Old Red Sandstone may recur in the lowest Carboniferous beds and locally give the appearance of transition and continuity between the two formations; but the characteristic Carboniferous strata are grey or blue-grey or black, and were formed in an environ-

28

ment in which lived a great abundance of organisms, animals and plants, whose decay prevented the iron-rich minerals from taking on the red and brown hues of the Old Red Sandstone. Many of the Carboniferous rocks were deposited in the sea, as their marine fossils show; but even where they are estuarine or non-marine they rarely disclose any reversion to the barren emptiness of earlier times in the conditions of their formation.

The heights of the Southern Uplands flanked the rift along its southern margin—a tract that was elevated not merely during the Caledonian earth-movements but that was repeatedly upwarped (while the rift subsided) throughout Upper Palaeozoic (and probably later) times. They formed a barrier between the Scottish province of Carboniferous sedimentation and the wide-spread seas of England and Wales. At times the barrier was breached as a result of temporary relative subsidence, and strata were then laid down more or less continuously over the greater part of the British Isles south of the Highlands; but the isolation of the Midland Valley during the Upper Palaeozoic era is reflected in the ways in which the Carboniferous rock-sequence differs from that of Northumbria, and even more from that of the English Midlands and Wales. In particular, the thick massive limestones of the Carboniferous Limestone are virtually unrepresented in Scotland, where the Cementstones, and still more the Oil-Shales, are almost unique in Britain.

Subsidence of the rift to receive the Carboniferous sediments was pulsatory, and there was constant fluctuation in the conditions of their formation with alternating dominance of marine and deltaic or estuarine or paludal influences. The rhythms of change were not uniform over the whole area of the rift, but within the Glasgow district the major groups into which the strata may conveniently be divided are fairly constant in their development, and are, in downward order of succession (Figs. 6 and 9):

4. COAL MEASURES: A group of sandstones and carbonaceous shales, mainly of non-marine origin, in which the comparatively thin coal seams are found more commonly in the lower part than in the upper; with a consequent subdivision of the group into

   (b) Barren Red Measures, without economically workable seams.

   (a) Productive Measures, highly carbonaceous in many beds, with workable coals making it the upper of the two formations in which extensive mining has been carried out.

3. MILLSTONE GRIT: Sandstones and thin shales, not greatly different from the Coal Measures in general appearance, but without important coals.

2. CARBONIFEROUS LIMESTONE SERIES: Shales, sandstones and limestones, many obviously of open-sea origin with abundant marine fossils; the name 'Carboniferous Limestone' only relative, most of the beds not being limestones, and the middle part of the group being highly carbonaceous:

   (c) Upper Limestone Group, dominantly marine with a number of fossiliferous bands.

   (b) Limestone Coal Group, the lower of the two Carboniferous formations in the Glasgow district containing extensively mined coal seams; an intercalation, without fossiliferous limestones, in the general sequence of marine beds.

   (a) Lower Limestone Groups like the Upper, with a number of thin fossiliferous marine limestones.

1. CALCIFEROUS SANDSTONE SERIES: A varied succession of lagoonal, non-marine, and marine sandstones, shales and limestones.

The names of the groups do not imply equivalence and correlation with rocks of similar names in England and Wales. As the goniatites show, much or all of the Calciferous Sandstone Group falls into the Viséan stage of the European Lower Carboniferous succession, and is to be correlated with most of the upper part of the Carboniferous Limestone of England and Wales. The Lower Limestone Group mostly belongs to the uppermost Viséan age, the upper part of the *Dibunophyllum* Zone. Its topmost bed, however, the Top Hosie Limestone, is the first member of the Namurian stage and is younger than any true Carboniferous Limestone farther south where beds of the same age usher in the Millstone Grit. No fossils that can be used for correlation have as yet been found in the Limestone Coal Group; but the overlying Upper Limestone Group has yielded goniatites at a number of horizons, and proves to fall into the lower *Eumorphoceras* Zone of the Namurian. The Millstone Grit of Scotland, very thin, contains few goniatites, but they suggest it continues the Namurian succession above the Upper

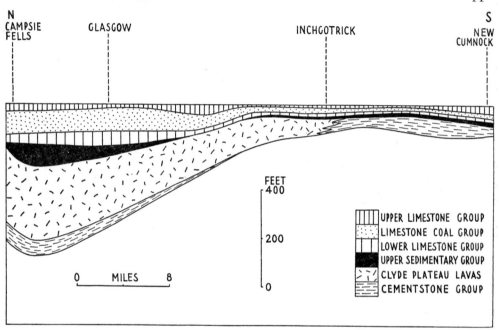

FIG. 9. Generalised section illustrating the development of the Calciferous Sandstone and Carboniferous Limestone series in the Glasgow district.

Limestone Group. There appears to be a great gap in the fossil sequence below the Coal Measures, all the zones except the *Eumorphoceras* Zone of the British Namurian succession being unknown in Scotland and scarcely likely to be represented in the greatly reduced Millstone Grit. Goniatites are rare in the Coal Measures, but the few that have been found indicate the *Gastrioceras* Zone: the non-marine lamellibranchs add confirmation in proving the occurrence of the *communis, similis-pulchra* and *modiolaris* zones of the Ammanian stage.

The Carboniferous sediments were interrupted at most stages of their formation by volcanic activity. This was especially powerful during Lower Carboniferous times, when the Clyde lavas were poured out. It continued on a diminishing scale until Millstone Grit times, and died away to insignificance in the Coal Measures. The centres from which the volcanic rocks were emitted changed their location from time to time, and the

30

regional influence of any one episodic outburst was usually limited to a comparatively small area. In consequence, the generalised Carboniferous sequence shows much local modification, the lateral changes in the Calciferous Sandstone Series, in which marker horizons cannot be traced for many miles, being particularly difficult to ascertain in detail. The volcanic extrusions were fed through necks many of which are now well exposed by erosion; and contemporaneous minor intrusions, including sills and dykes, are common and widespread.

THE CALCIFEROUS SANDSTONE SERIES

The thick piles of the Clyde lavas in the middle of the Calciferous Sandstone Series break the sediments into two major groups, differing not only in age but also in the conditions under which they were deposited and so in their lithology. The lower group, the Cementstones, is relatively uniform over the district and marks the beginning of a Carboniferous type of environment after the red beds of the Old Red Sandstone. The upper group, the Upper Sedimentary Group of the Calciferous Sandstone proper, laid down on the irregular and eroded surface of the lavas, shows much local variation in thickness and in details of sequence, and carries fossiliferous limestones and shales like those of the overlying Carboniferous Limestone Series and unlike any beds found in the Cementstones. Oil-shales, equivalent in age partly to the Cementstones, partly to the Upper Calciferous Sandstone, are thickly developed in the Lothians to the east, but diminish rapidly in importance as they are followed westwards and appear in the district only insignificantly.

The Cementstones are very well exposed along the foot of the Campsie Fells, where, as the Ballagan Beds, they reach a thickness of about 600 feet. They consist of alternations of thin-bedded soft shales and fine-grained impure dolomitic limestones, with some micaceous sandstone bands. The cementstone layers are almost completely unfossiliferous: they contain a relatively high proportion of argillaceous matter, and suggest in their nodular form and their composition an inorganic origin as precipitates from marine saline waters undergoing periodic evaporation in wide shallow pans. The rhythmic banding of the sediments is prominent in weathered sections, and implies climatic oscillations or more probably pulsatory subsidence without great downwarping as the rocks were being formed. The shale beds do not readily split, and suggest slow quiet accumulation. The sandstones reflect intermittent inflow of more disturbed waters, some of them being gently ripple-marked and current-bedded. Apart from drifted plant debris, fossils are rare and consist of a limited assemblage of ostracods, a few lamellibranchs, fish scales, and lingulid brachiopods: the saline waters were clearly inimical to the many kinds of organisms that presumably lived in the seas from which the salts were ultimately derived. The surfaces of the shale beds sometimes carry films of gypsum and pseudomorphs after common salt, and bedding planes showing desiccation cracks repeatedly occur.

The Ballagan Beds are overlain and underlain by thick sandstones that, like the intervening shales and Cementstones, show significant changes as they are followed northwards. The cementstones become less calcareous, more argillaceous; the shales contain a greater proportion of sandy layers; and particularly the upper thick sandstone —the Spout of Ballagan Sandstone—acquires a conglomeratic character, with pebbles of vein quartz, that suggests proximity to the contemporary land-mass from which the terrigenous detritus was derived. Eastwards along the outcrops (see Fig. 12) the Ballagan beds diminish in thickness, perhaps because of progressively earlier volcanic activity—some of the earliest lava flows have intercalations of shales and cementstones—perhaps because of internal overlap.

Cementstones occur underneath the lavas of the Kilpatrick Hills and of Renfrewshire; but in places they are thin or completely absent, and their variable development may well imply an irregular foundation on which they were deposited. In Ayrshire, especially south of the Inchgotrick fault that, although mainly of Hercynian age, was an important divide between notably distinct areas of Carboniferous sedimentation, the Cementstones are almost unaffected by vulcanicity and attain a thickness approaching 1,000 feet. They are comparable in lithology with the development at Ballagan, and contain a number of gypsum bands. Still farther south sandstones and conglomeratic layers become increasingly important, though their occurrence is highly variable; the group becomes thinner and there is repeated evidence of non-sequence and extreme shallowing; and in places, as near New Cumnock, the group may be entirely absent. It is clear that the floor on which the Cementstones was laid was of undulating relief, the beds of the group displaying internal overlap. Their attenuation towards the Southern Uplands is significant, and is a pointer to the existence of the rift margins in that direction. The similar complete overlap of the group on parts of the Lower Palaeozoic ridge running south-west from Lesmahagow implies that movement along the anticline was revived during Carboniferous times—certainly that the anticline stood up as an island above the flats of Cementstones sedimentation.

The lavas that overlie the Cementstones in the northern part of the Glasgow district reach thicknesses of 2,000–4,000 feet. They must therefore have stood well above sedimentation level when they were first outpoured, and their submergence in later Calciferous Sandstone times indicates the magnitude of the subsidence undergone by the Midland Valley as this short span of Carboniferous times elapsed. The surfaces of the uppermost lava flows, when finally vulcanicity died down, were initially uneven and were made still more irregular by intense subaerial erosion. With continued downwarping they were therefore submerged piecemeal, and some of them remained above sea-level as islands until after the close of Calciferous Sandstone sedimentation. The Upper Sedimentary Group of the Calciferous Sandstone Series is thus highly variable in its development, pocketed and discontinuous in its distribution, and not easily correlated from one outcrop to the next except by means of the fossiliferous marine horizons that form convenient marker bands.

In general, the group is without typical cementstone bands; and the subsidence that initiated its formation was sharp enough to allow access into the area of more normal open-sea waters than are ever suggested by the Cementstones. On the other hand, marine beds are by no means dominant in the group, which consists mainly of sandstones and sandy shales, fireclays and coal seams (some of them workable) that suggest deposition in alternating marine and paralic environments.

The basal sediments often consist of accumulations of volcanic detritus, reddish bole, mottled marls, and conglomeratic wash: they are diachronous in horizon, tending to appear immediately above the lavas at whatever place in the sequence sedimentation was renewed, and they thus are helpful in delineating local shore-lines. Laterally wedges of the volcanic detritus intertongue with the more normal sediments, becoming finer-grained in doing so but retaining the red-purple and green colours typical of their parent sources.

The thickest representatives of the Upper Sedimentary Group near Glasgow, reaching 1,000 feet, are found in and about Paisley, where the thin limestones contain common brachiopods (including large productids) and corals (*Syringopora*, *Lithostrotion*, *Dibunophyllum*, zaphrentoids), and some of the shales are rich in lamellibranchs. Both northwards and southwards the thickness diminishes by overlap. On the southern flanks of the Campsies the Craigmaddie Sandstones make up 400 feet of the sequence of 700 feet of sediments, and consist of conglomeratic and gritty layers that become finer-grained eastwards and diminish in thickness to insignificance. A comparable series of changes in the reverse direction is suggested by the development of the later members of the group in the outcrops immediately south of Glasgow, where the uppermost limestones rest with overlap on a thin basal residue of volcanic detritus (Fig. 10).

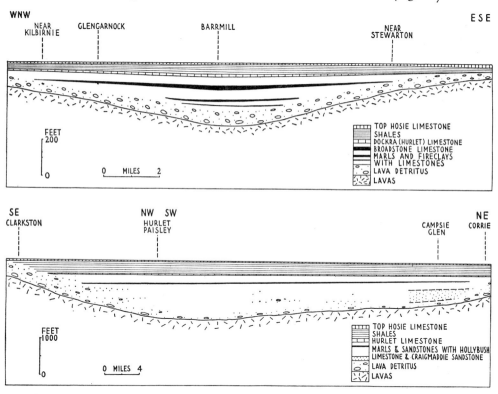

FIG. 10. Comparative reconstructed sections to illustrate the manner of sedimentation of the Upper Sedimentary Group in the Glasgow district. *In part after the Geological Survey.*

The Glasgow basin has its counterpart in the Kilbirnie-Stewarton ground, where the Upper Sedimentary Group reaches a maximum thickness of 300 feet in a depression on the lava floor, but thins to less than fifty feet north-westwards and south-eastwards, and probably was completely overlapped against an island core between Eaglesham and Galston (see Fig. 10). The rapid disappearance of the lavas in the neighbourhood of the

C

33

Inchgotrick fault is accompanied to the south by a more uniform development of the Upper Calciferous Sandstone, which follows the Cementstones conformably and is not always readily distinguished from them. The combined thicknesses of lavas and sediments belonging to the Calciferous Sandstone Group in the region of the Campsie Hills are probably more than 4,000 feet: the equivalent rocks south of the fault rarely exceed 1,500 feet and are mostly less than 1,000 feet. The southern part of Ayrshire was thus a positive area that subsided comparatively little in relation to the ground to the north and formed a shelf of slow deposition where the Upper Calciferous Sandstone (more or less equivalent to the Upper Sedimentary Group) is no more than a few hundred feet thick at maximum and may be as little as a few score feet, or even be completely extinguished. The sediments of the shelf usually contain fewer limestones than their northern counterparts and are dominantly sandstones and marls, with beds of conglomerate, fireclays, and occasional carbonaceous seams. Some of them are red and look like rocks of the Old Red Sandstone, and thin cornstones are known from the marly layers.

Into the south-eastern development of the Upper Calciferous Sandstone of the defined Glasgow district, the Oil-Shales may extend from the Cobbinshaw field of the Lothians. Lithological oil-shales are known to persist into Lanarkshire as far west as Strathaven: although they are thin and of poor quality, and do not compare with those exploited farther east, they are hints of a lateral passage from the western cementstone lagoonal facies to the paludal swamp-lake facies of the Oil-Shales. The changes were not radical, and in bulk the Calciferous Sandstone Series forms a unitary group of rocks in the Midland Valley; but the hint is one of landward approach to the east, seaward approach to the west, during Carboniferous times.

THE CARBONIFEROUS LIMESTONE SERIES

The initiation of the Carboniferous Limestone Series was by relatively rapid and abrupt subsidence of the rift floor and the consequent transgression of open seas across almost all the Midland Valley. The first bed of this transgressive group of sediments, the Hurlet Limestone, is identifiable from the Clyde estuary to the east coast, and is hence a marker horizon of great importance in the stratigraphy of the Scottish Carboniferous rocks. It began a cycle of fluctuating marine influence that persisted intermittently in all the sediments until the time of the Coal Measures, and that provides some justification for the nomenclatural analogy with the limestone sediments of England and Wales. The rocks show a well-marked sedimentary rhythm that is comparable with the Yoredale rhythm characteristic of equivalent beds in the north of England, each rhythmic unit beginning with a marine limestone formed during an episode of rapid subsidence and ending with a seat-earth and a thin coal as the area progressively shallowed.

The Lower Limestone Group of the Glasgow district is mainly composed of shales, many of them calcareous; and limestones, sandstones, fireclays and coals are subordinate. The sandstones increase in proportion eastwards on the flanks of the Central coalfield; and limestones in the Ayrshire coalfields. Correspondingly the thickness varies greatly from 600 feet in the north-eastern outcrops to less than 100 feet over most of the Ayrshire shelf. The variation is not merely due to different rates of deposition. A zone of thinning is noticeably developed in the neighbourhood of the Inchgotrick fault, about which there was significant movement as in earlier times: an erosion surface is to be

34

recognised at the top of the Hurlet (Dockra) Limestone in localities near Galston, the whole sequence above to the Top Hosie Limestone being reduced to fifteen feet at Inchgotrick itself. Some irregularity of the sea floor is also indicated by an island of lavas that probably persisted above sea-level in the ground about Eaglesham, against which the group was completely overlapped; and a confluent hill mass, or perhaps a separate island, was formed by the Lower Palaeozoic ridge running south-westwards from Lesmahagow.

The Limestone Coal Group extends from the Top Hosie Limestone to the base of the Index Limestone. Comparatively it is almost without marine beds—the chief being the Johnstone Shell-Bed with lamellibranchs and productid and other brachiopods—but is rich in coals. A classical transect illustrating the mode of sedimentation during a geological 'moment' is provided by the fossil lepidodendroid forest at Whiteinch, where the stumps and roots of a dozen trees, buried in shale as they grew and truncated by a sill of dolerite, are now exposed in the floor of an old quarry as petrified witnesses to the kind of swamp environment typical of Carboniferous times in Scotland. A comparable (but less well-preserved) example is to be seen as tree-trunks trapped by lavas in the Kilpatrick Hills. The contemporary geography was clearly one of extended estuarine flats, at times invaded by brackish or truly marine waters, at times invaded by fast-moving river floods: during the periods of quiescence the finer shales were laid down; during the flooding the coarser sandstones, often current-bedded, were brought in; and when surface-level reached just above sea-level the flats were converted into a richly vegetated swamp where in water-logged conditions the coal seams could accumulate.

In the northern development of the Limestone Coal Group, north of the Dusk Water fault, the thickness is 600–1,000 feet, and the group is conveniently subdivided, at the horizon of the thick carbonaceous shales forming the Black Metals, into a lower part with comparatively few, and an upper with common, coals and ironstones. Both these kinds of rocks have been extensively worked, the blackband ironstones, in which there is enough carbonaceous matter to allow smelting without the addition of charcoal or coal, being of particular importance during the growth of the iron and steel industry in the nineteenth century. South of the Dusk Water fault, however, there is relatively a sharp reduction in thickness, which rarely exceeds 300 feet. The reduction is intensified across the Inchgotrick fault, the group in central Ayrshire being of the order of 100 feet, the subdivisions being not separately distinguishable, and workable coals being reduced to insignificance. Still farther south across the Kerse Loch fault and the line of steep metals, the thicknesses increase almost equally abruptly and are between 200 and 300 feet. There can be little doubt that the faulting, though dominantly of Hercynian age, was initiated during Carboniferous times and broke up the western part of the Midland Valley into three or four more or less independent fault blocks undergoing differential subsidence. In some degree the rift was therefore multiple, much as the African rift is at the present day: but it is interesting that the successive steps made by the blocks were not consistently northward from the main Southern Uplands fault, the Inchgotrick-Kerse Loch block behaving as an isolated up-standing mass, relatively a small horst.

The Upper Limestone Group repeats the kinds of sediments found in the Lower: marine limestones return relatively commonly, and the sea had more ready access to the area than during Limestone Coal Group times. Nevertheless, the subdivision of the

Carboniferous Limestone Series is only a comparative one, and most of the rocks of the group are coarsely terrigenous and include massive beds of sandstone and grit, some shales and some coals. The group in the immediate neighbourhood of Glasgow is about 800 feet thick, and contains ten or a dozen well-marked limestone bands, most of them fossiliferous with common brachiopods (productids, spirifers, athyrids), corals (mainly small zaphrentoids), crinoids, lamellibranchs (including *Posidonia, Nuculana, Edmondia,* modiolids, pectens), cephalopods (including common orthocerates, and *Tylonautilus nodiferus*) and gastropods.

Southwards the group is affected by contemporaneous movements along active faults in much the same way as the Limestone Coal Group. Sandstones increase in relative importance, and some of the thinner limestones become extinguished. The thickness is reduced to 110-265 feet (thickening slightly southwards) between the Dusk Water fault and the Inchgotrick fault, and to about 100 feet (in places to less than 40 feet) between the Inchgotrick and Kerse Loch faults. Farther south there is the same sudden increase in the down-faulted block at the foot of the Southern Uplands, and between Patna and Muirkirk the group reaches more than 600 feet and the several limestones become again separately recognisable, though perhaps not at exactly the same horizons.

THE MILLSTONE GRIT

The Scottish Millstone Grit, resting upon the topmost limestone, the Castlecary, of the Upper Limestone Group, is a delta sediment, composed mainly of coarse sandstones with some shales and fireclays. It is almost without workable coals; and it contains few marine limestones, though fossiliferous layers are not uncommon in the lower part, of which the 'Roman Cement' lying towards the base is perhaps the most important. It has yielded abundant brachiopods (including productids, *Meekella* and *Prothyris*) and lamellibranchs from some of the richer marine bands. Much of it may well have been deposited in marginal seas under the control of powerful currents: the rocks are often tumbled and cross-bedded, and ripple-marks and rapid alternations of grain-size are usual. Plant debris is common including large drifted tree-trunks; and some of the coaly seams may be detrital.

In its lower part the group contains thick seams of refractory fireclay, of high economic value. They differ from the normal seat-earths of coal measures, most obviously in being without traces of roots or in rarely having a carbonaceous over-layer. Their mineral composition is also exceptional: the presence of very fresh felspars, hornblende and biotite suggests the erosion of igneous rocks, and they may well have been deposited by gentle currents as siliceous ganisters. In its upper part the group is much more strongly arenaceous, and includes thick beds of sandstone and grit, some of them pebbly or conglomeratic.

The Millstone Grit gives repeated signs of crustal restlessness, and in places lies with unconformity on the rocks beneath: thus the Castlecary Limestone is not to be found in parts of Renfrewshire, Ayrshire and Lanarkshire; and in south Lanarkshire the Grit rests on the Lower Limestone Group, in central Ayrshire on Cementstones. In consequence, it is not always easy to identify precisely the base of the Grit since the formation is negatively defined as the strata lying between the Upper Limestone Group and the Coal Measures. It is certain, however, that the formation is much reduced in thickness from about 340 feet near Glasgow to less than 100 feet in central Ayrshire. The effects of contemporaneous faulting are again to be recognised, notably by a great increase in thickness to over 400 feet near New Cumnock within a short distance of the Southern Uplands fault. At the same time it is evident from the sequence in the San-quhar and Thornhill basins that the Southern Uplands fault continued to be a formidable barrier to Carboniferous sedimentation; for in a thickness of only a few score feet of sediments beneath the Coal Measures, Lower and Upper Limestone Groups and Mill-stone Grit show various relations of overlap and overstep, including in places complete extinction by overstepping Coal Measures, that prove trivial net subsidence and inter-mittent revival of the up-faulted mass during sedimentation.

In Ayrshire, while the thickness of sediments may not be great, the full succession of the Millstone Grit is enlarged by the intercalation of basaltic lava flows, notably in the neighbourhood of Troon where they exceed 500 feet in thickness, that compare with the Clyde lavas in their effect on sedimentation. The rocks resting on their upper surface are unusual sediments: like the volcanic debris at the base of the Upper Sedi-mentary Group of the Calciferous Sandstones, they appear to be derived from the decay of ashy or lava detritus: as the Ayrshire Bauxitic Clays they contain much free alumina, layers that look not unlike laterite, ferruginous layers in which the mineral chamosite may be common, and haematitic pisolites—all features of rock-rot in humid subtropical conditions with some re-arrangement of the fragments by water transport.

THE COAL MEASURES

The Coal Measures of the district come to outcrop widely in the Central and Ayr-shire coalfields, over smaller areas in the Douglas coalfield and in the Sanquhar and Thornhill basins. They are sharply distinguished from the underlying Millstone Grit in containing a score of workable coal seams, a few of them thick, and in being almost without limestones except the important Skipsey's marine band that conveniently separates the Productive Coal Measures from the overlying Barren Red Measures. They are no less sharply distinguished in upward succession from the bright-red Permian sandstones of the Mauchline basin.

The rocks of the Coal Measures form an alternating sequence of sandstones, shales, fireclays, coal seams and thin ironstones. The rocks of the Productive Measures are generally grey or blue when fresh, though the sandstones weather to limonitic browns and yellows. The Barren Measures are red perhaps because of increasing aridity of climate during their formation—but the reddening may be secondary since red beds are known at horizons well below Skipsey's marine band, and the measures above it may be grey for scores of feet.

Numbers of mussel bands have been recorded from the Productive Measures, by means of which the beds have been shown to correlate with the Ammanian stage of other British coalfields, the Skipsey's marine band being equivalent to the Bolton marine band of Cumberland: the mussel bands are particularly important where, as in north Ayrshire, the marine bed is not found, and the top of the Millstone Grit is only to be defined lithologically. The lowest beds of the Barren Measures have yielded a few mussels of early Morganian age, but the group otherwise is without diagnostic fossils apart from plants.

The Productive Measures in the Central coalfield are about 1,200 feet thick. They thin to about 1,000 feet along the western outcrops, but without notable change in lithology. They consist of relatively fine-grained sediments, clays and shales with comparatively few sandstones. In north Ayrshire they are reduced to 500–700 feet: this may in part be due to late renewal of sedimentation after the volcanic episode of the Millstone Grit: it is not due to internal non-sequences, since all the Ammanian zones and most of the mussel bands have been recognised there. In south Ayrshire the thickness increases in conformity with what is known of the lower stratal groups, and reaches 1,400 feet at New Cumnock: the increase is due not to excessive development of sandstones alone but to a proportionate thickening of shales also; and the evidence must be accepted as again pointing to differential subsidence of the block adjacent to the Southern Uplands fault.

The Barren Red Measures, falling into the upper part of the Middle Coal Measures of current British classification, are highly variable in their detailed succession, and appear to have been deposited under less uniform conditions than the measures beneath. The general absence of coal seams and mussel bands is an obvious sign of a harsher environment for both plants and animals. At the same time, the red colouring in its patchy distribution may not be an original feature of the group, and staining, perhaps because of a former cover of New Red Sandstone, may well have contributed to the appearance of the strata.

The thickness of the Barren Measures is always residual, since they are followed unconformably by the Permian rocks. In the Central coalfield it is about 1,000 feet. It exceeds 1,500 feet on the southern flanks of the Mauchline basin, but diminishes to about 500 feet as it is followed northwards towards the north-western flanks. Though this reduction may reflect Permian overstep, it is not without significance in being parallel with that shown by the fully preserved Productive Measures beneath, and it may be due in part to tectonic causes.

ECONOMIC GEOLOGY OF THE CARBONIFEROUS ROCKS

The coals and ironstones of the coal measures have been the basis for the industrial growth of Glasgow and the West of Scotland during the past 250 years. Coals that at one time or another have been worked in the area are found in all the principal members of the Carboniferous formation, with the exception of the Cementstones; and it is to be recognised that there is a great contrast in the stratigraphical distribution of coal seams between Scotland and most of England outside Northumbria.

The coals of the Upper Calciferous Sandstone may sometimes reach considerable thickness—the Quarrelton Thick Coal of the Paisley-Johnstone ground is a multiple seam of 50 to 100 feet carrying a number of 'earth' partings—and have been extensively worked in the past, though they have a comparatively limited lateral range, like many of the individual rock beds of the group, and their reserves are limited even where they are not depleted. In the Lower Limestone Group a few coals, like the Hurlet Coal at its base and Lillie's 'Coal' (a highly bituminous shale) at a slightly higher horizon, were formerly worked especially in the Paisley district but now are of little or no importance.

The Limestone Coal Group is the most important coal-bearing group on the west flank of the Central coalfield, its strata as a whole being almost as thoroughly coal measures as those of the younger Productive Coal Measures—the nomenclatural distinction being essentially one of age and not of lithological contrast. Formerly the seams of the group were got over a wide outcrop extending from Stirling by Denny, Kilsyth and Kirkintilloch to Glasgow and Johnstone, and continuing again in north Ayrshire (where however the number of good seams is reduced to five or six). Over the whole of this outcrop signs of mining activity are ubiquitous, but the field has long entered a decline through the intensive exploitation of the more accessible coal; and although much coal remains still to be got it either lies at considerable depths beneath a cover of younger rocks or is so broken by faulting that the technical problems of working it make the cost of extraction uneconomic. Farther south in Ayrshire, between the Dusk Water and Inchgotrick faults, the outcrops of the group become diminished in extent and the workable seams reduced to only one or two. Still farther south, however, the group becomes thick and important again about Dalmellington, New Cumnock and Muirkirk, where seven or eight seams of good quality and from 2·5 to 7·5 feet thick (the Patna Thick Coal is a multiple seam reaching 17 feet) occur, and are comparatively undeveloped.

The Limestone Coal Group is of the age of the Millstone Grit of England, and although lithologically a precursor of the Coal Measures, is separated from the younger rocks by the Upper Limestone Group, in which workable coals are comparatively rare and only of local importance, and the Millstone Grit, from which they are virtually absent. There is thus in the cultural landscape usually a barren outcrop of intervening strata between the areas of bings and pit-heads where the older or younger coal measures occur to each side.

The Productive Measures form a wide expanse in the Central coalfield, though they occur in full development only in a few small areas centred chiefly about Bothwell and Hamilton. The seams of the series increase in thickness and value in upward succession, so that those of the smallest extension happen to be the most important. In consequence, the intense exploitation in the past of the better and higher seams has resulted in their near-exhaustion at the present day; and the reserves worth working are even smaller than those of the Limestone Coal Group. In Ayrshire, on the other hand, while the number of workable seams in the Kilmarnock basin diminishes eastwards from about a dozen to only four or five, those of the southern outcrops—from Ayr to Dalmellington and New Cumnock, and in the small Dailly coalfield—are relatively thick (about a score are two feet or more in thickness) and of good quality, and are a source of rich reserves.

Most of the coals of the Glasgow district are bituminous, rich in lustrous clarain, containing 80 to 90 per cent of carbon and 30 to 40 per cent of volatile matter: they are hence useful for a great variety of purposes—as house, gas and coking coals, and as steam-raising coals in industry. They are the product of the devolatilisation, probably through the effects of pressure, of plant humus accumulated *in situ* as a Carboniferous forest peat. They differ from the comparatively uncommon splint coals, which are usually rich in durain, dull and compact in contrast to the bituminous coals, and are sometimes cannels formed of carbonised washed-in plant detritus. There is no true primary anthracite in the Glasgow district—that is, coal of very high carbon (over 90 per cent) and correspondingly low volatile content—formed by the same process of coalification as the bituminous coals. Locally, however, anthracite has been accidentally produced by the metamorphism of coal seams in the neighbourhood of igneous intrusions. The conversion near Kirkintilloch of the Haughrigg bituminous seam into anthracite by the heat of a whin sill is a particularly well-authenticated instance where there is clear correlation of diminishing volatile content of the coal with proximity to and magnitude of the intrusion.

The ironstones of the Coal Measures are segregates mainly of siderite (ferrous carbonate) in shales usually rich in pyrite. They formed as secondary concretions, and may occur as isolated nodules or balls, usually strung along bedding planes, or may have become enlarged to grow by mutual contact into a continuous sheet or bed. They commonly contain intermixed clay minerals and are clay-ironstones that oxidise and disintegrate on weathering. The blackband ironstones are intrinsically no different, except in having been formed in shales containing abundant carbonaceous matter. The ironstones were exploited in vast quantities during the nineteenth century, but the exhaustion of the surface and near-surface resources, and the cost of working the bands by mining at depth, have caused the decline and virtual extinction of the industry.

CARBONIFEROUS IGNEOUS ROCKS

Contemporaneous igneous rocks are strongly developed in the Carboniferous groups of the Midland Valley, notably in the Calciferous Sandstone Series (as the Clyde plateau lavas) and the Millstone Grit of the Glasgow district. They form, and have controlled the erosion of, the hills encircling Glasgow to north, west and south; and on a smaller scale they contribute to the roughnesses of the landscape when as sills and dykes they project above the neighbouring general surface (Fig. 11).

The lavas of the Clyde group are more than 3,000 feet thick in the Campsie Fells, and are only a little thinner in the Kilpatrick Hills. They show some thinning in Renfrewshire, where, however, they exceed 2,000 feet; and are again preserved to the same order of thickness in the hills about Eaglesham. How far the lavas continue eastwards under the Central coalfield is unknown, or how far they formerly extended northwards beyond their present scarp limits; but at a conservative estimate they covered an area of not less than 600 square miles, even when the comparatively thin flows of Bute, Arran and central Ayrshire are ignored, and had a volume of perhaps 200 cubic miles when they were first outpoured. (See Plate VI.)

The original plateau of widespread lava sheets was, of course, not the product of extrusion from a single volcanic centre. There is abundant evidence of many vents where the lava cover has been removed by erosion; and many of the dykes to be seen cutting the lavas and the flanking sediments may also have been feeders to the flows. Moreover, the variations in chemical and physical characters of the lavas, both geographically and (not so markedly) in vertical sequence, leave little doubt that the flows must have been emitted from independent vents or fissures and were fed either from separate magma reservoirs or from segregated magma differentiates. In some instances, particularly in the Campsie Fells, it is possible to demonstrate the virtual identity of the igneous rock choking a volcanic vent with the rock of neighbouring lava sheets.

It is no less evident that volcanic activity waxed and waned independently in neighbouring centres. The high variability in thickness of the underlying Cementstones is almost proof of this: unless they were deposited on an extremely uneven floor, their thinning from 650 feet to zero along the front face of the Campsie escarpment is a sign of lateral equivalence of lavas and sediments—the lavas in the western Campsies

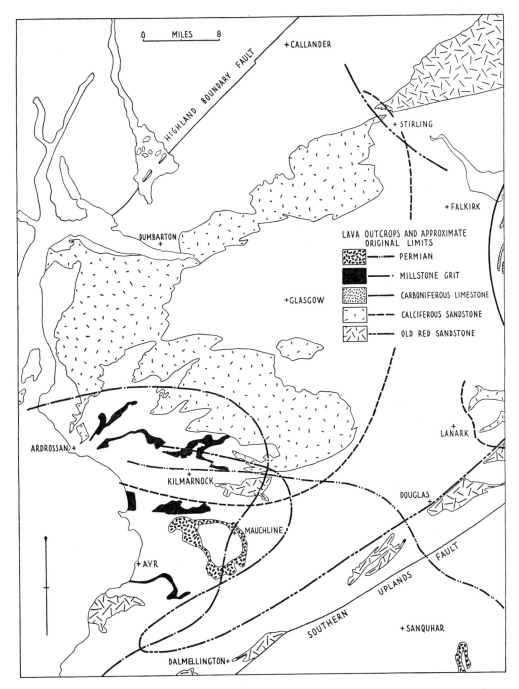

FIG. 11. Outline map showing the distribution of the principal masses of igneous rock in the Glasgow district.

not having been poured out until the sediments had accumulated. On the western slopes of the Renfrewshire Hills there is a similar chronologically transgressive descent of the lavas across the Cementstones on to Old Red Sandstone.

The lavas of the Clyde group are dominantly olivine basalts. Their conditions of cooling and of extrusion varied, and they fall into a number of conveniently recognised types distinguished by the larger and more conspicuous crystals they contain. In the flows forming the tiers on the Campsie scarp face—more than thirty have been counted —the lower members are mainly of Jedburgh basalt, a type with large (porphyritic) felspar and olivine crystals in a fine-grained matrix. The flows above are mainly Markle basalts, with smaller olivine crystals. Dunsapie basalts, with porphyritic augite crystals, are well represented in the Kilpatrick Hills; and Dalmeny basalts, with olivine alone as the common phenocryst, in the Eaglesham uplands. A single flow may occasionally be composite and show transition from one kind of basalt to another. Not all the flows are basaltic, however: more acid types, including trachytic and rhyolitic rocks, are known in Renfrewshire and in the Eaglesham hills, and there are common occurrences of intermediate rocks in most areas: the interlayering of the different kinds of flows implies notable chemical differentiation of the fluid magmas at depth.

Most of the extrusive rocks are the result of the non-violent welling of magmas, and fragmental products are comparatively rare. Towards the base of the Clyde sequence tuffs and fine ashes are widespread, but the explosive phase was short-lived. Detrital layers, sometimes with coarse fragments, on the other hand are of not uncommon occurrence between successive lava flows, and prove that the lava piles formed extensive land surfaces standing above neighbouring water level. They consist typically of bole— the rotted residues formed on the surface of a basaltic lava sheet exposed to subaerial denudation, especially when in a humid climate a cover of vegetation furnishes humic acids to intensify the processes of decomposition. The development of detrital layers between some of the Millstone Grit lavas of Ayrshire—mainly olivine basalts of Dalmeny type—may show more complex alteration of the slaggy lava surfaces, brought about by the soaking of the rock in shallow pools and by aqueous leaching and sorting to form not only kaolinitic and bauxitic residues like the Bauxitic Clay, but also small concretions and coagulated particles that give the detritus an oolitic appearance. In some instances the oolithic grains may be broken by desiccation, and the fragments re-cemented in newly grown ooliths.

Volcanic necks are numerous, usually forming prominent hills more or less round in plan, like the duns north of Glasgow, Dumbarton Rock, Neilston Pad. Those of the north face of the Campsie Fells are spectacular examples of aligned series (Fig. 12). They may be choked with basaltic agglomerate, or with normal basalt no different from the rocks of the lava flows. The well-known vent at Heads of Ayr, about 1,000 yards in diameter, dissected by the sea to show clearly its near-vertical walls and its internal structure, displays steeply inclined layering of the agglomeratic contents inwards, the successive layers indicating some lateral movement in the position of the main pipe as material was driven to the surface. In the vent, as in others, the agglomerate may consist of a mixture of many rock types indicating the structure of the crust through which the pipe was punched. (See Plates VI, VII, XIII.)

Of other intrusions of Carboniferous age in the Glasgow district, dykes and sills are

42

very common, but larger stocks and bosses are unknown. Some of the dykes are obviously associated with particular volcanic vents, notably dykes of Markle basalt in the Campsie Fells, and of trachyte around the agglomerate of the Meikle Bin vent north of Glasgow and around the Misty Law centre in Renfrewshire. But many of them are

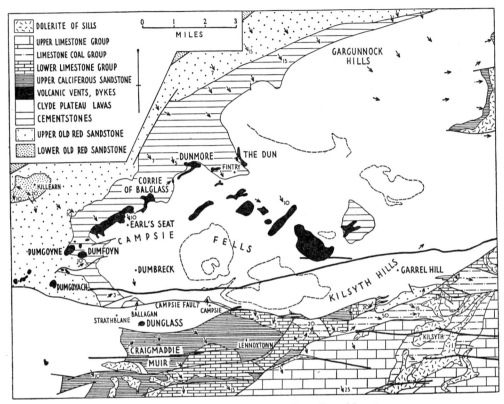

FIG. 12. Geological map of the Campsie Fells and neighbouring country.
After maps of the Geological Survey.

not certainly dated as of Carboniferous age, and may be Permian. The thick quartz-dolerite dykes that continue for long distances in the Midland Valley—the Campsie dyke runs from the Clyde to the Forth—have a consistent east-and-west strike that implies a major crustal fracture pattern as a component of the structural frame of the rift.

The large sills are sometimes manifestly off-shoots of the dykes; but they appear to be much more varied in composition (partly perhaps as a result of differentiation during intrusion), and their feeders cannot always be identified. Teschenitic and monchiquitic types are common, and often show differentiation or composite layering in place—the Lugar sill is especially well known for this characteristic. The quartz-dolerite sills, mostly of 'Permo-Carboniferous' age, are perhaps the most spectacular of the intrusions: they form asymmetrical hills showing scarp and 'dip' slopes, and form a base for large-scale crag-and-tail moulding by ice. Often they stand boldly above neighbouring ground and, notably in the Kilsyth-Stirling area, form conspicuous elements in the landscape.

43

In the Glasgow district rocks of Permian age, the lower members of the New Red Sandstone, are limited at the present day to the Mauchline basin; but since outliers are found in Arran and elsewhere in western Scotland, and in the Sanquhar and other basins in the Southern Uplands, it is probable that they formerly extended over much, perhaps all, of the Midland Valley and have since been removed by erosion.

The sediments, the Mauchline Sandstone, differ from any of the earlier strata in being almost wholly of wind-borne origin. They consist of bright-red sandstones of variable coarseness almost completely without other kinds of interbedded rocks. The high degree of sorting in most layers, the absence of water-borne pebbles, and the well-rounded highly polished 'millet-seed' sand grains that form the rock all point to transport by wind; and the individual massive sandstone posts show the violent cross-bedding that is characteristic of dune accumulations in open country. The sediments have the features of 'erg'—the vast piles of coalesced dunes that are typical of parts of the Sahara desert—and their red colouration reinforces the view that they accumulated on a land surface produced by the elevation of tracts of Carboniferous sediments above sea-level to form a continental area in an arid climate. The Permian rocks thus rest with unconformity on the underlying strata, and although the break in sedimentation is not revealed by notable difference in dip between the two formations, it marks the change from a marine or estuarine to a continental environment and is a sign of the beginnings of earth-movements that towards the close of Permian times were to become very powerful and to transform the structure of the Midland Valley.

In places the Permian rocks are desert sands where they rest directly on the Carboniferous; but the bulk of the Mauchline Sandstone, 1,500 feet thick, lies above a volcanic series that represents the last pulsatory outburst of igneous activity during Lower Palaeozoic times. The volcanic rocks, 500 feet thick, have thin layers of tuff near their base, and tuffs are also to be found towards the top of the sequence; but the bulk of the rocks is composed of olivine basalts of Dalmeny type occurring as numerous flows often separated from one another by thin films of red desert sand. The feeders of the flows are exposed in the truncated summits of over sixty volcanic necks in central Ayrshire. They contain agglomeratic accumulations of igneous material and of sedimentary fragments derived from the rocks punctured by the pipes. The possibility that some of the sills cutting the Carboniferous rocks are of Permian age has already been commented on.

THE HERCYNIAN EARTH-MOVEMENTS

The rôle of the Caledonian earth-movements was dominant in establishing the structural scaffolding of the Midland Valley and in controlling the distribution and manner of formation of the Upper Palaeozoic rocks. The movements were followed by a period of quiescence, when oscillations and warpings of the rift floor were comparatively gentle and affected structural form in only a minor degree. At the close of Permian times, however, a second major episode of crustal deformation imposed on the rocks of the area a system of folds and fractures that affected the younger strata no less than the older, and stamped a grain upon the country, and established a geomorphic pattern, that was to persist until the present day. Far more violently expressed in continental

Europe than in Scotland, the earth-movements have been given the name of Hercynian from their manifestation in the Harz Mountains.

The tectonic struts foundational to the structure of the Midland Valley—as of a great part of 'oldland' Britain—were laid down in Caledonian times and were in part congeneric with the crustal downwarp of the Lower Palaeozoic geosyncline. Their dominant grain is north-east-and-south-west; and they determined the place and controlled the mode of deposition of the Upper Palaeozoic sediments. The rift is their most obvious expression in Scotland; and in the rift there accumulated on the floor of Lower Palaeozoic rocks thicknesses of Old Red Sandstone, Carboniferous and Permian sediments and lavas that at their greatest were more than 10,000 feet, perhaps as much as 15,000 feet. Thicknesses varied significantly from place to place, and it is evident from the lateral changes displayed by the Upper Palaeozoic rocks that within the rift there were swells and fractures of Caledonian heritage that were influential in diversifying facies and in containing igneous activity. But these variations lie within the graben, which as a structural unit was a negative area throughout Upper Palaeozoic times, and which in its tectonic environment was in major contrast to the positive areas on its flanks—the Highlands and the Southern Uplands—receiving no more than a comparatively negligible veneer of sediments, perhaps 2,000 feet at most, during the same period.

Hercynian deformation was the product of crustal pressures that over the greater part of Britain—itself an outpost of European arcs of orogeny—were exerted broadly along meridional lines. The resulting east-and-west tectonic grain is well exhibited in southern England and Wales; but the dissipation of energy northwards is manifest in the resolution of force to be recognised in the derivative folds and faults of northern England and Scotland. In particular, the Hercynian pressures were incompetent to impose novel structural patterns on the Midland Valley, where the basic framework was too completely built-in to be over-ridden by later movement. In broad generalisation, the Hercynian structures of the Glasgow district, as of the whole Midland Valley, are the product of the re-direction of northward-driving pressures by the resistant Caledonian struts.

The main effects of the resolution of pressures in such a physical frame were to produce compression north-westwards and shear north-eastwards. The fore-shortening in the form of Hercynian folds thus has a grain virtually parallel with that of the earlier Caledonian folds. It is obvious that in outline the Midland Valley, conforming to expectation, is both a rift and a caledonoid syncline. Its oldest rocks broadly come to outcrop along its flanks, and its youngest in its central parts. Where the syncline has minor folds superimposed, they also take on a caledonoid trend, often an inherited caledonoid trend from minor Caledonian structures within the graben.

The simplicity of the theoretical arrangement is nevertheless obviously made more complicated by the lack of homogeneity of the Upper Palaeozoic rocks; and especially in the region of the thick and resistant Clyde lavas the asymmetry of the folded rocks is displayed in a corresponding asymmetry and distortion of the Hercynian folds. For parts of its length the main axis of the Central coalfield syncline, lying on the eastern margin of the lava masses, has a north-and-south alignment; and the longer axis of the Mauchline basin is even more oblique to the regional trend. In any particular instance the precise interaction of a number of independent variables that controlled the formation of the local structures—the relative competency of the several groups of strata, the form of the immediate Lower Palaeozoic foundation, the pattern of the surrounding structural context, the occurrence and magnitude of wedges of igneous rocks—is impossible to determine, and the local structure is a net product of deformation.

Similarly the caledonoid faults do not always provide proof of a strike-slip component of movement; but it is evident that the Highland Boundary fault and the Southern Uplands fault were active along their present courses in post-Carboniferous times, and that at least along the Highland border, where effective downthrow is towards the north near Balmaha and Helensburgh, towards the south at Toward Point, movement along the fault must have had a strong horizontal element. Within the rift it is no less clear that some of the major faults of caledonoid trend, like the Inchgotrick fault, are at the same time post-Carboniferous in age in their effects on the Upper Palaeozoic strata, and pre-Carboniferous in having controlled Carboniferous sedimentation. Other fractures in the district, notably those running east-and-west along courses adopted by some of the larger dykes, may be regarded as members of conjugate systems reflecting the north-westward direction of the principal compressive force.

However the genesis of the structures may be explained, in the result the Glasgow district occupies a multiple syncline between the margins of the rift. Glasgow itself lies in the core of a broken flank-fold of the basin of the Central coalfield, a minor syncline whose pitch is broadly delineated by the horse-shoe outcrop of the Clyde lavas. To the south-west a second minor syncline, pitching westwards, is occupied by the Kilmarnock coal basin, in which an elongate outlier of Barren Red Measures is preserved: it is incomplete on its southern limb, where the Inchgotrick fault throws up a wedge-shaped outcrop of Old Red Sandstone and Lower Carboniferous rocks that broadens eastwards and may be regarded as obliquely extending the anticline in Silurian rocks of the Nutberry Hill range. The wedge is followed southwards by the Mauchline basin, with its cover of Permian rocks the most deeply folded of the synclines of the Midland Valley. The basin has a counterpart in the small but tightly folded syncline of the Douglas coalfield, Barren Red Measures in its core, that is caught between the Silurian anticline of the Hagshaw Hills and the up-faulted Ordovician rocks of the Southern Uplands. (See Figs. 13, 14.)

A particular and economically important instance of the secondary effects of Hercynian pressures on primary Caledonian structures is provided in the mineralised Leadhills area, where a fracture pattern imposed on the tightly folded Ordovician grits and greywackes after the close of Silurian times was re-orientated by oblique Hercynian stress, and into the opened joints produced thereby mineralising fluids migrated from magmatic sources at depth to deposit the ore-veins of lead and zinc.

THE INTERLUDE OF MESOZOIC AND TERTIARY TIMES

The erosive stripping from the Glasgow district—as from the whole Midland Valley—of any former cover of Mesozoic and Tertiary sediments removed any direct means of interpreting stratigraphically the history of the area for the greater part of 200 million years. What inferences can be made of events during that long period of time are based on extrapolation of evidence from other parts of Scotland, or on the relics of past stages of geomorphic evolution that may still be recognised in the present-day landscape.

46

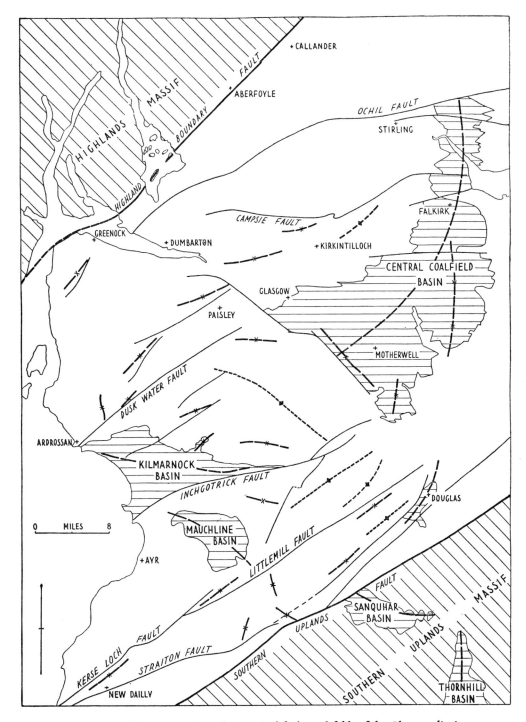

FIG. 13. Outline map to show the principal faults and folds of the Glasgow district.

47

The low-lying position of the area between uplands on both flanks is no present measure of its former altitude. The Hercynian folds, though not of such great amplitude as the Caledonian, had crestal ridges that are estimated to be of the order of thousands of feet above the synclinal troughs: the heart of the Mauchline basin, for instance, could have been not less than 5,500 feet lower than the edge of the Inchgotrick scarp five miles to the north at the time of the formation of the structures—or would have been if the scarp had not suffered erosive degradation as it was rising. The Midland Valley is thus a topographical feature that is the end-product of long-continued erosion during which the primary forms of the Hercynian folds—the latest pre-Glacial stratigraphical stage of which we have direct evidence—became almost totally obliterated.

The former extension of Triassic and Jurassic rocks into the area is now no more than a matter for speculation, though the Trias in nearby Arran makes likely the possibility that the formation extended eastwards to rest on the Permian at least of parts of Ayrshire. There is a greater probability attaching to the surmise that Cretaceous rocks, at least those of Chalk age, may have covered not merely the Midland Valley but the flanking uplands also. Their occurrence in Arran, and at several other localities farther north along the western Scottish coast, and their strong development in Antrim—all on the far side of the main Chalk outcrop in Lincolnshire and Yorkshire—has for long been regarded as a sign of a former cover that more or less completely buried all older rocks with gross unconformity.

The Chalk, if the hypothesis is accepted, formed a virtually continuous layer at first deposition. By analogy with its structural form in Antrim and England, it may be supposed to have been elevated above sea-level during early Tertiary times as a gentle dome whose crestal regions lay between the present-day low-lying Chalk outcrops. Doubtless the dome had minor folds on its flanks, and it certainly was broken by faults, some of them with throws of several hundred feet, along the line of the 'Hebridean rift'. But whatever its detailed form may have been, the dome as such is obviously now gone from mainland Scotland as a result of post-Cretaceous erosion.

The rivers that were the main agents in eroding the dome and removing the Chalk cover were initiated on the surface of the dome as it was uplifted. Hence, although the Chalk is now completely removed, the rivers, inherited by the underlying rocks from the Chalk cover, may still preserve the essential pattern they acquired on their inception, may still flow in directions that originally were directions of dip on the dome, may still be interpreted as form-lines of the structures imposed on mainland Scotland by the Tertiary earth-movements. That is, the present river pattern is superimposed on the underlying rocks and structures, the discordance of drainage and structure being itself an indication of the former Cretaceous cover. That the rivers are in fact superimposed is manifest: for instance, the Clyde follows a course that crosses indifferently all the major structures in its path, including the Southern Uplands fault and the complex basin of the Central coalfield; Loch Lomond, and the drowned valleys occupied by the sea lochs to the west, traverse the structures in the Dalradian rocks and the Highland Boundary fault, as though they did not exist; the Firth of Clyde, clearly an extension of Loch Long, truncates rock outcrops, dykes and faults on its margin with an equal disregard.

The stripping of the Chalk from its unconformable position above the older rocks saw also an exposure of the sub-Cretaceous surface, a plane of marine transgression which, if not completely mutilated by continued erosion, should still be identifiable in

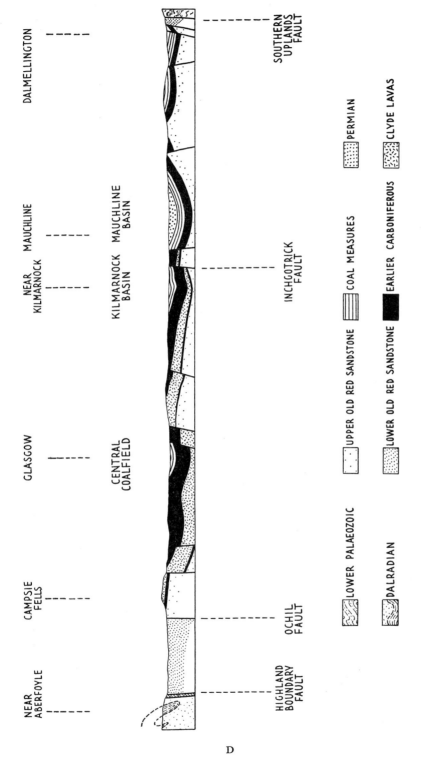

NEAR
ABERFOYLE

CAMPSIE
FELLS

GLASGOW

NEAR
KILMARNOCK

MAUCHLINE

DALMELLINGTON

HIGHLAND
BOUNDARY
FAULT

OCHIL
FAULT

CENTRAL
COALFIELD

KILMARNOCK
BASIN

MAUCHLINE
BASIN

INCHGOTRICK
FAULT

SOUTHERN
UPLANDS
FAULT

LOWER PALAEOZOIC

DALRADIAN

UPPER OLD RED SANDSTONE

LOWER OLD RED SANDSTONE

COAL MEASURES

EARLIER CARBONIFEROUS

PERMIAN

CLYDE LAVAS

FIG. 14. Cross-section to illustrate diagrammatically the structure of the Glasgow district. The length of the section is about 60 miles.

D

49

remnants on the flat-topped crests of the higher hills. Even when the primary upland surfaces are almost obliterated by the later paring-back of valley sides, the final residual hill peaks should display a general agreement in altitude to be integrated into the same reconstructed surface. Since many of the local hill summits are plateau-like or gently undulating, and truncate the strata without reflecting the underlying structure—the summits of the hill-rim around Glasgow from Nutberry to Hill of Stake and thence to the Campsies all rise to within a few hundred feet of the 2,000 foot contour and lie amongst hill masses of appropriate profile—they appear at first glance to be strong evidence complementary to the superimposed drainage-pattern that accords with and supports the hypothesis.

Nevertheless, the hypothesis, attractive in its simplicity and in its apparent accommodation of the facts, proves unsatisfactory on closer analysis: while the river system is truly described as superimposed, and the regional land surface into which the rivers have cut is a dissected plateau, it becomes impossible to accept the conclusion that these features of the landscape are the direct product of evolution from a Chalk cover when the plateau is transected by post-Chalk igneous dykes, and is a composite plateau made up of a staircase of platforms.

TERTIARY DYKES

Outside the Glasgow district, particularly in the Hebrides, early Tertiary times were times of igneous activity characterised by vast outpourings of lavas. Like the Clyde lavas, the Tertiary flows covered several hundred square miles in area (though perhaps not as completely unbroken sheets), and attained thicknesses in the neighbourhood of the volcanic centres of 1,500–2,000 feet. While some of the flows may have been extruded from dyke-like fissures, the majority appear to be the products of centralised vents of which five or six have been recognised. A measure of the age of the vulcanicity is provided by the manner in which the flows rest indifferently on older rocks from Cretaceous to Pre-Cambrian; and there is no doubt that they were poured out onto a varied and irregular land surface that had been subjected to long-continued erosion and from which the great part of any Chalk cover had been removed. Interbedded with the flows at a number of localities are sediments laid down during lulls in the volcanic activity in shallow lakes on the lava surfaces: locally the sediments are richly plant-bearing—some of them are lignites—and have yielded species of a warm temperate to subtropical flora that allow them to be dated approximately as of early Tertiary age. The whole rock-group thus helps to fill the wide gaps in Scottish stratigraphy, and provides glimpses of a landscape evolution that would otherwise be completely lost in obscurity. The evidence may to some degree be extrapolated to the Glasgow district.

Only one Tertiary volcanic centre, that of Arran, lay in the Midland Valley, but it was highly local in its effects and none of its extrusive products was carried much beyond the present limits of the island. It is improbable that the mainland rift received any cover of lavas—unlike its extension in Ireland, where the Antrim basalts flooded the whole depression and spilled over the bounding faults to north and south. If lavas had extended to the mainland in early Tertiary times, however, it is reasonable to suppose that they would then have covered much the same kind of surface as that flooring them in Arran—a surface as varied as the present-day surface, with rocks of all ages from

50

Lower Old Red Sandstone to Trias, folded and faulted by Hercynian and post-Triassic movements, coming to outcrop in it. It is clear that (as in some of the more northern exposures) the Chalk cover had been all but completely removed before the volcanic activity began, and much of the sub-Cretaceous platform with it.

More direct evidence is provided by some of the Tertiary dykes. The precise cause of the concentration of dyke swarms about each of the main volcanic centres is unknown, but it is evident that the dykes, fed from depth, reflect a relief of pressure in a deep-seated magma reservoir owing to tensional stress in the overlying crust. Their persistently maintained courses along north-west-and-south-east lines run normal to the tensional force, and distinguish them in areas, like the Midland Valley, where earlier dyke systems have caledonoid or east-and-west Hercynian courses.

Dykes from the Arran centre are comparatively close-set and have no great surface extension: although they exist in hundreds on Arran itself, few of them reach the mainland of Ayrshire, where, of coarse-grained crinanitic composition, they are seen notably near Heads of Ayr. None of the Skye swarm appears to have extended as far south as the Midland Valley; but the very much wider belt of the Mull cluster has a greater lateral penetration, and several of its members enter and cross the Midland Valley and continue through the Southern Uplands into northern England. Typically they are tholeiitic basalts or quartz-dolerites, and are usually much fresher than and recognisably different in mineralogical and chemical composition from any Palaeozoic dykes. The largest of them, 20 to 130 feet in width, have only short gaps in outcrop where they may confidently be interpolated, and have been followed for distances of over 100 miles.

The dykes are intrinsically important for the evidence they provide of Tertiary igneous activity in the Glasgow district, which lay just beyond the periphery of the extrusive phase. But they are even more important geomorphically in proving that at the time of their intrusion the present land surface where they now run had not come into existence: for manifestly a truncated dyke, from which no lava spills on either side, was truncated after intrusion. The Moneyacres-Hawick-Acklington dyke and the Barrmill-Muirkirk-Hartfell dyke cut through the Renfrewshire uplands almost at their highest point, the former also continuing through the summits of Nutberry Hill and Hagshaw Hill, and a branch of the latter almost through the summit of Cairn Table. In the Southern Uplands a short distance beyond the Glasgow district they similarly run through the summits of a number of residual hills in the regional plateau. The much more numerous members of the Mull swarm north of the Highland border in Argyll repeatedly crop out at altitudes above 2,000 feet. The evidence of the irregular and deeply eroded Chalk-stripped surface upon which the Tertiary lavas rest, the residual monadnock summits (as in Arran, on the mainland side of the 'Hebridean rift') of the volcanic rocks, the relatively severe deformation the volcanic rocks have undergone, and the erosion of the Tertiary dykes emergent on the present plateau surface, is strongly opposed to a hypothesis that any appreciable remnant of a sub-Cretaceous floor can now be recognised anywhere in the Glasgow district.

CYCLES OF EROSION

The much degraded surfaces of whatever high-level plateaus may still be represented in the Glasgow district are not now readily distinguished or correlated, partly because of the isolation of the remnants, partly because of glacial mutilation, partly perhaps because of a warping that can no longer be separated from erosive effects. Nevertheless, in parts of the area the occurrence of several cycles of plateau formation is clearly demonstrated by the association of geomorphic elements. Thus Ben Lomond is a spectacular outpost of the Highland plateau—itself probably a composite landform of complex origin, parts of it conceivably carrying a Cretaceous stamp—where summit heights commonly range above 3,000 feet. Immediately to the south-east there is a sharp fall, almost a cliff face, to much lower ground where summits are less than 2,000 feet but nevertheless repeatedly rise towards 2,000 feet—in Ben Uird and Ben Bhreac, the Campsie Fells, the Kilsyth Hills, the Renfrewshire Hills, Nutberry Hill, Cairn Table and the hills about, a number of the foothills of the Southern Uplands, and (a little to the east, outside the district) the Pentland Hills. The topography provides a strong suggestion that Ben Lomond (and its Highland neighbours) look down upon a greatly dissected surface that at one time impinged abruptly against their foot. (Pl. XIII.)

On the southern flanks of the Midland Valley the contrasts in relief are not quite so spectacular, but the Lowther Hills and Tinto, Blackcraig and Windy Standard, and just outside the district Culter Fell and Glenwhappen Rig, have approximately accordant summits at about 2,300 feet, and are relatively abruptly upstanding above the lower ground to the north. If there has been no significant warping they may therefore be looked upon as representing a third and intermediate member of a succession of stepped platforms.

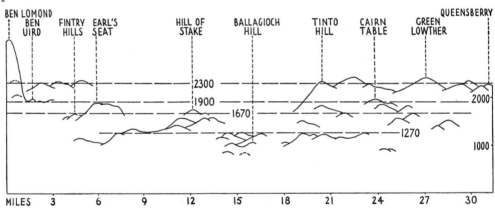

FIG. 15. Projected north-and-south profiles to illustrate benched landforms in the Glasgow district.

At lower altitudes the cover of glacial drift becomes thicker and more widespread, and the true form of the pre-Glacial surface increasingly difficult to determine. A full analysis of the possibilities in the district of integrating the summits in 'solid' rock has yet to be made: only in general and tentative terms can it be suggested that a statistical crowding of summit heights appears to be recognisable at three or four levels between about 1,600 feet and about 400+ feet, and that regionally the landscape is benched, the successive benches within the comparatively small areal limits of the district showing no significant warping (Fig. 15).

The benches, of age diminishing with altitude, are best, though perhaps not certainly, explained as being of marine origin, and as marking stages in the fall of sea-

52

level effectively under eustatic conditions. Each bench at its formation encroached upon and more or less destroyed earlier benches, not always symmetrically; and not every bench is necessarily preserved in relict form on the profiles of the higher hills. Thus the south face of the Campsie escarpment locally falls unbrokenly over 1,000 feet in less than a mile, and the north face of the Fintry and Gargunnock Hills as abruptly; and the Ayrshire plain at 400+ feet around the Ayr and Lugar valleys runs close under the hill range between Patna and New Cumnock whose summit levels are around 1,100 feet.

While the conceptual stages of landscape evolution are clearly enough expressed in the staircase of platforms, the field evidence at any particular locality of their real existence is thus commonly mutilated and obscured for various reasons; but despite an uncertainty that is inevitable in country degraded by intense river and ice erosion, the kind of landscape it is and the process of its formation appear to be sufficiently well established. It is evident that any Chalk cover that may at one time have been present was gone before the successive benches were planed. The higher benches truncate the Tertiary dykes and therefore are later than early Tertiary in age. In being insignificantly deformed they are also later than any Tertiary ('Alpine') crustal folding or fracturing that may have affected the area—folding and faulting not directly known in the Glasgow district, but causing strong deformation of the Tertiary igneous rocks in the Hebrides and (less markedly) in Arran. They are therefore probably of later Tertiary age (Neogene, perhaps mainly Pliocene), and were sculptured in a landscape, a product of long evolution during Mesozoic and early Tertiary times, of which in the Glasgow district almost nothing remains or is known.

The stepped fall in altitude of the benches is generally towards the central parts of the Midland Valley—a valley the imprint of whose present form emerged as the lower benches were planed. It is not improbable that differential erosion, controlled in part by rate of cliff recession, directly reflected geological structure; and although in places the planed surfaces transgressed the marginal faults (as on the southern slopes of Ben Lomond), in other places failed to reach the faults (as in the lee of Tinto), the present landscape secondarily reveals the main frame of the foundations laid in Caledonian and Hercynian times. Within the Midland Valley it is probable that at least some of the residual hill masses—notably the Campsie Fells edged by the Campsie fault—are further expressions of the control exerted on bench formation by geological structure.

Where the valley profiles have not been remoulded by ice, a number of the rivers confirm the evidence of polycyclic erosion provided by the benches in the occurrence of knick points and valley-wall shoulders. The Clyde is an outstanding example of such rejuvenation where, near Lanark, it leaves a wide open mature valley, filled with alluvium in which it meanders gently, and plunges over the Falls of Lanark to enter a steep-walled gorge through which it drops nearly 200 feet in little over a mile: the long profile of the upper reach, whose descent through the same interval spans nearly twenty miles above the Falls, is graded to a local base-level just below 600 feet.

DRAINAGE AND GLACIATION

It is difficult to recognise a consistent pattern in the river system of the Glasgow district. The primary streams, like the Clyde, were presumably superimposed by extension on the successive benches at each stage of emergence. At the present day, however,

53

most of them are too short, or have been too much changed in direction by glacial influence, for this relationship to be obvious; and nearly all of them have had their valleys over-deepened by glacial scour or choked with morainic debris so that profiles have lost their signs of rejuvenation. The headwaters of the Nith and the Afton reveal clear evidence of former high-level courses northwards before they were diverted to the existing Nith valley at New Cumnock; the streams of the Campsie and Kilpatrick hills hang steeply in their upper valleys; the River Calder and certain other streams draining from Hill of Stake show several well-marked knick points; and short reaches in a number of other streams conform to the expected profile. But over most of the lower ground, and in all the lochs north of the Clyde, it is now almost impossible to see behind glacial mutilation to pre-Glacial form.

A plausible reconstruction of the immediately pre-Glacial river system that has invited wide acceptance regards the Midland Valley, truly then a valley, as the site of a dominant longitudinal trunk stream. At the present day the stream has been dismembered, but the through depression running from the Clyde to the Forth, a low-lying dry gap at its crest at Kelvinhead a little east of Kilsyth, is the obvious relic of its former course, and was the route followed by the western members of the present Clyde drainage. Analogy may be made with the rivers of the Highlands, which fall into a pattern controlled by an asymmetrical principal watershed that lies very near the west coast and that gives to the east-flowing members long and comparatively gentle courses, and to the west-flowing only a few miles in which to tumble from sources high in the mountains into the sea. Extrapolated, the same watershed in the Glasgow district is surmised to have run from Cowal into Renfrewshire and thence south-eastwards. From its crest the original streams flowed east across what are now some of the larger lochs (including Loch Fyne, Loch Long, and Loch Lomond) and, combining as a reversed lower Clyde, met some of the Renfrewshire rivers to converge through the Kelvinhead gap on the Forth near Falkirk. The disruption of the original drainage to produce the present-day system was brought about by dismemberment and submergence that followed the work of the ice in trenching the discordant sea lochs across the earlier grain, Loch Long and its continuation in the Firth of Clyde being a principal pirate.

The reconstruction, in bringing the Clyde system into conformity with what is found farther north, and in regarding the Midland Valley as the unified basin of an enlarged Forth and its tributaries, has an obvious integrative appeal. In the details of its elements it uses dry valleys and wind-gaps, and aligned segments of now-dismembered streams, as guides to former courses, and is thus not without some support in the field evidence. As a first approximation the reconstruction is attractive, and brings order to apparent chaos; and it doubtless contains some truth.

On the other hand, if the evidence of rejuvenation of the Clyde at Lanark is to be accepted for what it seems, the river was already adjusted to the high-level bench in that area long before Glacial times; and its only possible course downstream for a number of miles was north-westwards. It could still have swung through a quarter-circle by Coatbridge to reach the Forth through the Kelvinhead gap; only if it was flanked to the west by high hills where its valley now lies. It is simpler to suppose that it continued westwards without hindrance.

In minor ways an interpretation of parts of the river system in terms of a secondary adjustment to underlying structure is obvious. Strathblane, for instance, linking the

Loch Lomond depression with the Kilsyth gap, owes its position in part to the alignment of the Campsie fault between the Campsie Fells and the Kilpatrick Hills; and the similar valleys, with dry cols, of the Johnstone and Barrhead gaps that break southwestwards through the Renfrewshire hills follow almost exactly the course of two prominent Hercynian faults.

In its main features, however, the origin of the drainage north and north-east of the lower Clyde remains obscure. While in a vague and general sense the south-running rivers and lochs of the Highlands are in accord with the inferences made of the benched history of the Midland Valley, the isolation of the several blocks of the Clyde lavas, and the numerous gaps in the divides of the Highlands, are elements of landscape that require systematic analysis, yet to be carried out, of both pre-Glacial and Glacial stages if a consistent integration is to be got. It may be that the work of the ice was too destructive to allow all stages of geomorphic evolution now to be recognised or a single comprehensive synthesis to emerge.

A complex association of landforms placed the Glasgow district in the path of ice-streams converging onto the ground from a number of centres. The main flows were from snowfields nourished in the Highlands. The flows descending northwards from the Southern Uplands were neither so large nor so powerful, but they were of sufficient magnitude to counter the force of Highland ice, and the massif of the Uplands stood throughout the Ice Age as an almost unbreached barrier against which the Highland ice broke. Smaller flows from more local centres made their contribution to the composite glaciers. The directions of flow and the interactions of neighbouring ice streams are revealed by such glacially moulded features as roches moutonnées, striated and polished surfaces, and drumlins, and especially by the distribution of closely identifiable erratics in the drifts.

To the west a major Highland glacier occupied the Firth of Clyde. It was directly fed by its own main stream and by tributary streams entering from the valleys of the present Loch Goil, Loch Eck, Loch Striven and Loch Fyne. The Renfrewshire hills fended off the flow for some miles, but south of the Cumbraes the great glacier was relatively unhindered and splayed out onto the Ayrshire plain as far as New Cumnock and Muirkirk and the front of the Southern Uplands. Along its route it not only scattered great numbers of Highland boulders (and more local boulders picked up from the Permian lavas of the Mauchline basin) but also carried far inland marine clays scooped from the sea bed over which it travelled. The clays contain an assemblage of fossils that include barnacles, foraminifers, and numbers of 'arctic' molluscs of which *Cyprina islandica* and *Pecten islandicus* are representative forms. The power of the ice is indicated by the finding of shelly boulder clay at heights above 1,000 feet. (See Fig. 16.)

Contemporary flows from the western hills of the Southern Uplands are plotted by the distribution of boulders of Doon granite, some of which descended as far north as Ayr, but most of which follow trails diverted either south-westwards to the main Firth glacier, or eastwards along the foot of the Uplands escarpment. At maximum pressure some ice was forced across the line of the Southern Uplands fault into the Nith valley about Sanquhar, carrying with it erratics of igneous rocks picked up in the Lugar valley of the Ayrshire plain.

Slightly farther east, Highland ice emerging from the valley of the Gareloch (possibly as an off-shoot from Loch Long), and the parallel flow descending Loch

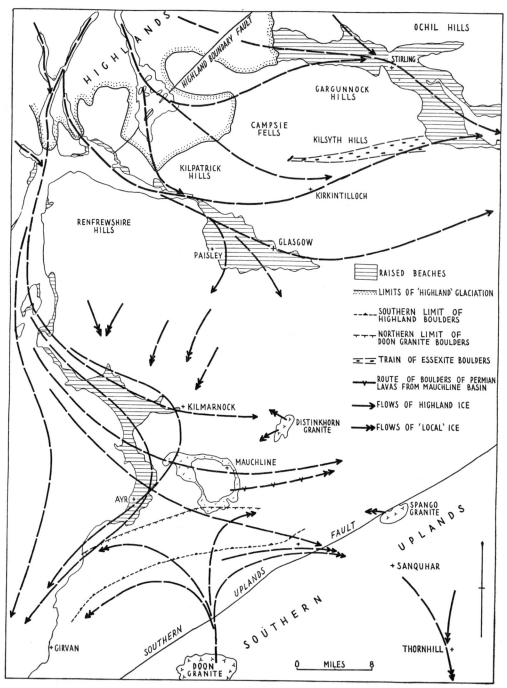

Legend (within map):

RAISED BEACHES
LIMITS OF 'HIGHLAND' GLACIATION
SOUTHERN LIMIT OF HIGHLAND BOULDERS
NORTHERN LIMIT OF DOON GRANITE BOULDERS
TRAIN OF ESSEXITE BOULDERS
ROUTE OF BOULDERS OF PERMIAN LAVAS FROM MAUCHLINE BASIN
FLOWS OF HIGHLAND ICE
FLOWS OF 'LOCAL' ICE

Map labels:
OCHIL HILLS, HIGHLANDS, HIGHLAND BOUNDARY FAULT, STIRLING, GARGUNNOCK HILLS, CAMPSIE FELLS, KILSYTH HILLS, KILPATRICK HILLS, KIRKINTILLOCH, RENFREWSHIRE HILLS, GLASGOW, PAISLEY, KILMARNOCK, DISTINKHORN GRANITE, MAUCHLINE, AYR, SPANGO GRANITE, UPLANDS, SANQUHAR, SOUTHERN, UPLANDS, FAULT, GIRVAN, SOUTHERN, DOON GRANITE, THORNHILL

0   MILES   8

FIG. 16. Map showing the lines of ice flow and other features of the glaciation of the Glasgow district.
The numerous small drumlins and other glacial mounds that stand as 'islands' above the level of the raised-beach sediments in the Clyde estuary and in Ayrshire are not represented.

56

Lomond, impinged on the Renfrewshire hills and were diverted eastwards along the Clyde valley. They brought with them shelly clays with 'arctic' molluscs like those of Ayrshire which they carried inland for several miles. Contained by the flanking hills of lava within the low ground of the Glasgow basin, the ice continued eastwards notably along what is now the Kelvin valley, spilling over the summit col at Kelvinhead into the Forth valley. A tributary flow passed through Strathblane to join the main stream south of the Campsie Fells, and other flows, following the grain of the country, occupied the upper Forth valley north of the Fintry Hills. Although the Campsie-Kilsyth-Gargunnock hill mass was influential in diverting the flows to north or south, it was itself completely overwhelmed by ice at maximum glaciation.

The whole of the Clyde-Forth depression is thus floored by glacial drift containing boulders, many carried from Highland sources, that prove the direction of ice movement. A particularly precise boulder train fans from the small outcrop of the essexite—the Lennoxtown essexite—at the foot of the Campsie escarpment, a highly individual rock easily identified. It never forms a wide spread but streams almost due east to the Forth near Grangemouth, and can be fragmentarily recognised along both shores of the Forth estuary as far as Queensferry. Drumlins moulded in the glacial drift by the movement of the ice are also very well developed in the ground between Glasgow and Edinburgh, most of them aligned west-east with their stoss slope facing west. Glasgow itself is a city whose topography and town planning have been largely controlled by the dozens of drumlins to be found within its limits. The mutual influence of Highland and Southern Uplands ice is reflected in the parallel courses erratics take in the Midland Valley: the Doon-granite and Tinto-felsite boulders transported into the Lothians are the complement to the essexite boulders carried to the Forth. There was, however, some fluctuation in the relative intensity of the ice-flows, and occasional erratics of Southern Uplands rocks have been found as far north as Glasgow.

The glaciation was multiple, 'glacial periods' alternating with relatively milder interludes when the glaciers melted in whole or in part and the ice fronts retreated. Stratigraphical evidence is provided in the Glasgow district by interglacial deposits of sands and gravels intercalated in boulder clay, found notably at Kilmaurs and Cowdon Burn in Ayrshire. From the water-borne sands have been obtained remains of water plants (*Potamogeton, Ranunculus*) and of a number of land animals including mammoth, reindeer and Irish elk. From gravels at Bishopbriggs (Glasgow) the woolly rhinoceros is also recorded.

At maximum glaciation the whole of the district—almost the whole of Britain—lay under a thick cover of ice. The deterioration of climate after the interglacial sands were laid down was accompanied by a second advance of the ice, which extended well south of the Midland Valley to leave deposits not readily distinguished from the earlier drifts where the intervening sands are absent or have not been found. In England there are records of yet a third period of glaciation, and elsewhere in Scotland of a fourth—or at least of fluctuations in the position of the ice-front. A fifth—the third clearly recognisable in the Glasgow district—is the last of any importance in Britain: as the Highland glaciation it was expressed locally by a renewal of valley-glacier movement down the larger lochs, the ice scarcely advancing beyond the Highland line. The limits of the glacier occupying the Gareloch are well shown by the terminal moraine at Rhu, and of the Loch Lomond glacier (which spread out as a piedmont fan between Helensburgh and

57

Killearn) even better shown in the drift mounds in Glen Fruin and around Drymen. At the time of this minor advance the lochs were occupied by sea water, the Lomond moraines containing dredged-up 'arctic' shells.

The effects of glacial movement on the landscape are spectacularly displayed in the sea lochs, whose bevelled walls and hanging tributary valleys disclose the erosive power of the ice. They are true glacial troughs, rock basins whose floors at their deepest were gouged to hundreds of feet (Loch Long nearly 300 feet, Loch Lomond nearly 400 feet) below present sea-level; and their moulding completely destroyed their pre-Glacial form. The smaller-scale erosion of corries in well-formed examples is displayed not only within the Highland border, but also on the north face of the Campsie and Fintry hills; and glacial lakes, moraine-dammed or in scooped-out basins, are common over the greater part of the uplands of the district. (See Plates V, VIIIa.)

In less direct ways, the ice, especially in its waning stages, moulded the landscape by choking valleys, holding back temporary lakes, and diverting melt-water streams. The lake that formerly occupied the Blane valley is noted for its varved clays. An over-flow channel from a Clyde lake forms the great gash of the Lochwinnoch gap through the Renfrewshire hills—though, sited on a downfaulted zone of Carboniferous sedi-ments, it was probably a pre-Glacial subsequent valley utilised by the glacial waters. West-flowing streams in the Renfrewshire hills, dammed behind a persistent glacier in the Firth of Clyde, formed lakes that spilled south-eastwards to open country. An elongate glacial lake in the upper reaches of the Kelvin valley may have drained east-wards through the Kelvinhead gap: its former existence is demonstrated by high-level delta gravels, and terraces of finer sands, at heights of about 170 feet on both sides of the valley below Kirkintilloch. The overflow from a temporary lake of a Clyde glacier, ponded against the hills of north Renfrewshire, carved the deep notch running from Gourock to Inverkip.

These instances of late-Glacial effects, and the common occurrence of such over-flow channels as one of their characteristic features, have a bearing on the inferred evolution of the drainage system. Many of the comparable dry transverse valleys that cut through the divides and form connections between the sea lochs farther west have the steep-walled flat-bottomed form of spillways temporarily occupied by the dis-charge from glacial lakes. It is very doubtful if they can properly be used as guides to the pre-Glacial drainage: they are often not aligned with appropriate streams, they are usually too narrow, they reach altitudes that cannot be correlated with one another or with the stream profiles, and there are too many of them. They do not offer strong evidence for relegating the broad courses of the lochs to a Glacial stage of geomorphic evolution, or for supposing that the trend of the courses cut across a pre-Glacial drainage pattern which they delineate.

During late-Glacial and post-Glacial times there was isostatic and eustatic recovery from the burden of the load of ice. The Glasgow district, like much of western Scotland, shows clear signs of changing sea-level in the occurrence of raised beaches at heights up to about 100 feet. Along the Clyde estuary the '100-foot' beach, approximately con-temporaneous with the Highland glaciation, is represented by deposits of clay (used for brick-making) that contain 'arctic' molluscs and other fossils. They lie about sixty feet above sea-level, and are inferred to have been deposited at depths of about forty feet. They extend up-river for several miles above Glasgow, form wide flats around

Paisley, and fill the Leven valley that links Loch Lomond with the sea. What is probably the same beach can be recognised along much of the coast of the Firth of Clyde, sometimes with a cliffed inner margin cut in glacial drift: thus it occupies the embayment, to a depth of two or three miles, from Saltcoats to Heads of Ayr, ascending in the larger valleys far up-stream, as from Irvine to Kilmarnock. (See Plate VII.)

Beaches locally occur at intermediate levels, but below the '100-foot' level the so-called '25-foot' 'Neolithic' beach is the most persistent and well developed. It was formed in a temperate climate, its fossil shells, often very abundant, including cockles, mussels, oysters and periwinkles; and it was sometimes a site for Stone Age settlements, as the occurrence of kitchen-middens and artefacts show. It is very well seen in the Clyde estuary, and forms much of the coastal region of the Firth, where it is commonly cut in solid rock and is backed by a well-defined cliff. Its variable altitude, however, is generally appreciably greater than twenty-five feet, and is a sign of the need for systematic study of the successive stages of post-Glacial emergence.

The coast, at the same time, is composite. The pulsatory uplift demonstrated by its raised beaches was complemented by widespread subsidence, and in general character the deeply indented estuaries and sea lochs, though owing much of their form to glacial excavation, make it a drowned coast. Stratigraphical evidence of oscillations in sea-level is provided by layers of peat that are found occasionally, as near Irvine, beneath the clays of the '25-foot' beach: they are composed of the humus, sometimes with boles and roots in position of growth, of pine, alder, birch, hazel and other forest trees, which must have grown on dry land before becoming submerged by the waters of the later beach. The second fall in sea-level that made the '25-foot' beach a raised beach is the last notable change in relative position of land and sea of which there is record in the Glasgow district.

THE PRESENT LANDSCAPE

There is in general a close reflection of geological structure in the present landscape, despite the effects of glaciation. Almost uniformly the hill-masses are up-faulted, like the Highlands and the Southern Uplands, or they are anticlinal inliers, like the Silurian outcrops near Lesmahagow, or they are floored by resistant lavas, like the rim of hills immediately around Glasgow. Locally the topographical expression of the geology is precise and detailed, as in the delineation of the Highland Boundary fault zone by the Conic Hill ridge east of Loch Lomond and by the notches running inland from Kilcreggan and Helensburgh; and in the similar etching along the line of strike of the Southern Uplands fault by a number of subsequent streams. It is well shown in the profile from the lava summits of the Campsies, across the abrupt fault-line scarp determined by the Campsie fault, over the shelf of tough Craigmaddie Sandstones, to the low ground of the Carboniferous outcrops on the outskirts of Glasgow. The synclinal basin of the Central coalfield is a low-lying tract complementary to the lava hills (though it is diversified by the occurrence of hard beds particularly in the upper Carboniferous rocks): and it is matched in Ayrshire by the Kilmarnock and Mauchline synclines which also now form plains flanked or roughened by outcrops of igneous rock. The carse of Stirling, between the Fintry Hills and the Highland border, widens eastwards as a sediment-filled arm of the sea lying on the outcrops of the comparatively soft strata of the Old Red Sandstone until, meeting the conjunction of the Old Red lavas of the Ochil Hills and the Carboniferous lavas of the Gargunnock Hills, it breaks through the narrows at Stirling along the line of the Ochil fault.

The geological structure clearly is responsible for the anomalous appearance of the lower Clyde valley, a drainage basin eight to ten miles wide from Johnstone through Paisley, Renfrew, and Bearsden, but narrowing downstream to little more than a mile or two about Dumbarton and Port Glasgow. The principal reason for the sudden gorge-like form that begins near Bowling is obviously the approximation of the lava hills on opposite banks, and their comparative resistance to a widening of the valley by lateral corrosion. The steepness of fall from the hill summits to the estuary intensifies the topographical constriction of the gorge, and is a great hindrance to human settlement. The narrow strip of flat-lying ground at the foot of the hills about Port Glasgow and Greenock, mainly composed of Glacial and post-Glacial deposits, is no place for the establishment of a large city or even of a great area of dockyards, and the natural features precluded any possibility of the growth of a Glasgow there: yet as a site for a port, far down the estuary and with deep water nearby not needing an artificially deepened channel or constant dredging, it has great advantages present Glasgow lacks.

Even in minor ways the intimate relationship of geology and landform is close. Small igneous intrusions, of which the wall-like dykes and the sub-circular volcanic necks and pipes are common, often have their outline almost exactly defined by the ridges and hillocks to which they give rise. The raised beaches, especially the '25-foot' beach, most recent and therefore least degraded, are cleanly delineated by their cliffs from the rough hinterland behind, and incidentally provide the ribbon of flat ground on which many of the Clyde coast resorts—Dunoon, Wemyss Bay, Largs, Fairlie, Millport—are sited. The streams coming off the hills, slightly stepped and rejuvenated by the uplift of which the beaches are the coastal expression, tumble over small falls in their lower reaches and provide a source of water power that was not without its effect in establishing local industries, notably textiles, in the eighteenth and nineteenth centuries. The sweep of the great embayment between the lavas and sills of the Ardrossan-Saltcoats headlands and the volcanic neck of Heads of Ayr—an embayment eroded in the comparatively soft rocks of the upper Carboniferous sediments, interrupted only by the promontory of the Troon dolerite sill—has been the natural environment for the long-shore drifting of some of the finest sandy beaches in the west of Scotland, and for the accompanying wind-blown onshore dunes, that have impeded the outfall of the Ayr and notably the Irvine rivers and have been the cause of recurrent flooding.

There is, however, a major contrast in landscape between areas of outcrop of solid rock and areas covered by glacial drift. The close relationship of topography to geological structure is usually to be looked for only in the uplands or along the rocky coasts: the lowlands are almost universally shrouded in morainic debris. The drift may be only a veneer slightly masking the form of the rock floor; but more often it transforms altogether the geomorphic aspect of the terrain and, deposited by thick ice that over-rode all but the larger hill masses, is wholly misleading as an indication of the sub-glacial surface. The most fully documented instance of the contrast is provided by some hundreds of boreholes in the valleys of the Clyde and its tributaries that have penetrated the cover of drift and disclosed in great detail the form and the depths of the floor of solid rock beneath. From the records it is clear that in what may have been pre-Glacial times the River Kelvin followed much the same course as it does at present from Kilsyth to its confluence with the Allander Water; but then, not swinging south and entering the Clyde in the heart of Glasgow, it continued for several miles westwards past Bearsden to unite with the Clyde perhaps at Drumry, possibly as far downstream as Clydebank. The general direction of the Clyde from Rutherglen to below Govan coincides with its pre-Glacial course, but thereafter the river now keeps to the Renfrew side of the valley whereas formerly it meandered northwards by Drumchapel. Above Rutherglen there is even greater divergence between the present and the pre-Glacial courses; and it is clear that the reaches where they appear to coincide are little more than accidentally aligned. A further contrast is provided by the profiles of the pre-Glacial channels, the Kelvin having much the steeper gradient and descending in a narrow gorge to depths exceeding 240 feet below sea-level near Clydebank, where (at the inferred confluence) the floor of the Clyde channel is probably little more than 100 feet below sea-level. That is, the pre-Glacial Clyde (to which the pre-Glacial Black Cart Water is similar) appears to have been a tributary hanging above a trenched Kelvin graded to a base-level not much less than 300 feet lower than present sea-level. There are obvious implications that the benched topography has a downward sub-glacial extension and that a pre-Glacial major river-system did not converge eastwards through the Kelvinhead gap, none of which are to be discerned in the present surface features.

In the Ayrshire plain it is equally improbable that the present drainage pattern, or much of the present surface (almost wholly formed in glacial drift), can be assumed to reflect even approximately the underlying solid floor. Sufficient borehole records like those available for the Clyde valley might well disclose the incongruent relationship that is the general expectation throughout the Midland Valley.

Anderson, J. G. C. The geology of the Highland border: Stonehaven to Arran. *Trans. Roy. Soc. Edinb.*, 1947, 61: 479-515.
Bailey, E. B., and others. The geology of the Glasgow district. *Mem. Geol. Surv.*, 1925.
Currie, E. D. Scottish Carboniferous goniatites. *Trans. Roy. Soc. Edinb.*, 1954, 62: 527-602.
Eyles, V. A., Simpson, J. B. and MacGregor, A. G. Geology of central Ayrshire. *Mem. Geol. Surv.*, 1949.
George, T. N. Drainage in the Southern Uplands: Clyde, Nith, Annan. *Trans. Geol. Soc. Glasg.*, 1955, 22: 1-34.
McCallien, W. J. *Geology of Glasgow and district*. London and Glasgow, 1938.
MacGregor, A. G. *British Regional Geology, Scotland: The Grampian Highlands.* 2nd edition. Edinburgh (H.M.S.O.), 1948.
Macgregor, M. Scottish Carboniferous stratigraphy: an introduction to the study of the Carboniferous rocks of Scotland. *Trans. Geol. Soc. Glasg.*, 1930, 18: 442-558.
——— and MacGregor, A. G. *British Regional Geology, Scotland: The Midland Valley of Scotland.* 2nd edition, Edinburgh (H.M.S.O.), 1948.
Pringle, J. *British Regional Geology, Scotland; The South of Scotland.* 2nd edition. Edinburgh (H.M.S.O.), 1948.
Richey, J. E., and others. The geology of north Ayrshire. *Mem. Geol. Surv.*, 1930.
Weir, J., and Leitch, D. Zonal distribution of the non-marine lamellibranchs in the Coal Measures of Scotland. *Trans. Roy. Soc. Edinb.*, 1936, 58: 697-751.

THE CLIMATE OF THE GLASGOW REGION

C. A. HALSTEAD

Lecturer in Geography, University of Glasgow

THE climate of Glasgow itself is not typical of that of the region, and therefore a factual summary of the climate of the city and a study of some of its features will be followed by a broad account of weather conditions over a wider area. In order to obtain full Atlantic exposure this will extend to Tiree and conditions at altitude will be exemplified by Ben Nevis and the Lowther Hill. For air masses, Stornoway must be referred to.

THE CLIMATE OF GLASGOW

The observations at the University Observatory, formerly situated two miles north-west of George Square and at a height of 180 feet, have been summarised without explanation by Professor Becker.[1] The principal features of these, derived from the graphical and tabular material of his work, are presented in Figure 17, the four parts of the diagram showing the yearly march of temperature, moisture, wind and 'atmospheric transparency'. The exposures of the instruments differed from those now considered desirable, especially in that the thermometers were in a north-wall screen at seven feet and not at the present standard of four feet screened from radiation from the ground. Major effects, almost certainly due to the expansion of the town to surround the Observatory, are noticed in the original work, but no attempt is made here to consider secular changes; the strict absence of comparability between recent and former records makes this very difficult and in any case is of little relevance to the following discussion.

The temperature curves show that shade temperatures ranging from 90° F to 3° F may be expected although the probable range in a given year is from 84° F to 14° F. Half the daily maxima and minima fall within the narrow bands shown. Maximum temperatures in January, just above 40° F, are thus comparable with minimum temperatures in May and October. If 58° F be considered a comfortable human environment, it will be seen that domestic heating will be needed on most days from mid-September to mid-May, in fact it is just possible for the coldest summer day to have the same temperature as the warmest winter one (53° F), so various are the sources of our air. In contrast to this, summer nights may sometimes be cooler than the warmer winter ones, although the chances that air temperatures will fall below freezing do not exceed one in three even during the winter. Ground frost may, however, occur at any time of the year and has more than an even chance of occurrence between the end of October and the middle of April. Since the growing season (when the mean daily temperature exceeds 42·8° F) begins in the first week in April and ends early in November, there is a definite risk of frost damage to new growth well into May, when for the whole month the chances of this are 1 to 6. This is well illustrated by the maximum frequency of

62

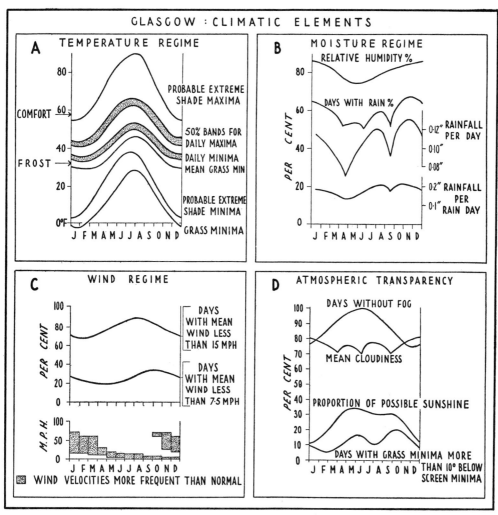

Fig. 17.   Climate of Glasgow.

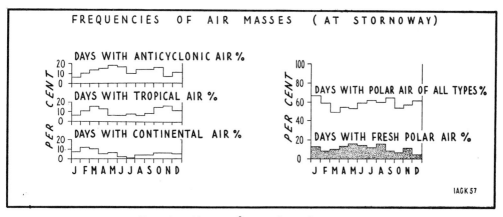

Fig. 18.   Air mass frequencies at Stornoway.

differences of 10° F between screen and grass minima (as illustrated in Fig. 17D) occurring in May and October when the screen minima are at about 42° F.

It is possible from Becker's five-day normals of mean temperature to recognise cooler periods than might be expected near the end of May, in early and late July, early in September and towards the end of October, as well as others outside the growing season. These may also be seen on other comparable records, for example at Fort William or Ben Nevis, and are discussed in the next section.

The humidity of the air in Glasgow is generally high, and from the curves (Fig. 17B) its mean value is seen to range from 74 per cent to 86 per cent. Since local saturation occurs on most nights, the yearly march of dew points is well illustrated by that of minimum screen temperatures, with a range from 34° F to 52° F. This is confirmed by a two-year (1955-57) sample of noon values [2] at Renfrew, half of which were between 38° F and 50° F. If the maximum temperatures are compared with the minima as dew points, it is found that mid-day humidities should range from about 75 per cent in winter to 55 per cent in summer, but in fact the most common noon value in the two-year sample was found to be 75 per cent, so that mean values are hardly representative. About one in 200 of the humidities was less than 35 per cent, but high humidities are very frequent and a not uncommon effect is condensation from moist air on to previously cooled surfaces, even indoors.

A close relationship may be seen between high mean relative humidities and poor visibilities, and there is a similar close relationship to the proportion of possible sunshine actually received. Further examination of cloud statistics shows that an additional effect is the more frequent occurrence of overcast days in winter and of fewer partly clouded days than in summer, a variation involving not only higher humidity but also less convection by heat from the ground breaking up the cloud. The mean cloud amount is seen from the graphs to show a much smaller annual variation. There is also a clear relationship between the occurrence of light winds in autumn and the frequency of fogs, but this is complicated by the oncoming of stronger winds at the same time of the year. It is to these that the general increase of rainfall may be attributed rather than to the absolute humidity which is greatest in summer, but a more detailed analysis of the variation of cloud and rainfall requires an analysis of weather types in the area.

WEATHER AND AIR MASSES IN THE GLASGOW REGION

Belasco [3] has made an analysis of the frequency of air masses from different sources during the eleven years 1938-49, and this has been compared with the two-year sample of noon weather previously referred to. However, since it appears from the frequency of wind directions that these are not representative at Glasgow because of shelter from the surrounding hills, the following table incorporates wind frequencies observed at Tiree.

From this it is clear that polar air dominates the circulation in this region, especially where moderate winds are concerned, and it is interesting that the Ben Nevis observations show that a very clear secondary maximum of northerly winds can occur at any time of the year. Although the sample study used a simple four-directional wind classification, the considerable contrast between the weather with northerly and southerly winds was brought out even when the southerly winds associated with convectional

Air Masses: Stornoway 1938-49	Surface Winds: Tiree, August 1955 to July 1957
Polar 58 per cent	Winds over 5 knots from north and west 56 per cent (and south when cumulus clouds are present)
Tropical 11 per cent ⎫ Fronts and ⎬ 23 per cent Depressions 12 per cent ⎭	Winds over 5 knots from south when no cumulus clouds are present 23 per cent
Anticyclonic 13 per cent Continental 6 per cent	All calms and winds less than 5 knots 8 per cent Winds over 5 knots from east 13 per cent

TABLE I. Percentage frequency of air masses and surface winds

clouds (a good test for polar air over the sea) were included. At Tiree almost two-thirds of the southerly winds are associated with cloud bases below 2,000 feet, but only one-third of the northerly ones had such a low cloud base; the contrast is even greater at Glasgow, where the north winds that do blow are coming downhill off the Highlands. At 2,400 feet, Lowther Hill, in the Southern Uplands, is in cloud for nine-tenths of the southerly winds but only one-quarter of the northerly ones, a clear indication of the moist character of the former; and it is apparent on the ground that the shelter provided by the Southern Uplands from such moist winds is the main reason for the excellent meteorological conditions of the international airport of Prestwick, the more exposed coastal areas having a much greater low-cloud frequency. Even the Highlands may benefit from such protection since it has been suggested that cloud conditions comparable to those on the Lowther Hill are not reached in the Ben Nevis area until 600 feet higher. At Glasgow and Tiree rain is most commonly associated with winds in the southerly quadrant, although on Lowther Hill (because of the normal wind veer with height) westerly winds bring most rainy days.

At Tiree further comparisons between other weather phenomena and general wind direction and therefore air-mass types show that visibilities there of less than six-and-a-quarter miles are six times more common with southerly than with northerly winds and in spite of the light winds coming from the north in Glasgow a similar effect may be noted there. At Tiree the relative humidities most commonly associated with northerly and southerly winds at noon are 75 per cent and 95 per cent respectively, a difference greater than the mean difference between summer and winter conditions; this amounts to a difference of 4° F in the respective dew points and makes the occurrence of dew points below 40° F three times as frequent in northerly as in southerly air, a clear factor in the development of frosty conditions.

The relative frequencies of such contrasted air-mass types throughout the year help in understanding the more complex seasonal variations in Figure 17 although the strong increase of wind with height may make detailed correlation hazardous. Although the area is one of dominant west or south-west winds, these are only well established from late June to mid-September; Becker gives tables showing the persistence of winds from various directions. Since these are the winds most to be expected by reason of the rotation of the earth, their interruption can only be understood as expressing the need for exchange of heat between high and low latitudes. In our own region this is most clearly seen in the outbreaks of cold air from the polar regions which tend to settle down as anticyclones on their way to be warmed in the south, either reinforcing the anti-cyclone near the Azores or the winter anticyclone over the Continent. These outbreaks are manifest as surges in the general polar air current which may be detected in Belasco's figures in May, August, November and January and may be contrasted with minor surges of moist tropical air in March, July and November (Fig. 18).

The pleasantest weather in the region is associated with the principal surges of cold, dry air beginning in April and lasting into June. The initial showers of this outburst (Fig. 17B) are often followed by a layer of cloud, formed as the moister surface air stagnates during the maximum of the anticyclone, which somewhat reduces the expected number of 'radiation nights' with large differences between screen and grass minima i.e. a tendency to surface chilling (both on Fig. 17D). Even easterly winds may dominate for a few days in mid-May if this major overflow of cold air produced by the long polar night amalgamates with the remnants of winter air from the Continent. By June these local anticyclonic pools of air have begun to warm and the clouds disperse, but the greater heating of the Continent restores the 'normal' westerly current which, as a gentle heat-induced indraught, becomes well established by mid-July. Disturbances, some-times of a thundery character, travelling slowly with this current, bring the secondary maximum of rainfall in August, and the cloud associated therewith results in the cooler periods (already mentioned) early in July and August and has a distinct effect on the pro-portion of possible sunshine received. But later in August there are also signs of renewed polar outbursts which begin to build up a September anticyclone. The air is still suffici-ently humid to form dew and prevent excessive radiation into the clear night skies until October (Fig. 17D), when the anticyclone reaches its maximum, but there are insufficient reinforcements of new polar air to give the vegetation its final blasting until November.

In early winter, however, moist air from the tropics tends to surge north and form stagnant foggy pools. These, however, are dispersed as the temperature gradients, building up around the growing masses of polar air, begin to accelerate the general circulation and outbursts of cold air—in early winter often via Scandinavia and later alternating between Pole and Continent—bring gales which are followed by fewer and fewer calms as the new year matures. Only in spring does the control of the developed pool of polar air seem to be almost complete, but its influence is steadily destroyed from below by the increasing heat of the sun.

REGIONAL AND ALTITUDINAL VARIATIONS IN WEATHER AND CLIMATE

Although such a sequence of events clearly explains the more complicated climatic data presented on Figure 17 and in some ways represents general conditions in the area, it

66

is clear that the climate of Glasgow is most unrepresentative of the region as a whole. The latter shows a complex variation with proximity to the sea and increased altitude and does not share in the urban warmth and smoke pollution of the Glasgow area itself. The separation of these influences into factors affecting individual climatic elements detracts from their reality since they often work together, but the application of the ideas in the preceding section to these variations is made very difficult by the virtual absence of high-level meteorological observations.

The influence of the sea which so invades the area must be very great at low levels, but the considerable mildness of the area for its latitude extends only slightly uphill; the rapid vertical decrease in temperature in the predominant polar air has been taken to explain the very shallow vertical zone of agricultural land and the general impression of rapid deterioration with height. But exposure to wind and rainfall also increases both seaward and vertically. A resemblance between the resulting decrease of annual and diurnal ranges of temperature in similar directions has suggested that conditions become 'oceanic' in the latter direction also, but it seems clear from the two-year sample that other factors outweigh this effect. On the Lowther Hill wind conditions are only slightly worse than at Tiree (Fig. 19A) and there are the same number of noons above 65°F. But there is an enormous contrast in the number of cold days (seven times as many noons below 40° F, forty times as many below 35° F) because the two frequency curves are skew in opposite directions (Fig. 19B). It is well known that plants and animals find effective cold increased by strong wind, and in the two-year sample it was found that on Lowther Hill twenty-six noons had temperatures below 30° F associated with winds stronger than 15 knots, an extreme condition never found at Tiree or Glasgow in the same period.

Such conditions are likely to make the problems of forestry, which is virtually the only alternative to continued deterioration of hill land, very difficult to solve other than by direct experimental planting. The present upper limits of planting are very low near the sea and at greater altitudes inland. These higher plantations may well act rather as an ameliorating influence on climate than as the quicker-yielding crop found at lower levels. Even there freak storms and turbulence effect may damage mature timber after a sudden thaw, whilst the absence of trees on the islands and close to the coast is probably an effect of sea salt or even blown sand (dunes are common on some coasts) rather than of climatic factors alone.

The general increases of exposure are by no means uniform. It is clear, for example, that Galloway benefits greatly from the shelter provided by Ireland in contrast to areas further north, where mean wind strengths at sea-level are an eighth greater and rainfalls more than a quarter greater at comparable levels. Effects of shelter from even more damaging winds are illustrated by the Ayrshire early-potato fields, where shelter inland by an old sea cliff is available against the dry north-east winds of April and May, the sea spray being kept away by low walls and sack-blocked gateways. The fruit lands of the Clyde Valley are probably sited as a result of a compromise between considerations of exposure to sun and shelter from certain winds, but precise climatic evidence here is lacking.

The previous reference to Glasgow, well sheltered from the north and partly from the south, makes it surprising to find that Becker demonstrates a clear land- and sea-breeze effect superimposed on the general winds. The sea-breeze component reaches a

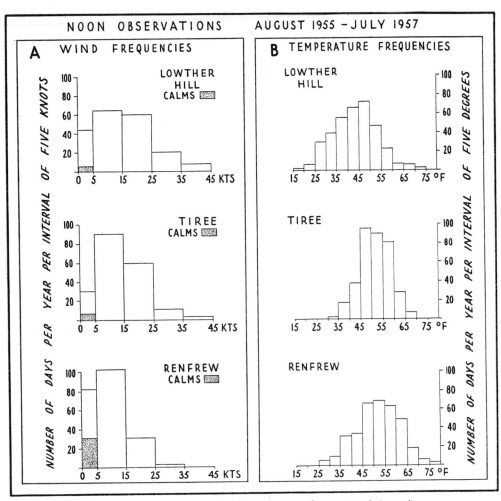

FIG. 19. Comparative wind and temperature frequencies (1955-57) at Lowther Hill, Tiree and Renfrew.

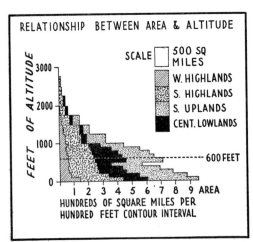

FIG. 20. Relationship between area and altitude in South-West and West Central Scotland.

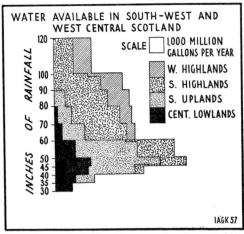

FIG. 21. Available water as related to rainfall in South-West and West Central Scotland.

maximum of 2 m.p.h. on July afternoons whilst a mean land-breeze of half this value occurs at night. This latter is partly due to the downhill drainage of cold air developed on the often badly-conducting, peat-covered moorlands surrounding the town and results in a smoke-trapping inversion of temperature occurring many times during the winter. Below 400 feet the lower Clyde Valley has only three mile-wide gaps for the escape of this polluted air, which is most commonly formed when dry north winds, walled away from the town by the Campsie and Kilpatrick Hills, are bringing brilliant weather to nearby places. The two-year sample provides thirty-one cases of fog even at noon at Renfrew compared with only one at Tiree, and there are seven times as many observations of 'visibility reduced by smoke'. Even the Tiree 'smoke' probably came from Glasgow (fourteen cases with winds between south-west and south-east, nine cases with winds south-east to north-east), since it is common to be able to follow the pall of smoke drifting downwind from the city, even into England; the clarity of the atmosphere during the otherwise humid Glasgow Fair fortnight is very striking! But in spite of such shelter—there are seven times as many calms as at Tiree or Lowther Hill— Glasgow does not escape the extreme gusts of strong gales funnelled through the Central Lowland gap, although strong winds (over twenty-five knots) are only one-sixth as common as at Tiree or one-tenth as common as on the over-exposed Lowther Hill (Fig. 19A).

The distribution of single climatic elements over the area is much better known than that of the weather conditions so far discussed. It is possible to consider rainfall and temperature in rather more detail, depending on the rainfall maps constructed by the Meteorological Office [4] and the results obtained on Ben Nevis [5] whence the effects of altitude on net available water and thermal conditions for plant growth may be estimated. Glasgow itself has between 37 and 40 inches of rainfall, which is unrepresentative of the region as a whole in amount and in monthly distribution since the local secondary maximum in August is quite overshadowed by the main December one in most of the region. It may be seen from Figure 20 that about half of the whole region is above 600 feet and is found to have more than 55 inches of rainfall per annum. Measurements of four rather arbitrary component regions show that whereas each has about half its area above the same height the distributions of higher land and rainfalls are remarkably different. The Central Lowland part of Western Scotland (excluding the Loch Lomond drainage and some moorland north of the Southern Upland Fault) has only 5 per cent of its area above 1,250 feet; the same height is exceeded by 9 per cent of the Highlands and Islands west of the Great Glen (Loch Linnhe) line, 12 per cent of the Western Southern Uplands and 20 per cent of the Southern Highlands. Combined with exposure as already discussed, this results in very different *average* relationships between rainfall and height (see Table II).

Perhaps the feature distinguishing these areas most clearly is the difference in the proportions of their areas with rainfalls greater than 60 inches. And since such a rainfall produces more than twice as much water as one of 40 inches when a general loss of 15 to 20 inches by evaporation (found by measurements of run-off in Scotland) is deducted from each, the relative importance of the areas as sources of water may be estimated. This is demonstrated in Figure 21, where an assessment of the water available is given for each region. Although the two Highland regions combined only just exceed the Southern Uplands in area they may produce almost twice as much water,

Region	Average elevation of isohyet of			Percentage of area with rainfall greater than		
	40″	60″	80″	40″	60″	80″
Western Highlands	—	80′	400′	100	88	63
Southern Highlands	—	400′	900′	100	66	32
Central Lowlands	400′	1200′	1700′	63	7	1
Southern Uplands	120′	1100′	1700′	90	16	3
Whole Area	120′	700′	1100′	87	38	18

TABLE II. Average relationships between mean annual rainfall and height in regions of Western Scotland—Argyll to Dumfries inclusive

whilst the Lowlands with one-third of the total area produce only one-eighth of the water. This excess of precipitation has had many repercussions, both natural and human. The fragmented and partly insular character of the Highlands is at least in part due to the glaciation, which may be attributed to a similar excess of snow in former times. The western areas are thus now isolated as water- and power-supplying areas as well as having smaller and lower drainage basins. Thus the most extensive hydro-electric developments in our area are those of the Galloway Power Scheme, while Glasgow's water supply comes from Loch Katrine, across the principal watershed and some 370 feet above sea-level. Apart from other considerations, Loch Lomond, being only 27 feet above sea-level, is not able to provide water by gravity. Those developments which have occurred in the Highlands have been rather remote, as at Kinlochleven, or have entailed considerable enlargement of the natural basins, as at Loch Sloy. Most of these systems are essentially peak-load schemes with more equipment installed than could be run continuously (the Galloway Scheme can run for about one-fifth of the time) and contrast with the larger systems of the less-fragmented Tay basin or even of the Clyde stations, which depend on a sharp break of slope well illustrated by the remarkable indentation in the histogram between 400 and 600 feet (Fig. 20). Many of the lowland stretches of the rivers were formerly used for industrial power (compensation water from the Glasgow Waterworks still supplying an early works near Doune), and the Clyde, Ayr, Endrick and Leven, together with the water fed to the early canals, were very important in early industrialisation. Even the first blast furnaces depended on such power sources, both in the Lowlands and on Loch Fyne and Loch Etive.

Although such superfluity of water has been and is very valuable, the deterioration of soils caused by leaching or gleying and its promotion of peat growth has been a major disadvantage. The 'debatable lands' of low slope still have fragments near sea-level which are unreclaimed from peat (Solway Moss itself, Linwood Moss, Shewalton Moss and the extensive Flanders Moss across the watershed) and peat is widespread on uplands where drainage is impeded by low slope or iron-pan development. Much agricultural land has been obtained laboriously from peat, and much is deteriorating for want of maintenance of drainage. There is little doubt that the 60-inch isohyet is a better guide to the extreme limit of profitable agriculture in our area than any considerations based on temperature, and the improved land, bounded by the 'head-dyke', tends generally to fall below this line.

Thermal conditions have greater relevance to the usefulness of hill grazings and the profitability of forestry. The occurrence of a continuous winter snow cover cannot be relied upon even on the highest hills, largely because of exposure to wind and spells of warm rain from tropical air-masses even in the heart of winter. The exception to this is perhaps the area above 3,500 feet; it has been shown that a January temperature of 27° F may be used as a climatic boundary over much of the world, and the observations on Ben Nevis show both that this value occurs at about 3,500 feet and that above this level snow covers are rarely interrupted until the spring thaw. Below this altitude another climatic boundary may be recognised where the mean monthly temperature in July is 50° F, commonly accepted as the poleward limit of forests. On Ben Nevis this occurs at 1,860 feet, so that on thermal considerations alone tree growth should be possible to this altitude which may rise considerably southward. But it is also clear from observations of the Snow Survey [6] that at this altitude also snow conditions are at their most variable and the absence of a continuous cover exposes the hills here to powerful frost action which, together with their great windiness, may prevent trees becoming established. A third thermal boundary suggested is that marked by the level at which the mean of the temperatures of May and September reaches 50° F, a 'summer' thus lasting roughly four months. From all the stations in our area and the relevant decrease of temperature with height found on Ben Nevis, it seems that this occurs at about 550 feet in hilly country but at almost 1,000 feet in Renfrewshire near the sea, a reasonable average figure being 750 feet. Both crops and trees can be grown above this level, but not with great success.

A more general idea of thermal patterns may be obtained by studying the period during which mean temperatures exceed 42·8° F, the growing period previously defined. But to obtain accurate figures upland stations at 1,310 feet at Leadhills (since discontinued but recently restored) in Lanarkshire and at 978 feet at Bowhill in Ayrshire have to be used as a basis for extrapolations in the Southern Uplands. If this is done, it is clear that from between 230 and 240 days at sea-level the growing season has fallen to 175 days at 1,000 feet, perhaps to 135 days at 2,000 feet and to 95 days at 3,000 feet. This is an average decrease of 55 days for each 1,000 feet, but the change may be as slow as 3 days per 100 feet near 1,500 feet. Not only does the length of the growing season decrease, but each day is of less value, the mean temperature of each growth-day falling off from about 51° F at sea-level to 50° F at 900 feet and thence more rapidly to 48° F at 2,000 feet and to 45° F at 3,000 feet. This is generally expressed as a decrease of 'accumulated temperature', which is in fact most rapid close to sea-level. These values are interestingly confirmed from the two-year sample figures which show that whereas noon temperatures above 49° F (43° F plus half the probable daily range) are equally as common at Tiree as at Glasgow, the frequency on the Lowther Hill at 2,400 feet reaches only half this value (Fig. 19B).

Experiment has suggested that biological activity increases geometrically with temperature so that such a rapid decrease of available heat with height must have a great effect. This is largely expressed in terms of yearly variations in yields rather than in the average conditions which we have been able to discuss. Other processes vary in a similar way; evaporation has been shown to increase with both temperature and sunshine (which may be only half its sea-level value at 3,000 feet), but the decrease which should thus occur uphill may be counteracted by increased wind and especially by the abnormally dry conditions known to occur occasionally at moderate levels in anti-cyclones. Similarly, evaporation will be less effective at high levels and run-off therefore greater. Soil leaching is more pronounced than at moderate heights and the danger of soil and peat erosion is ever present.

An over-all balance of these climatic resources cannot be struck. The disadvantages of high rainfall and rapid deterioration with altitude may be outweighed by the mild conditions near sea-level and the considerable water resources. Communities of former times and those of the future may assess the results of each factor differently, but although minor changes have been and may well be made, the broad climatic character of the area will long give it its major features as well as its local contrasts.

1 Becker, L. *Climatology of Glasgow*. Meteorological Office Geophysical Memoir No. 23, London, 1925.

2 Lowther Hill observations have been consulted by courtesy of the Director-General, Meteorological Office and the staff of the Ministry of Transport and Civil Aviation, London. Renfrew and Tiree observations were obtained from the Daily Weather Reports of the Meteorological Office, London.

3 Belasco, J. E. *Characteristics of Air Masses over the British Isles*. Meteorological Office Geophysical Memoir No. 87, London, 1952.

4 *National Atlas*, Sheet 1: Rainfall, Annual Average 1881-1915.

5 *Trans. Roy. Soc. Edinb.*, 1910, 44.

6 Published annually in *J. Glaciol.* until 1953; thereafter in *Met. Mag.*

PL. V.
FINNART DEEP-WATER OIL PORT

Looking up Loch Long, a typical sea-loch, from the south. Ben Arthur ('The Cobbler') in centre distance. Forestry Commission plantings on left. There is a pipe-line from Finnart to Grangemouth on the Forth.

British Petroleum Co. Ltd.

Pl. VI. THE CAMPSIES, looking north through Strathblane.

Volcanic neck of Dumgoyne on left; scarp edge of Carboniferous lavas centre; apparent secondary outcrop, right centre, is large landslide.

Pl. VII.   THE VALE OF LEVEN

Ben Lomond in extreme right-distance dominates Loch Lomond which drains through the alluvium-filled Vale to the Clyde in foreground. Dumbarton, with its harbour in the Leven estuary, and its one road bridge, on left. Dumbarton Rock in foreground with Denny's shipyard behind, right.

Pl. VIIIa.   UPPER LOCH LOMOND

A heavily glaciated valley with bottom 600 feet below sea-level. Ben Vorlich left, Ben Lomond right with Rowardennan Lodge (Y.H.) at foot; Forestry Commission property eventually to be planted. Scrub woods, mainly deciduous above waters of low faunal productivity.

Photograph by Dr J. K. St Joseph, University of Cambridge

Pl. VIIIb.   FORESTRY COMMISSION PROPERTY NEAR ABERFOYLE

Mixed coniferous species on Menteith Hills; new houses for foresters at Bravall.

THE LAND AND ITS UTILISATION

I. VEGETATION

JOHN WALTON

Professor of Botany, University of Glasgow

THE Glasgow region contains a wide range of types of vegetation and has a varied flora, but no attempt has been made to publish a complete list of the flora since the production of *The Flora, Fauna and Geology of the Clyde Area* edited by Scott Elliott for the British Association Meeting in Glasgow in 1901. John R. Lee's *Flora of the Clyde Area* brought the list of flowering plants and ferns up to date in 1933, and there is also a card catalogue of plants including Bryophyta and Algae in the Clyde Area kept by the Andersonian Naturalists' Society in Glasgow as well as publications in the Society's journal. Druce's *Comital Flora* (1932) and more recently *The Flora of the British Isles* (1952) by Clapham, Tutin and Warburg, provide vice-county records for the species of flowering plants and ferns which occur in the area. Also, there is in preparation a new distribution survey of vascular plants by the Botanical Society of the British Isles, and in the Department of Botany of the University of Glasgow there are considerable herbarium collections from the area.

The upper part of the Clyde Valley lies in the Southern Uplands, where sheep farming has had a profound influence on the vegetation. The hill slopes and summits, for the most part destitute of trees, carry acid moor and grassland. On the drier well-drained slopes *Calluna* heath occurs in places, but owing to heavy grazing and over-burning it is steadily diminishing in extent. *Scirpus* and *Eriophorum* and their associates cover the more level areas. At lower altitudes alder and willows fringe the stream banks.

Much of the Lanarkshire plateau, between 600 and 1,000 feet, is under cultivation or grazing, but in the deep, narrow valleys cut by the tributaries of the Clyde through the drift cover and the underlying Carboniferous and Old Red sandstones and shales, there are relict oak and ash woodlands in which a rich ground flora is found. One of the best examples is where the river Nethan passes below Craignethan Castle in a deep wooded gorge and enters the Clyde near Crossford; also, in the High Parks at Cadzow Castle near Hamilton there is parkland with some very old hollow oaks. The few summits which exceed 1,000 feet are, for the most part, covered with grassland and heather moor or, on the level areas, with thick peat.

The lower reaches of the Clyde are ringed in by hills built of Carboniferous lavas which form extensive plateaus whose highest point is Earl's Seat at 1,896 feet. Above about 1,400 feet, on the gently sloping upper parts of the hills, there is blanket peat and *Rubus chamaemorus* occurs, but on the slopes where the drainage is better there is grassland. On the escarpment facing the north, between Balfron and Gargunnock, there are two corries which have a few arctic-alpine species. However, there is no doubt that birch scrub once existed up to a height of 1,500 feet on most of the hill sides, but owing to grazing, natural or semi-natural woodland is found only on the steep sides of the stream gorges and on the talus slopes; Campsie Glen affords one of the best examples of such a wooded glen.

The upper part of the valley of the Forth between Stirling and Aberfoyle is of great interest and is an area to which a good deal of attention has been paid by Glasgow botanists. In post-Glacial times it was a freshwater loch which filled up with sediments and later developed into a raised bog; the Lake of Menteith is all that is left of the original loch. In the seventeenth and eighteenth centuries Dutch engineers reclaimed a large extent of the eastern part of the area by removing the peat, but Flanders Moss still remains, largely in a natural state. Among the more characteristic plants *Vaccinium oxycoccus* and *Andromeda polifolia* occur in abundance. *Ledum palustre* was recorded many years ago in bogs near Stirling, and about fifteen years ago a number of bushes of *Ledum groenlandicum* were found on Flanders Moss and it is unlikely that it was introduced by human agency. Parts of the Moss, particularly round the drier margins adjoining the reclaimed agricultural areas, bear birch woodland.

The South-West Highlands include several mountains of over 2,400 feet, the highest, Ben Lomond, attaining 3,192 feet. The rocks are for the most part schists, gneisses and grits, and it is a region of high rainfall. The climax vegetation of most of the valleys in the area is oak woodland with ash, birch, rowan and holly. Very little natural woodland is left, but on the lower slopes of Ben Lomond, between Rowardennan and Inversnaid, there is quite a large area of oak wood. This has been cut over in the past and many of the older trees appear to have developed from stools left from this felling. There are also considerable oak woods in the Trossachs, and mixed woods partly of oak occur around the shores of Loch Long and Loch Fyne.

The oaks vary considerably in character. Both *Quercus petraea* and *Quercus robur* occur with numerous hybrid forms. After the woods were felled in the seventeenth century to provide charcoal for the bloomeries—traces of which are widespread in the area—both species were probably used in whatever re-afforestation was effected. Pine forest may have existed in places over 800 feet, and there are traces of pine forest further north in Glen Falloch. Some of the area originally occupied by woodland or scrub now provides rough grazing, but large areas have been densely colonised by bracken which, owing to the rocky nature of the terrain, cannot be economically eradicated. These bracken-infested areas are quite unproductive and it is only by afforestation that they can be rendered productive. Above the limit of the oak woods, birch woods occur; while in wetter areas alder and birch woodland are found. In the largest stream gorges woodland may occur at much greater altitudes than on the open hillsides.

Above the present tree limit are grassland and heather communities, and scree vegetation such as occurs in the Lake District hills is rarely found. This is probably due to the more rapid colonisation by Bryophytes in this wetter climate and to the less fissile nature of the rocks. This grass and heather zone is succeeded near the summits of the higher peaks by arctic-alpine grassland. On the rocky summits of 1,700 feet and more *Salix herbacea* and *Juncus trifidus* are almost always to be found.

The corries which are so characteristic of these mountains present special features of interest. Their steep sides and crags with rock ledges out of reach of grazing animals have a rich flora—usually richer in those facing north than in those facing southwards;

this is possibly because they do not dry out so readily on hot summer days. On the rock ledges of the corries one finds not only characteristic arctic–alpine species but also many plants which are characteristic of lower altitudes. These are found extending their range up the sheltered ravines and on the corrie ledges and crevices. A quite common example of this is the Globe Flower (*Trollius*) which is frequently present at high altitudes on rock ledges. Species found at high altitudes on the open mountain-sides are also found at much lower altitudes in sheltered gorges and ravines. *Alchemilla alpina* may be found in such places as low as 200 feet above sea-level. The series of corries on the Ben More range on the east side of Loch Eck and the crags just below the summit of Ben Lomond provide particularly good examples of chomophyte floras.

FRESHWATER LOCHS

In the lowland districts most of the freshwater lochs are utilised as reservoirs and have little natural shore vegetation. There are a few, however, which are too near sea-level to be of use as reservoirs. They are of the highly evolved type, usually shallow, with water relatively rich in mineral nutrients derived from the surrounding cultivated land. Lochwinnoch in Renfrewshire is the best example. It is a large, shallow loch with marginal reed and sedge swamps and in places extensive floating mats consisting largely of Bog Bean (*Menyanthes*) on which black-headed gulls nest. The largest freshwater lochs, however, are Loch Lomond and others in the Trossachs, all occupying over-deepened glacial valleys. Being a large loch, the open shores of Loch Lomond are wave-swept and it is only in sheltered bays that reed swamp can develop. The water is relatively poor in mineral salts, but where the rivers enter, and there is deposition of silt, the underwater vegetation is richer than elsewhere. In the sheltered deep-water bays, such as that at Balmaha, there is a richer submerged flora in which *Potamogetons* are dominant. The shores where there are alluvial deposits have a fringe of alder thicket with *Rubus saxatilis*, *Scutellaria* and other associates, grading into oak woodland.

The Lake of Menteith is a relatively small, low-altitude loch, with *Phragmites* swamps and water lilies. The flora consists principally of *Lobelia*, *Myriophyllum*, *Litorella*, *Isoetes*, species of *Potamogeton* and water lilies, (*Nymphaea alba* and *Nuphar lutea*).

MARINE AND COASTAL VEGETATION

The shores of the sea lochs or fiords are mostly rocky, except where the entering rivers have formed alluvial deposits. There is a flora of marine algae, largely dominated in the intertidal zone by *Ascophyllum nodosum*. At the shallow heads of some of the lochs the remarkable unattached *Ascophyllum Mackaii* is found, and there are salt marshes consisting of *Glyceria* and *Armeria* turf. The more open rocky shores bear a rich seaweed vegetation and exhibit the characteristic zonation of brown seaweeds extending from the *Pelvetia* zone on the rock surfaces above the intertidal region down through the *Fucus* and *Ascophyllum* zones to the *Laminaria* zone below low-tide level. On the particularly exposed rocky shores, however, the red seaweed *Gigartina* associated with the brown seaweed *Himanthalia* may replace *Ascophyllum* as the dominant alga, and during the war it was harvested on quite a large scale for the preparation of Scottish Agar employed as a substitute for Japanese Agar which was then unobtainable.

The raised beaches, backed by the old sea cliffs, are a conspicuous feature of the topography. Most of the area immediately surrounding the Firth is windswept, and where the raised beach is rocky and unsuited for cultivation and is flushed with drainage from the old cliffs and inland slopes, a rich flora is found. Coastal sand-dunes attain their greatest development along the Ayrshire Coast between Ardrossan and Ayr, but, owing to the establishment of golf-courses on most of the sand-dune areas, very little natural stabilised sand-dune vegetation exists. At Prestwick, *Rosa spinosissima* is a noticeable and abundant constituent of the flora of the stabilised dunes.

II. AGRICULTURE

Donald S. Hendrie

Professor of Agriculture, University of Glasgow, and Principal of The West of Scotland Agricultural College

Since Glasgow and its neighbouring urban districts are the only big, yet not too distant, market for the farm produce of South-West Scotland, it is convenient to describe this large farming area as a whole. Its unity is recognised in its grouping into one 'province' for agricultural education and advisory work.

The visitor of 1958 who gets beyond the confines of the urban area will see a farming countryside which has changed beyond recognition in a couple of centuries. William Aiton, commenting on the records of agriculture in the county of Ayr in the mid-eighteenth century, describes farm houses then as hovels; cattle starving and the people wretched; no fallows and no sown grass; no carts; hedges and ditches non-existent or dilapidated; the plough not yoked till Candlemas; and the land scourged by oat crop after oat crop till it lapsed into sterility. He relates that, as elsewhere in Scotland, cattle were often bled in winter and the blood mixed with oatmeal for human food.

As late as 1800, it was still thought necessary to record that feudalism had disappeared in Perthshire. Sixty years earlier, the countryside was treeless, hedgeless and desolate; enclosure was in its infancy and the land was held in runrig, *i.e.* in *annually re-allotted* strips cropped on the crowns and full of stones, weeds and water in the intervening hollows. Leases were non-existent or arbitrary and of short duration. Dr Robertson, writing in 1793, says of this earlier period:

'The farmers were wretchedly poor. Want sat on every brow; hunger was painted on every countenance and neither their tattered clothes nor their miserable cottages were a sufficient shelter from the nipping cold. Their crops were late and scanty and their half-starved cattle, like themselves, stood exposed and shivering to every blast.'

Today, things are different in South-West Scotland and farming is big business. Some of the important statistics of its farms—which constitute one-quarter of Scotland's 32,000 full-time holdings—are shown in Table III. The figures bring out the preponderance of small farms, the high proportion of grassland occupied by leys, the relative and absolute large acreage of rough grazings, the predominance of oats among cereal crops,

76

	Argyll	Ayr	Bute Dumb. Renf.	Stirling Clack.	Dumf.	K'bright.	Lanark	Wigtown	Total	Percentage of Scottish Total
ACRES										
Agricultural Land (000)	1,668	632	356	261	611	493	454	281	4,756	31
Arable Crops and Fallow	21,254	53,525	29,182	33,555	52,447	32,337	53,997	38,481	314,778	19
Temporary Grass	29,454	77,624	31,392	21,539	76,604	57,766	53,651	55,079	403,109	26
Permanent Grass	48,963	154,322	66,997	61,020	100,758	72,325	109,684	49,136	663,205	54
Rough Grazings (000)	1,558	343	227	160	380	325	236	138	3,367	31
Oats	13,670	34,032	16,789	18,857	32,403	20,729	31,169	23,434	191,083	23
Wheat	25	1,011	1,051	2,520	550	136	1,670	220	7,183	9
Barley	172	600	253	1,192	1,678	410	475	700	5,480	3
Roots for Livestock	3,119	6,209	3,457	3,004	10,136	6,927	6,654	8,810	48,316	17
Potatoes	1,654	6,744	4,880	3,609	3,045	849	5,791	2,286	28,858	18
Vegetables	24	248	350	125	45	24	850	27	1,693	15
Land under Glass (000 sq. ft.)	26	1,874	795	759	82	62	5,717	32	9,347	73
NUMBERS										
Cows and Heifers in Milk or Calf	29,068	86,902	33,262	20,600	53,399	39,398	55,157	44,367	362,153	53
Breeding Ewes (000)	357	169	72	62	227	146	105	60	1,198	37
Breeding Sows and Gilts	222	3,030	2,716	2,025	2,115	1,066	2,714	1,122	15,010	29
Poultry (000)	130	629	263	211	476	203	400	114	2,426	26
Tractors (over 10 h.p.)	1,004	2,566	1,144	1,175	2,153	1,248	2,171	1,232	12,693	26
Combined Harvester-Threshers	0	24	12	26	95	31	13	10	211	12
Pick-up Balers	5	174	24	33	286	113	83	62	780	40
Combined Seed and Fertiliser Drillers	22	110	50	171	155	41	111	43	703	16
Agricultural Holdings	3,022	3,331	2,149	1,653	2,599	1,466	2,860	1,210	18,290	25
Regular Workers on Farms	2,146	5,149	2,368	1,818	3,542	2,378	4,327	2,353	24,081	33

TABLE III. Selected Agricultural Statistics for the counties of South-West Scotland, 1956

Dumb.=Dumbarton; Renf.=Renfrew; Clack.=Clackmannan; Dumf.=Dumfries; K'bright=Kirkcudbright.

Source: H.M.S.O. Agricultural Returns for 1956.

the ubiquitous dairy cow, the importance of sheep and the vital place occupied by the tractor although much of the area is unsuitable for forms of mechanisation now common-place over most of Britain. Comparison of these statistics with those for 1939 (omitted for lack of space) indicates an increase in the growing of oats; a bigger acreage of roots; rather more land under the plough—doubtless reflecting greater efforts at self-sufficiency; a sizable increase in cattle numbers (mainly dairy cows); the disappearance of the heavy horse; more pigs; fewer low-ground sheep but static hill-flock numbers; and a material drop in the regular labour force. The published statistics also reveal that the change from tenancy to owner-occupation has been accelerated since the Second, as it was after the First, World War.

In assessing the economic and social significance of the physical statistics of a selected area such as this, one is largely reduced to qualitative comment. But it is at least clear from the evidence of city banking, manufacture, commerce and tax collection—and from the economy of many a thriving county town—that farming is probably the biggest single producer of wealth in the area and that it constitutes an important market for industrial products which is prized and energetically sought after. By its own progress in raising efficiency it has also been an important source of labour-recruitment for other expanding trades and industries.

The character of farmers and their workers is at least as important to a study of the agriculture of the area as is the consideration of the crop and animal husbandry which is practised. This human breed has its strengths and weaknesses. In the former category must come the willing acceptance of personal hard work—a characteristic which has made the *émigré* farmer from Ayrshire and Lanarkshire something of a menace to the more graciously ordered farm life of other parts of Britain! Traditionally, the farmers of South-West Scotland are not 'collar and tie' men. They are not lavishly given to public utterance, letters to the Editor, political economics or the staging of farm demonstrations for the edification of their peers. But, on most holdings in the area, 'the Master'—if put to it—is the number-one craftsman of the enterprise. On the other hand, tradition —so excellent a *guide*—sometimes becomes too much the *master*. The gift-horse of research is looked very closely in the mouth and the use of borrowed capital is often regarded with dread by the small farmer.

But the picture is changing as productivity responds to two or three generations of good husbandry. This is as it should be; indeed, it would be intolerable if all the hard work and application of science had not brought a good deal of prosperity to the highly capitalised farmer on the better class of low-ground holding. What is much more significant is that not only have the successful ones learned how to enjoy their rewards— whether by a day with Hounds, an afternoon with a favourite football team, overseas travel or in paying fees at famous Scottish schools—but that such marks of lifemanship are now held to be creditable and worth working for.

Notable contributions made by South-West Scotland in earlier years were the institution of the Ayrshire Cattle Herd Book in 1877, the beginning of Milk Recording in 1902, the advent of commercial tuberculin-testing of dairy herds in the late nineteen-twenties and the elimination of tuberculosis from all cattle since the last War. Although probably of gradually declining importance relative to total farm output, the breeding of pedigree stock is a strongly traditional feature of the area and to omit it from this pen-picture would be to miss something which is inherent in the temperament of its farmers. To many of them, perfection of animal form is, in itself, an end worth seeking and the artistry required to improve on Nature's raw material adds intoxicating fascination. For such—and indeed for most of the others who may eschew the hard work involved but love to look at the result—scientific gibes about the futility of breeding on outward characteristics and about the folly of 'paper' pedigrees very largely miss the point and will certainly be ignored as long as farm incomes suffice to meet the cost of such enjoyable activities.

In this region, the Ayrshire, the Clydesdale, the Galloway, the Blackface and the Border Leicester have originated or have, at least, been brought to present-day perfection on farms whose names (Bargower; Lessnessock; Auchenbrain; Hobsland; Craigie Mains; Dunure Mains; Gilchristland; Castle Milk; Hazelside; Glenbuck; Eglinton Mains; Skerrington Mains) are household words all over the English-speaking farming world. In Argyllshire, the visitor will see some of the best folds of the picturesque Highland cattle, beloved of the tourist but having to fight for a continuing place against breeds such as the Galloway.

It is pleasant to find official statistics indicating that, contrary to some gloomy views, the Scottish farm labour force is in good and, indeed, probably in improved shape. In the 'thirties, the industry employed, to an unhealthy extent, youths under twenty who had no hope of permanent employment at reasonable remuneration in farming and who tended to leave as soon as they could claim a man's wage in industry. Now, youth and maturity are more soundly represented and, as a result, farm work can be a career. This is, of course, a matter of fine balance and very little would tip the scales dangerously in the other direction and leave agriculture suffering from under-recruitment and a population of ageing workers. It is excellent that farm workers too have shared agriculture's increased prosperity and that, like so many other wage-earners in Britain, they can now aspire to small cars and mind-broadening travel.

It is, of course, true that agricultural workers have declined in numbers since 1939, but, in the same period, physical output has gone up by well over 50 per cent. This apparent contradiction (in itself the biggest farming change in modern times) has been made possible by rapid mechanisation and the increased use of fertilisers. The tractor is found everywhere and, after a period during which it did little more than replace the motive power of horses, mechanisation is now gradually assuming its real function of reducing unpleasant toil and lowering, or at least holding, costs. The milking machine is universal; forward-loaders, elevators and manure-spreaders are common in an area which once made a virtue of personal prowess in weight-lifting; a considerable proportion of the hay crop is baled; silage-making machinery is increasing in quantity and specialisation; the bulk collection of milk has appeared and is eminently successful; the milk-pump replaces the dairymaid's perambulations; precision-drilling of root crops is well established; 'down the spout' fertilising of drilled cereals is commonplace; hormone weed-killers are now old friends; and combined harvester-threshers and grain-drying facilities are being used on farms with cereal acreages so small as to make agricultural economists raise their eyebrows. 'Work study' is now a respectable phrase and its benefits are being sought. As elsewhere in Britain, the artificial insemination of dairy cows is common practice.

Fertiliser usage in South-West Scotland is relatively high with a tendency, within this generalisation, for farmers to be sceptical about the wisdom of using nitrogen in

79

the quantities which most advisers would say is profitable. Some comparative figures are given in Table IV.

	Overall average pounds per acre (Crops and Grass)			
	Nitrogen (N)	Phosphate (P$_2$O$_5$)	Potash (K$_2$O)	Total
S.W. Scotland	16	40	22	78
Scotland	20	40	25	85
Eire	4	12	6	22
United Kingdom	22	27	22	71
Holland	71	40	66	177
Iceland	77	39	26	142

TABLE IV. Fertiliser Consumption 1955-56
Source: Official Statistics

That the use of fertilisers—a key factor in modern farm efficiency—is much higher than average in some parts of the area will be seen from Table V, which gives the average rates of application in 1956 in two sample areas.

	Overall average pounds per acre (Crops and Grass)		
	Nitrogen (N)	Phosphate (P$_2$O$_5$)	Potash (K$_2$O)
Six Ayrshire Parishes	26	58	34
Five Wigtownshire Parishes	19	73	38
	Average actual pounds per acre applied		
	Nitrogen (N)	Phosphate (P$_2$O$_5$)	Potash (K$_2$O)
Six Ayrshire Parishes	40	86	54
Five Wigtownshire Parishes	48	149	84

TABLE V. Fertiliser usage in certain areas of South-West Scotland
Source: Survey of Fertiliser Practice in Scotland, Reports Nos. 1 and 4, W.S.A.C. and A.R.C.

While the area retains its traditional faith in the ley (here more than half the acreage of grass is of short duration whereas south of the Border the proportion has crept slowly upwards from one-seventh to its present level of one-quarter), it cannot be said that farmers have taken at all enthusiastically to the stock-in-trade of the modern grassland enthusiast—the electric fence, strip grazing, simple grass-seed mixtures, heavy nitrogenous manuring and so on. Indeed, except for the good work which has been done by plant breeders and the consequent improvement of strains and mixtures (dairy farmers are now able to put their cows to grass in the spring three to four weeks earlier than formerly and to leave them there for a similar longer period in the autumn) there has been relatively little general change in grassland management for many years. The value of much that is now accepted as sound practice in other areas is regarded by many Scottish farmers as 'not proven' under their harder climatic conditions, heavy rainfall and fertility-generating leys. It has, however, been shown that the production of utilised starch equivalent per acre in dairy pastures in this area can be brought to figures of 30 cwt per acre and more. Dairy pastures at Auchincruive, the West of Scotland Agricultural College's farm, have given 33 cwt per acre; and from 1954-56 ten farmers applying, in accordance with College advice, intensive grassland methods secured from 19·7 to 36·9 cwt per acre as against 13·8 to 21·1 cwt per acre from other pastures on the same farms treated in the more traditional manner.

In spite of two world wars, there has been surprisingly little change in the over-all economic pattern of farming, which forms a relatively mature background determined more by climate, soil and market than by the need for technical change. On the whole, the ways of doing things have changed much more than the things which are done. Farm 'exports' are mainly livestock and their products. Exceptions to this generalisation are oats and other cereals, ryegrass and timothy seed, seed potatoes from Perthshire, horticultural produce and the early potatoes of the coastal strip. The last mentioned are the product of an important branch of farming carried on with a degree of risk, intensity of effort and success which give it an air of considerable glamour. The industry, in its birth in 1870, was taking firm hold ten years later and really came into its own with the appearance of the variety Epicure (still the growers' favourite) in 1906. The main horticultural product is tomatoes, but strawberries (staging a come-back as a result of the intervention of science against disease and degeneration), plums, salad crops and the more pedestrian vegetables are also important. The growing production of flowers, particularly chrysanthemums and the forcing of bulbs, marks prosperity in the towns and the reaction to the grey Scottish winter. In remote Atlantic-swept Tiree, a small band of enthusiasts are founding a co-operative island industry for the growing of flower-bulbs.

Milk is, of course, the main livestock product being sold from two out of every three farms in the South-West. Probably no animal has better withstood the economic blasts of two wars—and, from a farming angle, the even more dangerous vicissitudes of peace—than the Ayrshire cow. British grassland may be producing a good deal less than that of the more intensive farms of the Netherlands, Denmark, Belgium, Norway and Western Germany but at least the dairy farmers are the keenest of all in this country to grow and utilise grass efficiently. Milk output has risen since 1939, partly due to keeping more cows but to a much greater extent because of larger yields per cow.

The volume of, and the increase in, milk sales are shown in Table VI. The period of increase is not yet over for the figures for 1956-57 are 5·9 per cent above those for 1955-56.

Before the First World War, farm cheese-making was an important enterprise in the South-West. Now, alas, there are only about twenty cheese-making farms left, but the factories of the area turn out Cheddar—and the traditional Dunlop—cheese in large amounts. Livestock come after milk in importance, *viz.* surplus dairy stock, store lambs and cast ewes from the hills and hill-bred store cattle. Lesser products are wool, fat lambs and a relatively small amount of beef cattle from pure beef breeds. There is also the big weight of meat—both good and second-rate—which is a by-product of the dairy industry.

Area	1938–39	1955–56	1956–57
	Thousand Gallons		
Argyll	3,015	5,618	6,139
Ayr	31,286	40,050	42,145
Bute	1,053	2,001	2,158
Dumfries	10,459	20,631	22,350
Dunbarton	3,044	4,008	4,292
Kirkcudbright	8,527	15,738	17,107
Lanark	18,853	25,054	26,250
Renfrew	7,067	8,023	8,197
Stirling	4,958	6,675	6,899
Wigtown	14,593	21,086	22,669
S.M.M.B. Area	122,769	184,117	194,994

TABLE VI. Milk Output in South-West Scotland. 1938-39 year ended 30th September ; 1955-56 and 1956-57 years ended 31st March.

Source: Scottish Milk Marketing Board Statistics

The preceding section of this chapter describes the natural vegetation of the area. The agricultural use to which the land is put is as would be expected from the information already given and from considerations of soil, altitude and market. (See Figure 22.) On the lower ground, with an average annual rainfall up to about 50 inches, dairying predominates wherever there are serviceable roads and potentially productive grassland. In the more favoured parts (with limited rainfall) cropping assumes more and more importance until it even predominates in some small areas—for example, on the Ayrshire coast. The high, wet parishes (the slopes and tops of the Southern Uplands, the West Renfrewshire Hills, the Campsies, the Argyllshire mountains and the southern foothills of the Grampians) are devoted to hill sheep farming. Between these and the dairy farms there is an important and very mixed group of marginal and upland stock-rearing farms, some of which provide a living from a considerable variety of lines of production. Finally, there are the horticultural holdings of the Clyde Valley and of the environs of towns and, of course, numbers of sporadically distributed pig and poultry enterprises.

An idea of the numerical importance of these various farming types (within the category of full-time holdings) is given in Table VII.

Types of Farms	Number of Farms	Per Cent of all Farms
All full-time farms	9,234	100
Hill farms	614	7
Stock-rearing	1,690	18
Cropping	400	4
Dairying	5,801	63
Horticultural	328	4
Intensive pig and poultry	314	3
Other farms	87	1

TABLE VII. The Number and Distribution of Farm Types in counties of Ayr, Bute, Dumfries, Dunbarton, Kirkcudbright, Lanark, Renfrew, Stirling and Wigtown. *Source: Types of Farming in Scotland*, Edinburgh, H.M.S.O., 1952

Clearly, the dairy, livestock and hill farms, which constitute 88 per cent of the whole, are the backbone of the region's farming—as indeed they are of Scotland as a whole. But statistical descriptions on ' national farm ' lines make, at best, cold reading. What sort of *human* units are involved ? What would be revealed by visits to typical farms ?

A characteristic dairy farm of the area would occupy 150 acres and carry perhaps forty home-bred cows and their followers. There might well be two-score of breeding ewes, but, on the majority, dairy cattle would be the only grazing stock. All would have at least one tractor, but not a few would still bring in an indolent horse or two for haymaking, moving cattle food in winter, harrowing in grass seeds, sowing row-crops and so on. A few hundred poultry on deep litter—or quite possibly a smaller number kept on free-range lines as a sideline—would be in evidence. The regular labour required—apart from that of the farmer and his wife—would probably be three, of whom one might well be a son.

The main product of the farm is, of course, milk, which would contribute about two-thirds of the gross farm revenue. The production of milk is spread pretty evenly over the year with a slight current trend towards an increased proportion in summer. Other sources of income might include cast and fat cows (5 per cent), surplus dairy cattle (4 per cent), fat bullocks and heifers derived from crossing the heifers and worst cows with a beef bull (4 per cent), sheep (3 per cent) and direct subsidies (1 per cent). *Any* dairy farm visited in the area would be selling ' Tuberculin-Tested ' milk or milk from an 'Attested' herd, because all dairy farmers have now reached at least this goal, while many sell the even higher ' Certified ' grade.

One in three of the farms are milk recorded. Few would achieve more than 750 gallons of milk per cow per year actually sold. The intensity of land use for milk production is indicated by saying that on the average about three to four acres is used to support each cow and her followers; in addition, 'concentrates' are purchased. Since, in spite of all current preachings, grass and roughages seldom, *over the year*, contribute in this part of the world more towards milk production than the provision of the maintenance requirements of the cows, concentrates are prominent in cow rations often to the extent of four pounds or more per gallon for every gallon of milk produced.

Where these supplementary concentrates come from depends, of course, on the land resources available. Where the land is good and in sufficient supply in relation to stocking, 50 per cent or even more of the concentrates may be grown on the farm. In many other cases, oats alone would make a rather modest contribution to home-mixed rations rounded off with a proprietary 'balancer'. But in a great many of the poorer, more upland dairy holdings, bulk foods and home-grown concentrates together would do little more than support the cows, leaving production mainly to purchased dairy foods. The bills for these then swallow up one-third or even more of the gross receipts from milk sold.

What standard of living may be expected from the dairy enterprise described? Obviously, the answer must vary with the quality of land, the efficiency of management, the amount of indebtedness, the seasonal hazards of weather and so on. Since about 1950, the information collated by the West of Scotland Agricultural College's Economics Department indicates that net returns from dairying have been falling and that the year-to-year position is erratic. A gross revenue of perhaps £9,000 ought to be obtained, of which expenditure would swallow up over £8,000. The balance of under £1,000 represents the value of manual work done by the farmer and his wife (usually worth some £400 to £500 per annum), interest on tenant's capital and the rewards of enterprise. On the whole, therefore, the smaller dairy farmer of the area is far from over-paid and might well be excused some bitterness about those more highly organised sections of the community who are in a position to command a bigger share of the national cake. In terms of tenant's capital, the College's data suggest a yield of from 7·5 to 15 per cent during the five years ending mid-1956. Nor is the future reassuring. Milk production in the area has increased since pre-war by some thirty million gallons per year and, as in the United Kingdom, the shadow of over-supply darkens the scene. Already, well over 40 per cent of the South-West's production has to be sold for manufacturing purposes at prices per gallon far below its present cost of production.

So much for the dairy farm. The hill sheep farm is perhaps the most colourful and distinctive of all British farming-types and, more than any other, it justifies the claim to being a way of life as much as a business. There is, of course, a great variety of sheep farms in the area from the wet, heathery Blackface-populated hills of Argyllshire to the grassier grazings further south, sometimes carrying Cheviots. Everywhere there are big individual differences between holdings in the relative proportions of hill, 'intake' from the hill and arable land. As already stated, such farms do not exceed 7 per cent of holdings in the area, yet the South-West has nearly one-third of all the sheep farms in Scotland.

A hill farm in Argyllshire might typically extend to 2,500 acres, including from twenty to fifty acres of ploughable land. The mid-summer sheep stock would be about 1,500, and the ewe flock of 800 at the beginning of winter would be running on the hill at about one sheep to three acres. The labour force would be two shepherds, of whom one might be a son of the family. Some extra assistance at lambing-time (occasionally in the form of an agricultural college student seeking experience) would be taken on, if procurable. The lambing percentage would vary between 50 per cent and 85 per cent according to the season and the character of the hill. Depending on the situation and the

terrain, there would probably be a small acreage of oats and swedes, but the main con-
servation of food for winter is haymaking from twenty to thirty acres.

The cattle position varies a great deal, the conservative view being that cattle must
compete with sheep to the latter's disadvantage. However, hill cow grants, calf subsidies and the gradual realisation of the beneficial effects of cattle on hill herbage are
leading to the introduction of more of them. Farmers converted to such views might
run one cattle beast to ten ewes, but forty to fifty cattle—including perhaps fifteen
breeding cows—would more commonly be the position on the 2,500-acre farm
described.

The influence of veterinary science on this branch of farming has, in recent times,
much increased and the 'health' of the hill ewe is now very commonly fortified by the
hypodermic syringe and the dosing gun. The benefits of this degree of disease control
are gratefully acknowledged, but the labour involved and the cost of the treatments
cause rueful reflection. Although blow-fly has been conquered, the spread of bracken
and the decline of heather are still serious problems.

Our typical hill farm would, according to College reports, probably be making a
gross revenue of about £3,500—this statement is being written before the averages of
the satisfactory returns from the 1957 lamb crop have been analysed—to which
sheep, wool, cattle and subsidies would each contribute about one-third. From this, the
profit might be £750 to £900, which has to meet interest on capital, provide some
payment for the manual work of the farmer and his wife and reward management.
A surprising number of sheep farms are part of a larger farming business and these
figures may not, therefore, give the complete financial picture of many such enterprises.
During the five years ended 1956, the data collected by the College suggest a return on
tenant capital from hill sheep farming of from 12·5 per cent to 20 per cent.

Into such reckonings must be taken the fact that, in many cases, the fertility of hill
farms is slowly declining as lambs and wool are sold faster than Nature can replenish
the fertility removed—the application of fertilisers being normally uneconomic or
physically impracticable. If proper financial expression is given to this loss, it is very
doubtful if hill sheep farming has ever—taking the rough with the smooth—adequately
recompensed the expenditure, the exceptional risks and the hardness of the life involved.

But the problems of the high-country sheep farmer of the area are probably as
much social as economic. The penalty of remoteness in a gregarious and pleasure-loving
age, the limited help possible from mechanisation, long distances from school, the
tardy arrival of electricity and the preference of young people for the tractor rather than
the animal, all come into the picture. It seems that, as a result of it all, a smaller number
of each generation of shepherds is prepared to remain in the hills. Yet the hill grazings
of Scotland total some eleven million acres. A survey of the production from hill land
in the United Kingdom by Davidson and Wibberley suggests that, although the contribution of such land to total farm output is only of the order of 4 per cent (including
about 3 per cent of milk and about 6 per cent of cattle), it is worth £40,000,000 per
annum and provides about 40 per cent of the national production of sheep and lambs
and one-third of the country's wool clip. The future prosperity of such land is therefore,
in its own right, important.

Lastly, a glimpse at a horticultural unit in the Clyde Valley. Here is the very
antithesis of the hill farm—low altitude, compact size, good communications, proximity

to school and place of entertainment and many crops a year. Left in the cold by the price-guarantee provisions of the post-war Agriculture Acts and much bedevilled by G.A.T.T., commercial horticulture is a colourful but highly competitive enterprise. Especially in so far as it operates under glass, it uses a more accurately controlled environment and must constantly deploy correspondingly rich resources of science and engineering.

Visualise an enterprise comprising an acre of tomato-growing 'glass' and capitalised to the extent of at least £15,000. A reasonable aim would be to sell fifty to fifty-five tons of tomatoes. What this will bring in is anybody's guess. If the problems of hill farming are long-term, deep-seated and well-known as part and parcel of the unchanging hills which cause them, those of commercial horticulture are of the present hour and border on the fear of the unknown which even the next day may bring forth. Is it cold and are people still eating roast beef and 'two veg'? Is it hot and are salads the thing? Has the Guernsey crop arrived or has an unexpected shipment from Spain or the Canaries upset all calculations? What on earth will happen if the European Free Trade area does, after all, extend to horticulture? Has a market-seeking surplus come up over-night from Covent Garden? Are the porters or the pitchers on strike? Has the salesman gone on holiday or merely temporarily insulated himself by lifting his telephone off the receiver? But if the answers to these and other questions are satisfactory—and if there is enough working capital to buy enough coal to get the crop on to the market reasonably early—the gross revenue might be of the order of £6,000. Of this amount, payments for coal, soil sterilisation, plants and, above all, labour might leave about £1,500 (or threepence per pound of tomatoes) from which to provide interest on the large amount of capital and the profit-reward for quite exceptional risk-taking.

What has been said of the financial position of the dairy farmer, the hill sheep man and the horticulturist adds up to a picture of reasonable prosperity among occupiers of good land, side by side with very hard work for small return under more marginal conditions. The figures quoted indicate the earnings of capital invested on a 'tenancy' basis; it needs no detailed arithmetic to show that, if the 'ownership' capital is brought into account, the return on total capital must, more often than not, be inadequate. For many years past, this situation has settled into a pattern in which the agricultural cake has provided no more than a few crumbs for the owner of the land and its fixed equipment.

The area has its full share of technical problems for the future. Can bracken be eradicated, and how is the drain of fertility from the hills to be reversed? Inflammatory conditions of the udder of the dairy cow demand fundamental work which has scarcely begun. The intensive exploitation of grassland carries with it a potential risk of little-understood animal metabolic disturbance. How is the over-production of milk to be absorbed? Are milk costs more likely to be reduced—or at least held—by the traditional attachment to high yields, purchased foods and conventional but laborious methods of housing *or* by loose-housing, minimum labour and maximum self-sufficiency, even if they mean lower average yields? The last is all the more of a dilemma in that a great deal of money has been spent in recent years on making the existing cow-byres of South-West Scotland the best in Britain. Above all, where is the terrifyingly large amount of new capital (required for increased efficiency) to come from at a time of declining returns from poorer land and ever-increasing interest by the Tax Inspector in the life and operations of the larger farmer?

86

Such problems lead to thoughts of the agricultural education, advisory services and research facilities which are available. Specialised research is not a subject for regional description, but the other two educational fields mentioned are an essential part of the subject-matter of this survey. The degree level of agricultural education is provided by Glasgow University (the first Agricultural Ordinance was approved in August 1895), the teaching of the subject of agriculture itself being based, by formal agreement, on the fullest use of the wide resources of the West of Scotland Agricultural College; the College became a corporate entity in 1899 by the fusion of a dairy advisory service dating back to 1860 and of agricultural classes begun in Glasgow in 1886. This arrangement is highly advantageous and economical because the teaching is thus richly nourished by the half-century of day-to-day advisory contacts with 15,000 farmers in twelve counties of Scotland, by the wide range of investigational work undertaken by the College specialists and by the use of 600 acres of land owned by the College at Auchincruive.

The Agricultural College, in its own right, provides more vocational training at the level of the two-year Scottish Diplomas (in agriculture, dairying, poultry husbandry and horticulture) and by a varied range of Short Courses and Evening Classes. In the fields of dairy technology and poultry husbandry, the College offers the only post-school teaching facilities in Scotland.

There is thus at the disposal of the agriculture and dairy industries as much as could reasonably be required. But the use made of them falls short of expectations. A negligible number of farmers' sons take the University degree course in agriculture and they seldom return to the farm. More surprisingly, even the two-year Diploma courses—designed on an applied basis and intended to support practical application—secure an insignificant enrolment from farm families. It is, of course, true that the quite excellent young men and women, from town and city, who swell the classes form a most valuable source of new blood to the industry and that this contribution amply justifies the efforts of the teaching institutions. It is also true that a further small number of people receive some agricultural training at farm schools of one sort and another. But it is a matter of concern that, at a critical time in farming history, so very few farmers in the area invest in an early training in the fundamental and durable scientific principles which are, in the long term, so much more valuable than the transient items of information which are so readily available when required. This state of affairs is in sharp contrast to the high proportion of agriculture's present *leading men* who did invest in agricultural education.

The use of the advisory services presents a more rewarding picture. Indeed, it may well be that the ready availability of reliable advice has tended to obscure the basic need for systematic training! Be that as it may, the official statistics reveal that each year some 24,000 advisory visits are made, 18,000 attendances take place at lectures and demonstrations and 17,000 samples of agricultural materials are analysed.

Advisory work is in the hands of about forty agricultural and horticultural staff stationed in the counties with central support from specialists ranging through the fields of chemistry, botany, zoology, bacteriology, plant pathology, veterinary science, architecture, animal, crop and grass husbandry, horticulture, dairying, poultry husbandry, bee-keeping and economics. As far as Great Britain is concerned, the marriage of central teaching and of advisory work is peculiar to Scotland and, given conditions in which the system will work, its advantages are very great indeed.

The extension services have never faced greater demands. Gone are the days when straight advice on a ration, a seeds mixture, the drainage of a field or manuring was so great a boon to the majority of farmers as to be, in itself, sufficient. A generation of educational activity in the young farmers' club movement, the efforts over the years of the stalwarts of the advisory services and an extraordinarily good agricultural press have brought great changes in needs and outlook. Indeed, the best farmers nowadays often feel the urge to seek the answer to their more complex problems direct from the specialist worker at the Research Institute. The demand is, therefore, for highly trained county advisers who not only have at their fingertips the latest scientific and engineering knowledge but who can discuss, on equal terms, the economic organisation of the enterprise.

III. FORESTRY

J. E. James
Conservator of Forests (West Scotland), Forestry Commission

The history of forestry in Strathclyde is rather difficult to follow, and in the upper reaches of the river the extent of the woodlands was small until fairly recent times. In the 1794 Statistical Account for the Parish of Douglas it was stated that there was very little natural woodland in the parish, but referring to Douglas Castle grounds it states that there were '... very aged ones [trees] which, tradition says, were used in barbarous times for hanging their enemies—the English'. It is also stated in this Account of Douglas Parish that about the year 1774 some 300 acres were planted with oak, elm, beech, plane, ash and firs of different kinds, and that ten years later a further 800 acres were planted with similar species. The 1845 Statistical Account for Douglas Parish indicates that the woodland position was still poor and that out of 28,000 acres in the parish only 1,500 were woodland. The position today is much better and there are very extensive plantations on Douglas Estate. From these and other Statistical Accounts it is evident that the natural woodlands in this area in the eighteenth and nineteenth centuries were very few. Naismith, in his *Agricultural Survey of Clydesdale* published in 1794, records that there were only 1,800 acres of plantations in the whole area and most of these were about twenty years old. The remaining forest area was of hardwood coppice worked on a planned rotation for tan bark and for charcoal.

Many other writers of this period commented on the bareness of the countryside and on the great advantages which might result to agriculture if more shelter were provided. In the areas bordering the Firth of Clyde, however, more activity seems to have taken place and sizable plantations were being formed at Inveraray on Loch-Fyneside and in the Dunoon and Kilmun districts during the early part of the nineteenth century. It is recorded in the 1845 Statistical Account for Dunoon and Kilmun that, between the years 1818-41, 2,100 acres had been planted with larch, Scots Pine and other coniferous species on the estates of Castle Toward and Benmore. At Inveraray the first planting of any size was carried out by the Marquis of Argyll from 1653-85 and by his son the ninth Earl, and in this connection that shrewd observer of the countryside, the

88

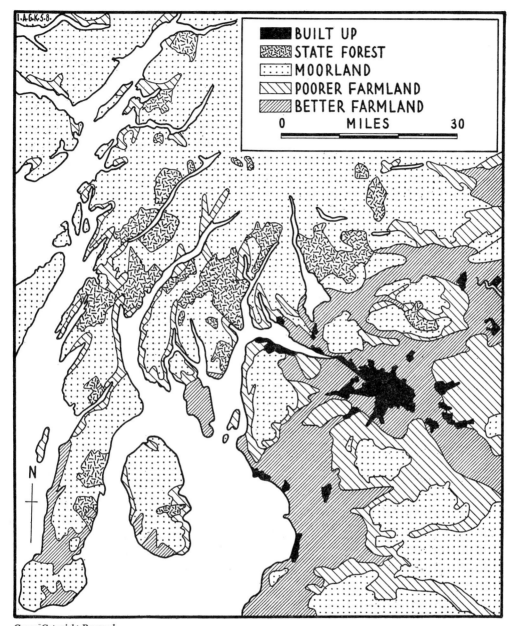

BUILT UP
STATE FOREST
MOORLAND
POORER FARMLAND
BETTER FARMLAND

0   MILES   30

N

FIG. 22. Land use : generalised from National Atlas and information from Forestry Commission.

Rev John Smith, a minister of Campbeltown, writes in his *General View of the Agriculture of the County of Argyll*, published in 1798, 'of plantations we have not a great many nor can we boast of the extent of any of them except of the Duke of Argyll's which may be ranked among the greatest in the kingdom'. In other areas along the coast of the Firth of Clyde most of the woodlands consisted of oak coppice which was managed on a short rotation and exploited for charcoal and tan bark, together with the natural hardwoods occurring in the valley bottoms and described in the section of this chapter dealing with vegetation. It is interesting to note that at Inveraray in these early days of afforestation, hardwoods were nearly always planted together with conifers.

In the upper Forth valley there was a greater area of natural and semi-natural woodland than in the Firth of Clyde region, and from records it would appear that these were run on a reasonably well-planned programme. The system of management was what we now call 'coppice-with-standards', and it was generally the practice to work the coppice on a twenty-four-year rotation. In 1794 regulations were promulgated to ensure the adequate stocking of the ground with standards, and the number of standards to be retained per acre was carefully laid down.

It is perhaps interesting to note that in these days, as is now the case, the cost of transport was a ruling factor controlling the price of timber, and it is recorded that in the Aberfoyle district the price obtained was only sufficient to cover the cost of cutting and stripping the oak bark. The profit was in the bark itself, which was sold for one shilling and sixpence per stone and despatched by road to Stirling, where it was loaded into boats. The coppice-with-standard system was in force in the oak woods on both sides of Loch Lomond, but from records it would appear that in this part of the region the oak woods were enclosed after felling to prevent grazing and a carefully planned system of thinning of the coppice woods was undertaken. The oak grew well on Loch-Lomondside and it is recorded that in the Bandtry Wood the best oak trees had a mid-girth of seven feet and three inches and a volume of forty-five cubic feet solid at ninety-six years of age. Some of the oakwoods on Loch-Lomondside continued to be worked on the coppice-with-standard system up to the end of the nineteenth century, though by 1845 the Lairds of Luss Estate had begun the formation of plantations of conifers on a large scale.

If the State Forests formed in the last thirty years are excluded, it cannot be said that at the present time the region under consideration is a very important one from a forestry point of view. There are within it, however, a number of estates with a long forestry tradition and where forestry is now being actively practised. In that part of the central lowland belt which lies within this region, forestry has been regarded as of minor importance and the land which has been devoted to it has been, in the main, of the less fertile soil types which could be spared from agriculture. Such areas are frequently of heathland or moorland type, but also included is land of higher fertility where topographical factors, particularly steepness of slope, ruled out arable farming. To the west and north of the Firth of Clyde the demands of sheep farming and to a certain extent sporting interests have resulted in forestry being practised mainly on the steep sides of the valleys and on precipitous lochside slopes. Towards the north of the region in the valley of the River Forth there are some extensive woodland properties mainly on heathland and moorland soils. Throughout the whole area, however, much good land was planted around mansion houses and in the associated policies. A considerable amount of hedgerow planting was also done when such planting was fashionable, mainly in the eastern half of the region.

On many estates the efficiency of management has depended on whether or not the owner at the time was personally interested in forestry. In some cases if the woodlands were able to supply the timber requirements of the estate and if the young plantations provided some cover for game, little more was expected of them. Nevertheless, the privately owned woodlands of this region, as elsewhere in Scotland, were of great importance in helping to provide timber for essential purposes in two world wars. Unfortunately, all too frequently many years were allowed to elapse before the planting of these felled areas was undertaken, and at the present time much still remains to be done.

Many of the earliest plantations formed were of broad-leaved trees, mainly oak, beech and sycamore with some elm and ash, but from the middle of the nineteenth century conifers, chiefly Scots Pine (*Pinus sylvestris*), European Larch (*Larix decidua*) and Norway Spruce (*Picea abies*), began to replace the hardwoods. In the plantations of the twentieth century, particularly those formed after 1919, many exotic coniferous species were used, and plantations of Sitka Spruce (*Picea sitchensis*), Japanese Larch (*Larix leptolepis*) and Douglas Fir (*Pseudotsuga taxifolia*) are now frequently seen. In the Ardgoil Estate plantations, on land east of Loch Goil owned and formed by Glasgow Corporation, a wide variety of exotic conifers have been used, including Western Red Cedar (*Thuja plicata*), Noble Fir (*Abies procera*), Grand Fir (*Abies grandis*), Western Hemlock (*Tsuga heterophylla*), Cypress (*Cupressus macrocarpa*), Jack Pine (*Pinus Banksiana*) and Weymouth Pine (*Pinus strobus*). Most of these have grown extremely well in the maritime climate of Argyll. Although current estate practice tends to favour the use of the faster-growing exotic species, Norway Spruce (*Picea abies*), Scots Pine (*Pinus sylvestris*) and some European Larch (*Larix decidua*) are still used on suitable sites.

The bigger estates of the region have a total woodland area of some 35,000 acres and it is estimated that about 30 per cent of the woodlands on these larger estates are being managed under definite management plans. In the case of estates which have no proper plans the standard and intensity of management varies from estate to estate. On some, the woods are well cared for; others maintain their existing productive woodlands in a satisfactory way but have done little towards re-stocking the unproductive areas, while on a number of estates little or no forestry is being practised. It should be stated, however, that some woodlands in those parts of Argyll and Dunbarton, within the region under consideration, consist mainly of scrub oak or oak/birch/alder scrub and are valued more for the shelter which they provide for stock than for their potential value as forests.

On the State Forest side, the position is more encouraging and in the upper Forth/Clydesdale area plantation work has proceeded rapidly since the formation of the Forestry Commission in 1919. The most extensive afforestation has taken place in the Cowal area of Argyll and in the Aberfoyle district (Pl. VIIIb). Table VIII shows Forestry Commission forests within the region being considered and the dates of first planting at each forest. (See also Figure 22.)

It will be seen that Forestry Commission work started first in Glenbranter Forest within the Cowal district in 1921. This was followed closely by the acquisition and planting of Benmore Forest in 1925 which was gifted to the Forestry Commission by the late Mr H. G. Younger. In 1929 Mr Younger also gave Benmore House to the nation for the furtherance of forestry education and it has since been used as a training school for foresters. Acquisition of land in this area proceeded steadily prior to the Second World War and the Cowal peninsula now contains one of the greatest concentrations of Forestry Commission plantations in Scotland. The total area owned by the Forestry Commission in this locality is some 80,000 acres, of which 25,600 acres

91

have now been planted. In the Aberfoyle district afforestation began in 1929 with the acquisition of Loch Ard Forest, and this Forest now comprises a total of 32,000 acres, of which 17,600 have been planted. The rate of planting on Loch Ard was stepped up very considerably after the Second World War and Table IX shows the progress from 1928-56.

The Forestry Commission has always endeavoured to preserve as much as possible of the natural hardwoods, particularly where this was desirable for considerations of amenity. In districts which are much frequented by tourists, they have left considerable areas unplanted in order to preserve expansive views. The nature of the soil and climate of this region, however, is best suited to the growing of spruce and in many areas pure plantations of this species have been inevitable. In some of their earlier work the Forestry Commissioners were guilty of planting their forests so that the edges of the plantations were straight lines. This gave the woodlands an artificial appearance which has been adversely criticised. In recent years the aesthetic value of plantations has been given greater consideration and more success has been obtained in making the new forests blend with the natural scenery.

Although within this region, with its essentially maritime climate, Sitka Spruce (*Picea sitchensis*) and Norway Spruce (*Picea abies*) thrive better than many of the other commonly used conifers, they are not used exclusively. Scots Pine (*Pinus sylvestris*) is still planted on hard knolls and gravel sites of the more inland areas and great attention is always paid to the importance of using Scots Pine of the correct provenance. This species does not thrive well near the sea coast, where it has generally to be replaced by other species. Lodge Pole Pine (*Pinus contorta*) is planted on difficult morainic soil types and to replace Scots Pine near the coast. It is also frequently used to nurse Sitka Spruce on the more intractable peats. European Larch is used sparingly within the region as it is a species more at home in Central Scotland and in the drier east-coast districts. Here it is limited to selected sites—mainly free, well-drained loams. Japanese Larch (*Larix leptolepis*), once extensively planted, is now restricted to the less fertile grass and heather/ bracken sites where its rôle is primarily that of a pioneer. As has been previously recorded, the Spruces are widely planted. Norway Spruce is now confined to the better flush-sites at low altitudes. Ubiquitous Sitka Spruce is used on a wide range of sites including the poorer peats. It does best, however, on the intermediate types which are characterised by a vegetation of purple moor grass (*Molinia caerulea*), and heather/purple moor grass (*Calluna vulgaris/Molinia caerulea*). One of the most useful characteristics of Sitka Spruce is its ability to withstand exposure, and this factor has naturally in- fluenced its use in the West of Scotland. It is not surprising, therefore, that in this region 67 per cent of all planting is done with Sitka Spruce. In recent years there has been a tendency to increase the use of other exotic species most of which come from North America. Douglas Fir (*Pseudotsuga taxifolia*), Western Hemlock (*Tsuga heterophylla*), Western Red Cedar (*Thuja plicata*), Grand Fir (*Abies grandis*) and the Noble Fir (*Abies procera*) all do well in the western parts of the region and are big volume producers.

Successful afforestation in any locality depends on the correct selection of species in relation to the soil type and the prevailing climatic conditions. This applies equally in West Scotland, but for the successful establishment of new plantations in this area of high rainfall, great attention must be paid to adequate drainage. When afforestation was begun by the Forestry Commission in the early nineteen-twenties drainage had to be done by manual labour and was often inadequate. The general introduction after the Second World War of forest ploughs drawn by powerful Caterpillar tractors has

Forest	Date of Commencement	Total Area	Plantations	To be Planted	Balance (including unplantable and agricultural land)
Ardgartan	1924	20,974	4,950	1,832	14,192
Benmore	1925	9,584	3,043	300	6,241
Carron Valley	1936	6,637	4,485	36	2,116
Corlarach	1945	4,879	2,257	70	2,552
Garadhban	1931	1,297	1,204	42	51
Garelochhead	1948	1,004	612	256	136
Glenbranter	1921	8,712	3,519	237	4,956
Glendaruel	1946	7,045	1,985	1,010	4,050
Glenfinart	1926	8,712	3,105	101	5,506
Lennox Castle	1927	777	633	88	56
Loch Ard	1928	32,284	17,636	2,677	11,971
Loch Eck	1921	5,502	2,413	29	3,060
Rowardennan	1950	9,468	1,737	1,624	6,107
Strathlachlan	1945	7,616	2,702	266	4,648
Strathyre	1930	10,616	5,792	3	4,821
Torrie	1947	1,157	995	42	120
Totals		136,264	57,068	8,613	70,583

TABLE VIII. Forestry Commission forests within the region

Years	Acreage Planted
1928–1932	430
1932–1936	2,610
1937–1941	2,700
1942–1946	1,500
1947–1951	3,000
1952–1956	6,550

TABLE IX. Planting progress on Loch Ard Forest 1928–56

not only cheapened the cost of ground preparation but has allowed more intensive drainage to be carried out. On the better *Molinia* sites in this region it is generally sufficient to plough at twenty-one-foot intervals using single-furrow or double-furrow drainage ploughs. Turfs are cut from the plough 'slices' and spread between the furrows at the appropriate spacings. On more difficult sites where a greater intensity of drainage is needed, the plough drains are put in at a closer spacing. When thoroughly degraded sites have to be prepared or where planting has to be done on hard morainic ground covered by a sealed peaty layer, ploughing may be done with advantage at a five-foot spacing, but for this closer ploughing it is customary to use tine or disc ploughs in preference to the type of equipment which has been designed primarily for hill draining. With the advent of ploughing it has been possible to use smaller and therefore cheaper plants than was previously the case. For most species which are to be planted on turfs or on ploughed ground, a two-year-old transplant is adequate and a fair measure of success has been obtained with well-grown, one-year-old seedlings.

Planting is generally done in the spring, and March and April are considered the best months for this operation. Losses seldom exceed 10 per cent and are generally caused by the drying east winds which are frequent during the late spring and early summer. In some parts of the Clyde valley late spring frosts do severe damage and Sitka Spruce is particularly susceptible. It is, therefore, important to avoid using this species in frost hollows and to replace it with Norway Spruce, Serbian Spruce (*Picea omorika*) or with a pine. Maintenance of the young plantations in this locality does not give rise to much anxiety provided the choice of species has been correct and the initial draining well done. It is of the utmost importance, however, that the plantation drainage be well maintained throughout the entire life of the crop.

Many of the plantations formed by the Forestry Commission both in the Cowal area and in the Aberfoyle district are already well into the thinning stage. In Cowal there are some 8,000 acres under thinning at present and at Loch Ard about 600 acres. The growth in Cowal is more rapid than in the eastern part of the region, and because the predominant species are spruces, the plantations generally come to the thinning stage a little earlier than is the case in the Aberfoyle area. Thinning normally starts when the plantations are from eighteen to twenty years old and all species are thinned on a three-year cycle.

The type of thinning practised in the Forestry Commission woodlands in this area has been a heavy, low thinning, and it is found that this method suits both the silviculture and management of the district. In the first thinnings of spruce the average output per acre is generally in the nature of 200 to 250 cubic feet hoppus but increases to 300 to 400 cubic feet hoppus in the second and third thinnings. Many of the older plantations had reached the thinning stage during the last war, but they failed to receive the necessary attention owing to the shortage of labour. In 1946 thinning work got off to a slow start as it was still difficult to recruit a labour force which was adequate both in numbers and in skill. A small programme was, however, completed in 1946 and thinning has increased steadily each year up to 1957. Owing to the accumulation of growing stock the number and volume of trees per acre removed during these years were probably higher than would be normal had thinning begun at the correct time, and out-turns of 600 to 650 cubic feet hoppus per acre were not uncommon. Now that arrears in the Cowal district have been overtaken, lighter thinnings which produce an average of 250 to 350 cubic feet hoppus per acre in spruce are being carried out. In 1957 the production was 502,500 cubic feet hoppus from thinnings and it is anticipated that the quantities of produce from future thinning operations will increase steadily. By 1960 the district should produce about one million cubic feet hoppus and by 1970 it is estimated that one-and-a-half million cubic feet hoppus will come from Forestry Commission plantations in the region. At the present time approximately 20 per cent of the timber produced is large enough for sawmilling and the greater part of the remainder is used for the preparation of pitprops, but with each succeeding year the percentage of mill timber will increase.

The problem of disposing of logs of sawmill size which are produced from thinnings has already been partially solved by the establishment of a Swedish sawmill of the Ari type at Strachur, a small village situated at the north end of Loch Eck in the county of Argyll. The set-up of the Ari Mill has been the first step in this part of the country towards a planned utilisation of logs produced from the great concentration of Forestry Commission forests in the Cowal district. It was established with two main objectives: first, to ensure the fullest possible utilisation of local log supplies, and second, to place on the market well-sawn and adequately seasoned timber from the exotic species now so commonly used in large-scale afforestation. The mill uses circular sawing methods, each saw unit being coupled with adequate conveyor belt systems so that the whole mill works smoothly as a single unit. The round-log requirements of the Ari Mill are approximately a quarter-of-a-million cubic feet hoppus per annum and logs of a minimum size of six feet in length with a six-inch top diameter can be sawn. A modern kiln has been erected to work in conjunction with the Ari Mill and about one-half of the sawn timber produced is kiln seasoned. In this way it is possible to market a product of known specification and guaranteed moisture content. This has already done something to overcome the prejudice against home-grown timber which is so firmly held in the building trade and other timber-using industries in this country.

The large-scale development of forestry in the Cowal district and around Aberfoyle naturally resulted in increased employment and in a larger resident population. The Forestry Commission have endeavoured to keep pace with this by building adequate numbers of houses for their workers. Wherever possible such building schemes have been added to existing villages, though in some cases almost new centres of population have been developed. Following this increase in building, the local authorities have been forced to recast plans for education and they have co-operated by adding to existing schools or by building new ones. Where industry has come in, even on such a small scale as at Strachur following the setting up of the Ari sawmill, local authority housing has also been necessary. As increasing areas of plantations reach the thinning stage it will become more necessary to augment departmental working by selling marked thinnings standing to timber merchants. The housing of these merchants' employees will probably call for the building of many more local authority houses. (See Plate VIIIb.)

No description of the forests in this region would be complete without mention being made of the National Forest Parks. Some of the finest scenery in the Western Scottish Highlands is to be found within the boundaries of land owned by the Forestry Commission and the advantages to the public of such areas for recreation and enjoyment has been appreciated by the Forestry Commissioners. The Argyll National Forest Park which is formed from Forestry Commission forests in the Cowal area (Pl. V) together with the Glasgow Corporation's property on Ardgoil Estate affords excellent recreational facilities for the people of Glasgow. The more recently established Queen Elizabeth Forest Park includes much of the land between Loch Lomond and the Trossachs. It is extensively used by the people of Glasgow and Edinburgh who can find within its boundaries scope for walking, hill climbing and pony trekking.

BIOLOGY IN THE CLYDE AND ITS ASSOCIATED WATERS

WITH A NOTE ON LAND ANIMALS IN THE CLYDE AREA

W. D. RUSSELL HUNTER
Lecturer in Zoology, University of Glasgow

IT is historically appropriate to survey in this chapter something of the fundamental biology of the extensive natural waters in the West of Scotland. On the marine side, the laboratory at Millport of the Scottish Marine Biological Association can trace its origins among the earliest-founded of such institutions. Particularly during the last thirty-five years, workers on its staff have been concerned with research into the most fundamental problems of marine biology—those concerned with the factors controlling organic productivity in the sea. The published results of such work at Millport during this period are uniquely important in world literature on the subject, and will always remain among the bases of our knowledge of the productivity of animal plankton. On a smaller scale, and more recently, investigation of similar problems in the natural fresh waters of the area has begun. Ten years ago, the Zoology Department of the University of Glasgow established a Field Research Station on the shores of Loch Lomond—the largest body of fresh water in Great Britain.

The fertility of any body of natural water—whether salt or fresh—depends ultimately on the interaction of certain factors: first, the amount of energy gained by the body of water from solar radiation; secondly, the physical and chemical characteristics of the water itself, notably its content in solution of certain nutrient salts; and thirdly, the nature of the substratum on which the body of water lies, and its configuration. In turn, all these factors are affected by the topographical setting, not only by the landforms which surround the waters but also by the underwater continuations of these forms. An obvious example is that the availability of solar energy is determined by bathymetric characteristics like the surface/volume ratio of the water body. In other chapters of this book the topography of the coastal region lying to the west of Glasgow is considered in more detail, but it is worth noting here certain general characteristics of the numerous sea lochs and freshwater lochs of the area, before passing to consideration of them as environments for plants and animals. (See Plates V and VIIIa.)

Separated from the Atlantic on the west by the long protecting arm of the Kintyre peninsula and on the south (see Fig. 23) by the shallower waters of the submarine plateau which stretches from the Mull of Kintyre to south Ayrshire, lies the body of sea water which has long been known as the Clyde Sea Area. The Area can be subdivided into two main regions; the southern or seaward part consisting of the broad open waters of Kilbrannan Sound along with the main channel of the Firth of Clyde, these being bordered mainly by lowland country of gentle slope. It is, however, with the northern region of the Area, that is north of Bute and the Cumbraes, that the present account is more concerned. This northern landward part of the Clyde Sea Area consists, besides the estuary of the Clyde itself, of long narrow fiords, cutting deep into a land mass of largely highland character. These fiords, the sea lochs, run northwards from the Firth of Clyde, some trending east of north and some west of north, and are generally regarded as submerged land valleys, over-deepened by ice erosion. In one case, two of these fiord valleys, with an easterly and westerly trend respectively, are connected distally, forming the Kyles of Bute. In certain other cases, similar pairs of sea lochs approach each other at their northern, inner ends but without meeting: for example, Gareloch and Loch Long, Loch Goil and Loch Fyne. As a result of their glacial origin, these sea lochs share certain characteristic features. They are usually U-shaped in cross-section and have their greatest depths where the valley they occupy is narrowest; bathymetrically, there may be several distinct deep basins in each loch separated by transverse bars of shallow water, while similar shoaling bars occur across the mouths of each of the long fiords where, at their southern ends, they unite with each other or with the waters of the Firth. This typical depth-restriction of the mouths of the sea lochs is of significance in relation to the occurrence in the area of other long, narrow, north-south valleys, *not* submerged to form sea lochs, but occupied by the great freshwater lochs of the region: Loch Eck, Loch Lomond and, less typically, Loch Awe. It has often been noted that a rise of sea-level in this area of some thirty feet would convert Loch Eck and Loch Lomond to sea lochs, whereas a fall of sea-level by a similar amount would isolate the Gareloch, Loch Goil and Loch Riddon as freshwater lochs, and would, incidentally, separate the Kyles of Bute into sea lochs of more typical form. The essential feature is of course the height of the land surface at the southern debouchement of the long valleys, since the deep rock basins occupied by the fresh waters of Loch Lomond and Loch Eck lie far below present Mean Sea Level (M.S.L.). The water surface of Loch Lomond lies only 27 feet $\pm$7 feet above M.S.L., while much of the northern part of the loch has water depths of over 525 feet and one extensive depression, the 'Tarbet deep' reaches 620 feet. In the sea lochs this same characteristic of a deep basin contained within a shoaling bar makes possible to some extent the hydrographic and thence the biological study of each sea-loch basin as an isolated unit. The present account will survey briefly the seasonal variation in factors affecting the fertility of a typical sea loch, Loch Striven, and of a typical freshwater loch, Loch Lomond, before turning to consideration of the over-all faunal productivity of the marine and fresh waters of the region.

SEASONS IN A SEA LOCH

Loch Striven provides a most suitable sea loch for investigations of organic productivity, on account of its relatively small size, simple basin shape and the low proportion of land drainage which it receives. For over thirty years it has been the locus of studies conducted by workers from the Millport Laboratory—notably Drs Marshall and Orr—into the physical and chemical variations which occur in its waters, and the resultant changes in the plankton (passively drifting organisms of the surface waters). The greatest part of the basic pasturage in Loch Striven is provided in spring by chains of one species of planktonic diatom, *Skeletonema costatum*. Like all green plants, to live, grow and multiply, *Skeletonema* requires light, water, carbon dioxide and certain mineral salts in solution—notably phosphates, nitrates and silicates. In Loch Striven, as in other bodies of sea water, the numbers of diatoms present in the waters vary greatly through the seasons, and follow closely the same seasonal pattern of change

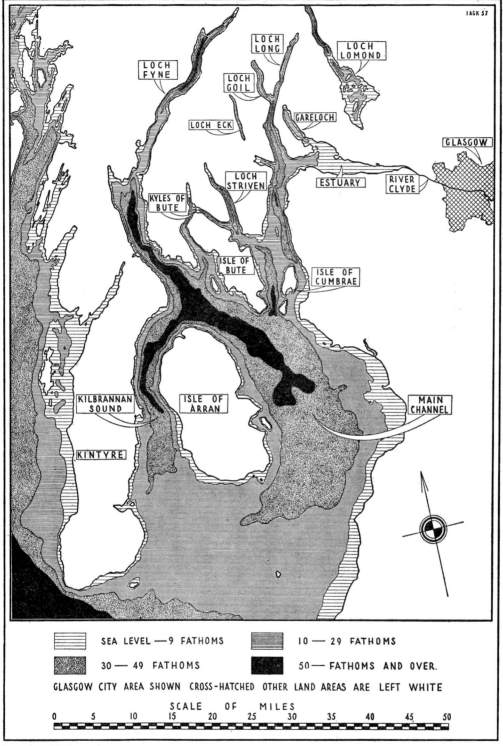

FIG. 23. The Clyde Sea Area (after H. R. Mill).

99

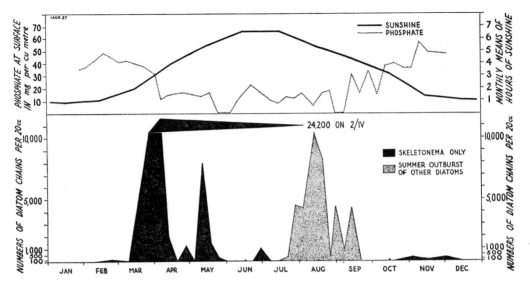

FIG. 24. Seasonal cycle of diatom production in Loch Striven in the year 1926.
Monthly averages of hours of sunshine per day, and the concentration of phosphates in the surface waters of the loch are shown. The concentration in the surface waters of the most important diatom in the spring diatom increase, *Skeletonema costatum*, is shown by the black frequency polygons, while the other diatom species of the summer outburst are shown stippled. Data are taken from tables and graphs in Marshall and Orr (1927).

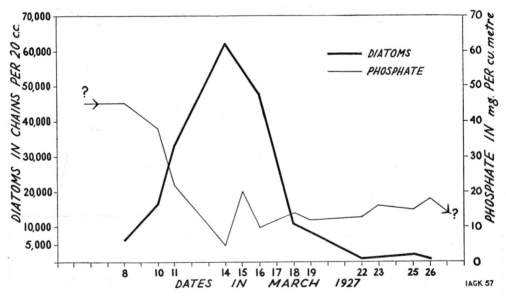

FIG. 25. The course of the spring diatom outburst in Loch Striven showing the concentrations of phosphates and of diatoms in the surface waters. Data are taken from tables in Marshall and Orr (1930).

100

year after year. In the surface waters of Loch Striven (see Figs. 24 and 25) the greatest numbers of diatoms are found in late March or early April. It is now generally agreed that the onset of this 'Spring Diatom Increase', which in Loch Striven occurs every year within about a week of 20 March, is due to a threshold being reached in the total available light (see Fig. 24). The exceedingly rapid multiplication of diatoms uses up the nutrient salts available, for example reducing the concentrations of dissolved phosphate found (which had previously stood at a relatively high and very constant level through the winter). That is to say, since it is likely that the concentrations of other nutrients follow essentially similar seasonal changes to those of phosphates, amounts of all nutrients sufficient to support a diatom increase are present throughout the winter. Since the other green-plant requirements of water and of carbon dioxide are likely never to be limiting factors in the surface waters of the sea, the environmental changes which produce this spectacular outburst of diatoms regularly each spring must therefore be changes in the available light-energy, almost entirely directly—the amount of light penetrating to and impinging on the diatom cells—but also to some extent indirectly by way of changes in water temperature. Dissolved *organic* salts have never been clearly shown to exert any controlling influence on diatom production in the sea. In other areas of the sea the Spring Diatom Increase is brought to an end by the complete exhaustion of nutrient salts, though in Loch Striven the increase seems to fall off each year before all the available phosphate is utilised. In the surface waters after the end of the Spring Diatom Increase there are usually several smaller maxima of *Skeletonema* and other diatoms in the late spring and again in the autumn. In Loch Striven there is often also a summer diatom maximum in July or August, which is less constant and made up of other diatom species including those of *Nitzchia*, *Leptocylindrus*, *Eucampia*, *Chaetoceros* and *Rhizosolenia*. Characteristically, each diatom increase begins in the surface waters and gradually spreads deeper, decreasing at the surface as it does so. This condition is ended in Loch Striven in October/November when the temperature stratification typical of the summer breaks down and there is general vertical mixing of the waters. The result is replenishment of the plant nutrient content of the surface waters from the concentrations built up in the bottom water in the late summer and autumn, by bacterial breakdown of plant and animal material which has fallen there from the water above during the course of spring and summer.

The pasturage provided by the planktonic diatoms (and to some extent by dino-flagellates and μ-flagellates) is primarily grazed by the animals of the plankton, of which the most important are the copepod crustaceans, mostly a few millimetres in length. By far the most important of these in most temperate, and some polar, waters is *Calanus finmarchicus*. In its turn *Calanus* provides the main food for Herring and Mackerel, for the young of many other fishes, for the largest true fish in European waters—the Basking Shark *Cetorhinus*, and for certain whalebone whales in the Arctic. Drs Marshall and Orr have recently brought together all existing knowledge of *Calanus*—much of it from their own researches in the Clyde Area—in their book *The Biology of a Marine Copepod*. *Calanus* hatches from the egg as a nauplius larva and during development this stage is followed by five other similar moult-stages before giving rise to the Ist copepodite stage; there are then four more copepodite stages (II-V), followed by the moult to the adult male or female *Calanus*. Seasonal variations in the numbers of these stages present throughout the year are indicated in Figure 26, and it can be seen that in Loch Striven

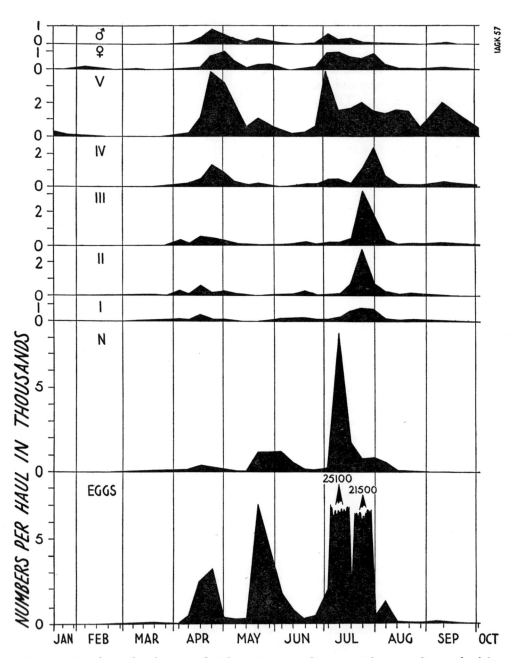

FIG. 26. Numbers of each stage of *Calanus* (eggs, nauplii, Ist to Vth copepodites, and adult copepods) in Loch Striven in 1933 (after Marshall and Orr, 1955).

the annual populations of *Calanus* are made up of three successive broods (see also Fig. 27). The whole cycle takes about two months in summer in Loch Striven, one month for development from egg to adult, and up to one month for maturing the eggs. The over-wintering stock in Loch Striven consists of Vth copepodites, and the slowed development of this pre-adult stage means that the over-wintering brood has a life-cycle

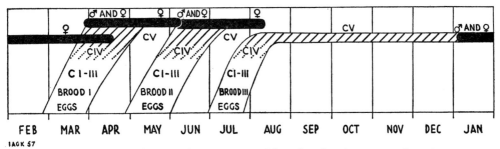

FIG. 27. Diagram showing the succession of broods of *Calanus* in Loch Striven; the size of the stages is indicated by their positions on the vertical scale; adult copepods shown full black, Vth copepodite stage cross-hatched; CI—CIII, CIV and CV=Ist to Vth copepodite stages (after Marshall and Orr, 1953).

lasting through eight or nine months. The greatest numbers of *Calanus* and of other animals of the zöoplankton are found in the summer, following the outburst of diatom growth in the spring. Throughout temperate seas the 'biomass' (or total weight of organisms per unit of volume, or under unit area of the sea surface) in summer is of the order of one hundred times that in the same locus in the winter months. In the Clyde, concentrations of *Calanus* can give rise to a biomass, measured wet, of 100 mg. per cubic metre of sea water at the summer peak value—that is to say, concentrations corresponding to 200 adult *Calanus* per cubic metre can be met with.

MARINE FAUNAL PRODUCTIVITY

In Loch Striven and most of the Clyde Area, *Calanus* can be regarded as the most important constituent of the zöoplankton, other copepod crustacea which occur in comparable numbers being much smaller in size (*e.g.* the species of *Oithona, Pseudocalanus, Microcalanus* and *Acartia*). To put it another way, *Calanus* is the most important agent at this stage in the conversion of the plant crop into fish. In a few places, such as the upper basin of Loch Fyne, certain other planktonic crustacea, although not occurring in such high numbers as *Calanus*, are by their larger body-sizes important as fish food. In Loch Fyne these include the euphausids *Meganyctiphanes norvegica* and *Thysanoessa raschii*, and the larger copepod *Euchaeta*. As well as the phytoplankton, vegetable detritus (partly derived from land plants) may be of importance in feeding these larger crustacea. The zöoplankton produced in the Clyde is consumed directly by such fish as the Herring (*Clupea harengus*) and the Mackerel (*Scomber scombrus*), and some idea of the plankton numbers involved can be given. At Millport, in one sample of young herring (about seven inches in length), the average content of each gut was nearly 2,000 *Calanus*. It is well-nigh impossible to make any numerical estimates of the food of the largest plankton catchers: the basking sharks which occur regularly around Arran and in lower Loch Fyne, and the whales which occur occasionally in the area. Stomachs

103

of the former killed in summer in the Clyde may have a capacity of about 120 gallons and are usually distended with a packed mass of pure *Calanus*.

Not only those fish which feed directly on *Calanus* benefit from the plankton production of the surface waters of the sea, but in addition all fish and other animals living on the sea bed are provided with food either directly or indirectly from the 'rain' of dead or dying planktonic organisms sinking down to them from the surface waters. Besides fish like Herring (pelagic fish), which can feed throughout their life on animal plankton, those bottom-living (demersal) fish, which may eat shellfish as adults, are still directly dependent in their young stages, and indirectly dependent through their adult food, on the crop of plankton in the waters above them. An important aspect of such indirect dependence on the varying conditions of plankton production is that in populations of many of the larger marine invertebrates living on the bottom, and in populations of certain fish, we find marked fluctuations in the relative proportions of different age-groups. Good examples of this in the Clyde are provided by the bivalve molluscs of sandy shores. For example, a population of *Tellina tenuis* at Millport sampled each year for twenty-five years showed that in only four of these years could the spat-fall be regarded as successful, and the young bivalves settling in each of these successful years made up the bulk of the population for several years after. This is even more markedly the case in populations of the Cockle (*Cardium edule*) in the Clyde Area, in which a particular year-group may remain dominant for ten years or more. Similarly, predominance of one age-group in populations occurs in many other bottom-living invertebrates, and is well known in several commercially important fish. On average, only in one year in every four does the breeding of Haddock (*Gadus aeglefinus*) result in a marked replenishment of numbers in the population. In all these cases there is an annual breeding season, and it is almost certain that the reproductive activity of adult animals in the populations is the same each year. The variations in age-groups may well result from conditions in the plankton being favourable for the developing young of each particular species only in certain years. That is to say, it is not annual fluctuations in numbers of eggs produced that matter, it is annual variations in the number of larval fish surviving to become young adults, or in larval bivalves achieving a successful spat-fall in the right place.

It has often been pointed out that human exploitation of the productivity of the sea is analogous to that of the hunter on land rather than that of the farmer, in spite of the enormous value of food gained (in 1956 amounting to £12·5m. landed in Scotland alone). It is undoubtedly true that over-fishing has reduced fish stocks and thus the profitability of fisheries in many cases, and much fishery research is concerned with the elucidation of the factors controlling the yield of each particular fishing. International regulation of fisheries has lagged behind the national control—itself belated—of British fishing. However, the Firth of Clyde has been the locus of one major piece of fishery regulation since 1889, from which year all trawling has been prohibited in the Clyde Sea Area. It has not been possible during these years to prevent occasional operation of foreign trawlers within the Area (but outside the three-mile limit), and such trawling, mainly by Belgian and French vessels, has been a constant source of resentment among local fishermen. Almost all the herring landed in the Clyde are from ring-netters, and the great bulk of the demersal fish are from seine-net vessels, only very small landings by liners being made in the Area. The Clyde herring fishing fluctuates markedly from year to year and the fluctuations are only partly explicable in terms of survival of specific age-groups. In a good year (*e.g.* 1950) over 400,000 cwt may be landed, in a poor one (*e.g.* 1946) about one-fifth of this. At the height of a good season over 300 boats (about 2,500 fishermen) may be employed, and a good season's catch in the Clyde may have a value of nearly £0·5m. The most important demersal fish caught in the Area are Haddock, Whiting (*Gadus merlangus*) and Cod (*G. callarias*), with Hake (*Merluccius merluccius*) and Plaice (*Pleuronectes platessa*) also valuable. In 1956 landings of these whitefish, mainly at Ayr, Campbeltown, Tarbert, Portpatrick and Girvan, amounted to 101,215 cwt (with a value of £324,381). Landings of shellfish in the Clyde are relatively small, amounting to a total value of just over £40,000 in 1956; the most important item being lobsters with the next most valuable scallops (miscalled 'clams' by Clyde fishermen). Local demand for shellfish is low, and extensive stocks of mussels, cockles and periwinkles are not exploited thoroughly. In the case of mussels, however, many of the major beds occur in regions polluted with sewage and, as mussel purification tanks have never been built in the Clyde Area, sale of mussels from these beds has to be prevented. Other edible shellfish which occur in the Clyde Area are not used at all, including various Butter-clams (*Paphia* spp.) and *Mya arenaria*, the prized 'Soft-shell Clam' of North America. Abundant throughout the area a century ago, the Oyster (*Ostrea edulis*) is now limited to some very small beds in Loch Ryan, though breeding and re-establishment experiments have been carried out for some years by workers from the Millport Laboratory.

In summary, it can be said of commercial fishing activities in the Clyde Area that several species of demersal fish are fully fished, lobsters are probably over-fished in some regions, that mackerel, most molluscs and crabs are probably under-exploited, and that the economic position as regards herring remains obscured by the large natural variations which occur in the stocks.

FERTILITY IN A FRESHWATER LOCH

The factors affecting plankton production in the offshore waters of a large body of fresh water like Loch Lomond are essentially similar to those already discussed in the sea, but most physical and chemical factors vary over a wider range in fresh water, and as a result the productivity of different bodies of fresh water varies enormously. The incidence of solar energy, the physical and chemical conditions of the medium and of the substratum are all determined by topographical features. The case of Loch Lomond is best understood if it is considered as two different loch regions, very distinct in their configuration, which will be termed here the highland loch and the lowland loch (see Fig. 28). Their differences reflect not only the solid geology of the rocks on which they lie but also their erosional history. The highland loch, north of Inverbeg, is a deep, narrow trough running through metamorphosed rocks of Dalradian age (mainly mica-schists)—a pre-Glacial valley over-deepened by ice action. This twelve-mile-long trough has an average width of just over half a mile and an average depth of over 300 feet, with much water between 500 and 600 feet deep. In contrast, the lowland loch south and east of Luss is wide, relatively shallow, and studded with islands and submerged banks. It lies largely over sedimentary rocks of Carboniferous and Devonian age, mainly coarse-grained sandstones and conglomerates, and occupies a shallow depression which results partly from 'ponding' when it was an area of glacial deposition during the erosion of the highland loch, but also partly as a result of marine incursions interglacially (see Chapter 2 of this book). This lowland loch, some six miles by four miles wide, has no water deeper than seventy-five feet, and considerable areas shallower than fifty feet deep. The region north of Luss and south of Inverbeg is in many ways intermediate in character. Characteristic echo-sounding records prepared by Dr H. D. Slack across the highland and lowland lochs are shown in Figure 29, and, though these records must be interpreted with caution, one further significant feature shown is the occurrence in the lowland loch, but not in the highland, of a series of deposits as infillings of depressions in the rock floor. Significantly, the country surrounding the lowland loch has extensive cover of drift deposits, mainly boulder clays along with some marine and fluvial deposits, while the only extensive cover in the highland region is blanket peat. (See Plates VII and VIIIa.)

There have been many theoretical discussions on the biological classification of larger lakes throughout the world. One fundamental concept which is widely accepted is that of eutrophy/oligotrophy. Lakes termed eutrophic are those whose waters are relatively rich in plant nutrients (such as phosphates and nitrates), usually have much rapidly decaying organic mud on the lake bottom, and usually show reduced oxygen tensions in their waters in summer. Oligotrophic lakes are those whose waters are always low in plant nutrients and usually highly oxygenated, and which have relatively small amounts of slowly decaying organic material in their bottom deposits. Eutrophic lakes are usually relatively shallow with gently sloping banks supporting wide belts of littoral vegetation; oligotrophic lakes are mostly deep with steep rock sides. The former class is typified by many lakes in Denmark and Fennoscandia, the latter by most Alpine lakes. It is obvious that in a eutrophic lake the plankton will be richer and the entire annual turn-over of organic material, and the resultant total faunal productivity, greater than those in oligotrophic conditions. Of course, when a large number of lakes are assessed, a series of gradations between these two types can be found.

Certain authorities distinguish as a third lake type, termed dystrophic, those typically brown-water lakes with a relatively high content of the acidic, organic materials in solution which are known as 'humic acid'. The important biological effect of this chemical condition is to reduce the rate of, or even prevent, the processes of bacterial breakdown which result in the return of plant nutrients to the water from dead organic material on the bottom. The bottom deposits of such lakes consist largely of unrotted organic material which accumulates as peat. As a result, humic acid waters are infertile and the faunal productivity of such lakes is very low. The present writer believes that lake-classifications could better be regarded as falling within a system of three distinct and *continuous* variates. This can be conceived as a three-dimensional system of rectangular co-ordinates: along one axis would range values from nutrient-sterility through oligotrophy to eutrophy (expressed best as late-winter concentrations of nitrate and/or phosphate); along the second axis, values for humic content of the water; and along the third, values for calcium content. A lake with maximal organic production would correspond to optimum calcium content, minimum humic content, and eutrophy. Generally speaking, extremely humic and most extremely oligotrophic lakes are poor in lime, while many, though certainly not all, eutrophic lakes have hard water. It is also important to make such lake comparisons only within similar climatic conditions; for

106

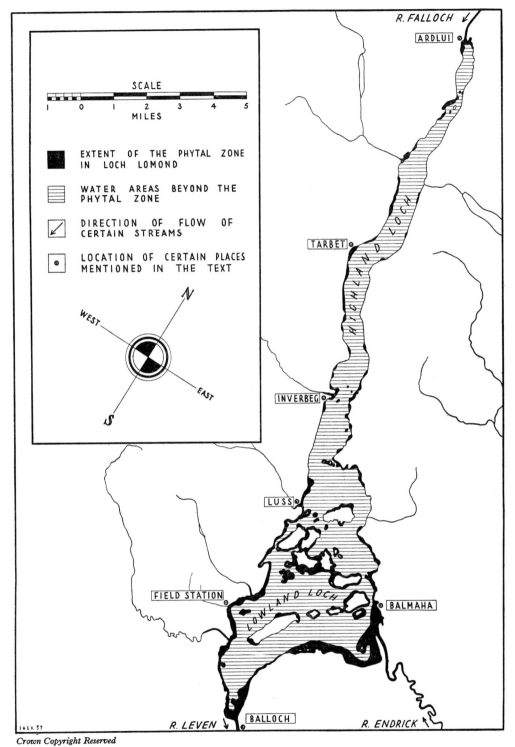

FIG. 28. Map of Loch Lomond showing the extent of water (less than 13 feet deep), which is shallow enough to permit the growth of rooted green plants, *i.e.* the potential phytal zone (after Slack and others, 1957).

107

example, change of latitude, and of altitude, have complex effects on productivity. Finally, it is essential to realise that no lake can permanently be classified at the same point in any system; the trophic and other characteristics of each lake are changing continuously. This reflects the transience (in a geological time-scale) of the environment provided by any body of fresh water.

Returning to consideration of Loch Lomond, it will be obvious that as a result of their shapes the highland loch receives markedly less light-energy per unit volume of water for the plants of the plankton than the lowland loch. A further physical difference is that temperature stratification in the deeper highland loch persists through more than half of each year (approximately May to December), while any stratification in the lowland loch is transitory. The chemical nature of the waters flowing into Loch Lomond is again dissimilar in the two regions. The highland loch has a catchment area of metamorphic rocks yielding little in the way of nutrient salts, and largely covered with peat. The Devonian and Carboniferous sediments which surround the lower loch, with their overlying beds of boulder clay and other drift deposits, are richer in soluble nutrients. For example, from the figures available it seems likely that the calcium content of waters inflowing from the Endrick Water at the south-east corner of Loch Lomond is some fourteen times greater than that of the River Falloch at the northern end of the loch (see Fig. 28). This disparity is enhanced by markedly different agricultural utilisation of the two areas (see Chapter 4 of this book): the highland region being only used as rough grazing for sheep, while the lowland is largely arable farmland which receives additional nutrient salts in the form of fertilizers. As a result of all these factors it is undoubtedly true (although no total biomass assessments can yet be made) that the plankton production of the lowland loch is considerably richer than that of the highland part. A detailed study of the carbon and nitrogen content of bottom deposits throughout Loch Lomond by Dr H. D. Slack shows that the highland loch deposits have greater organic content and a higher carbon/nitrogen ratio, and indicates that the highland loch is both more dystrophic and more oligotrophic than the lowland loch. Such comparison should not obscure the fact that, considered in a general eutrophic-oligotrophic scale, even lowland Loch Lomond is poor in nutrient salts, and would be assessed towards oligotrophy. An example of a larger loch in Scotland which is nearer eutrophy is Loch Leven in Fife; there is none such in the West of Scotland. The seasonal cycle of plankton production in fresh water is similar to, but more variable than, the marine pattern.

One other aspect of fertility in fresh waters is shown in Loch Lomond. In the highly oxygenated waters of oligotrophic lakes (including in this case Loch Lomond), bottom sediments may be largely overlaid by colloids of ferric iron which can absorb nutrient salts. In more eutrophic lakes conditions of low oxygen tension may bring about a reduction of part of this layer to the ferrous state at certain seasons, resulting in release of nutrient salts. In Loch Lomond, dissolved oxygen concentrations are always high and such release never occurs. On the other hand, on several occasions the phosphorous content of the water has been observed to be higher in the waters of the lowland loch immediately after periods of strong winds. It is thought that under these conditions wind-induced currents in the water are strong enough to lift sediment from the bottom and bring about some release of absorbed nutrients. Although this has not been followed up in Loch Lomond, it is obvious that such temporary increase in

108

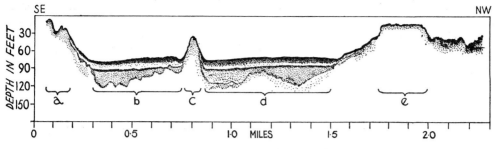

Fig. 29a. Lowland Loch Lomond.

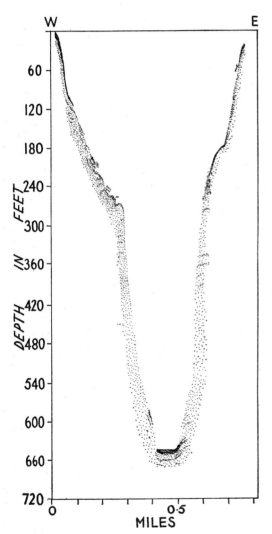

In the transect across the lowland loch the reefs and banks under shallow water (*a*, *c* and *e*) are apparently not covered by any fine deposits, while in the troughs (profundal zone—*b* and *d*) there are two types of deposits as infillings of the irregularities of the rock floor. In the transect across the highland loch the traces obtained by echo-sounding demonstrate the return of a relatively weak signal from the very steep slopes, while the bottom shows no layered deposits.

Fig. 29b. Highland Loch Lomond.

FIG. 29. Echo-soundings across lowland and highland Loch Lomond. From Slack, 1957.

dissolved nutrients could, in the summer, result in a short diatom outburst. Further, the extent of the spring crop of phytoplankton may well depend on the frequency of gale-force winds (greater than 7 on Beaufort scale) in the preceding winter. Such events may largely account for the seasonal pattern of plankton production in fresh water being less stereotyped than that in the sea.

FAUNAL PRODUCTIVITY IN FRESH WATER

Plankton production in Loch Lomond, and in similar bodies of fresh water like Loch Eck, provides one part of the basic food supply for the attached and crawling animals of the lake-bottom—the benthos—and for the free-swimming fishes. In such fresh waters, another major part of the basic pasturage consists of the attached plants, both microscopic diatoms and filamentous algae, and rooted 'higher' vegetation. In considering animal productivity in general, some of the most striking differences between Loch Lomond and a sea loch of similar size arise from the enhanced importance of such marginal attached vegetation—and also of vegetable detritus from land plants drifted into the fresh waters—as a direct or indirect source of food for animals. In Loch Lomond at depths of over thirteen feet, insufficient light penetrates for green plants to survive. Certain diatoms can persist to greater depths, utilising light of longer wave-length. True green plants can live on the bottom only in those marginal waters of the loch which are shallower than this threshold depth for light penetration. In the case of the phanerogamic vegetation a further limiting factor can be the need for soft bottom substrata for rooting. The marginal zone of attached vegetation, or phytal zone, is of greatly varying extent around Loch Lomond. Once again there is a marked difference between the lowland section of the loch and the highland part (see Fig. 28). In the former the potential phytal zone over mud, sand and gravel shallows may be hundreds of yards wide, while in the latter, on the steep-to, eroded rock-surfaces, the zone may only be a few feet in horizontal width, or on the smoother rock faces be non-existent. However, in the lowland part of Loch Lomond not all shallow water, suitable in respect of light penetration and substratum, supports a dense vegetation. A new limiting factor here is exposure to wind and wave-action, a high degree of which results in unstable sand or gravel bottom deposits which do not support a real phytal zone. The lowland country surrounding the lower loch allows considerable exposure to winds, and this, with a 'fetch' of up to nearly five miles, can produce considerable wave-action. Only in the more sheltered inlets are eutrophic conditions found, and all around southern Loch Lomond there are extensive shallows of exceedingly low productivity. In spite of this, the phytal zone of the lower loch is still far more extensive; water of from zero to thirteen feet in depth lies below about 10 per cent of the total surface area of Loch Lomond, but only 2 per cent of this is around the deep rock-basins of the upper loch.

As a result, the benthos of the highland part of the loch is markedly smaller in numbers of species and of individual animals than that of the lowland loch. These differences in relation to number of species are most marked when the benthic animals living deeper than the phytal zone (in the sub-littoral zone and the profundal zone) are considered. Where a phytal zone does occur in the upper loch it, somewhat surprisingly, supports almost the same species of animals as the more extensive zone does in the

110

lowland loch. Of course, the total number of individual animals—the total biomass of animal tissue produced—must be vastly greater in the lowland loch.

Among several groups of benthic animals, certain species seem to be limited in their distribution to the lowland part of Loch Lomond. Considering the freshwater snails: fourteen species occur in the lowland section, but only seven of them have been found to extend into the highland part of the loch. This is paralleled among the bivalve molluscs: among the species of the minute, but numerically important, genus *Pisidium*, it is likely that *P. amnicum* and *P. henslowanum* are even more limited in distribution, occurring only in the southern part of the lowland section. Further, although the pearl mussel *Margaritifera margaritifera* occurs to the north and west of Loch Lomond, other large mussels (*Anodonta anatina*) live in Loch Lomond only around the outfall of the Endrick Water in the south-east corner, and do not occur in the Highlands north and west. Similarly, certain species of insects are largely limited to those well-sheltered inlets which provide the most eutrophic habitats in the whole of Loch Lomond. In such places Agrionid dragon-flies are more numerous and there is a significant increase in Corixid bugs; *Cymatia bonsdorffi*, *Corixa scotti*, *C. falleri*, and *C. distincta* being present in addition to *C. lacustris*, which is more ubiquitous and abundant. As a generalisation, many species of benthic animals occurring in Loch Lomond must be limited in their distribution to the lowland loch or to specific habitats occurring only within it. A species-distribution, very unusual for Loch Lomond, is presented by another minute bivalve, *Pisidium conventus*, which seems to be limited to the deepest profundal waters of the upper loch. *P. conventus* is an uncommon species of limited distribution in Britain, being more typical of Swedish Lapland and northern Norway, and occurring as the only mollusc in certain summer fresh waters in the high Arctic. Its status as a *relict* species is emphasised when it is noted that the water temperature at the bottom of the Tarbet deep where it occurs is low and has varied only from 4·7° to 6·4°C over four years of recording.

Returning to consider the total numbers of benthic animals in the different zones of Loch Lomond, the most extensive quantitative data are for the phytal zone of the lowland loch, where mean densities of over 6,000 animals per square metre occur. Detailed data for the phytal zone of the highland loch are lacking, but even if similar densities are achieved, which is unlikely, the considerably less extensive phytal areas of the highland loch can only support a much smaller biomass. In deeper water the disparity is even more marked: quantitative sampling of the profundal bottom fauna in summer has yielded densities of 25–30 animals per square metre in the highland region, 400–500 animals per square metre in the lowland part.

The fishes which occur in Loch Lomond include species which feed on plankton, on benthic animals and on plant and vegetable detritus. Both in the distribution of particular fish species and in the relative abundance of fish populations the difference in fertility between lowland and highland waters is again demonstrated. Although Sea and Brown Trout (*Salmo trutta*) are the commonest fish in the highland loch, and Pike (*Esox lucius*) and Perch (*Perca fluviatilis*) occur in it, these species are all probably much more abundant in the lowland loch. On the other hand, there are probably six species, including Loach (*Nemacheilus barbatula*), Roach (*Rutilus rutilus*) and Flounder (*Platichthys flesus*), which are *limited* to the southernmost part of Loch Lomond. Somewhat special cases of distribution are presented by Salmon (*Salmo salar*) and three species of

Lamprey (*Petromyzon marinus*, *Lampetra fluviatilis*, and *L. planeri*), the occurrences of two of which, Salmon and *P. marinus* are related to their migratory routes to appropriate breeding places. Perhaps the most interesting fish in Loch Lomond, however, is the salmonid Powan (*Coregonus clupeoides*), sometimes miscalled the 'Freshwater Herring', found elsewhere only in Loch Eck. Powan form large shoals throughout most of the year and can be taken by seine- or ring-netting. The greater part of the food consists of crustacean plankton taken near the surface in open water, almost like the Herring in the sea lochs, but in the case of the Powan, bottom animals are also consumed to a lesser extent. There is a significant seasonal variation in this: the summer diet (June to November) of adult Powan is 85 per cent planktonic by volume, and over 80 per cent of individual fish taken are found to be feeding on plankton only. In the winter months, more feeding on benthos occurs. The planktonic diet is very largely made up of two species of cladoceran, *Bosmina obtusirostris* and *Daphnia hyalina*, and the bottom animals taken in greatest numbers include the snail *Lymnaea peregra* and the isopod crustacean *Asellus aquaticus*. After spawning, powan eggs are consumed in very large numbers. Nearly all Powan have been found to spawn in early January, and this is significant when it is considered that *Coregonus* became a freshwater genus in northerly temperate regions at the close of the last glaciation. Coregonid species or 'Whitefish', including the Pollan of Ireland, the Gwyniad of North Wales, the Schelly of the Lake District and the Vendace of Mill Loch, Lochmaben, are typically dwellers in deep, cold lakes. In Loch Lomond, shoals of Powan often move through the littoral shallows in the summer, and thus are surprisingly tolerant of the highest water temperatures which occur in Loch Lomond. In this case the temperature limitation characteristic of a relict species is found only in breeding and development. The Powan in Loch Lomond appears to spawn only when the falling water temperature of winter nears 6° C, and subsequently the embryonic development proceeds through about sixty-five days of the coldest months of the year. During laboratory rearing of powan eggs, higher temperatures have been found to result in the death of developing embryos.

So far as is known, the biology of Powan living in Loch Eck is similar, though in some specimens examined the principal food was the planktonic cladoceran *Bythotrephes*. Only recently a new subspecies of the other glacial-relict genus, the Charr (*Salvelinus alpinus youngeri* Friend, 1956), has also been found in Loch Eck. Peculiar genetic characters might be expected in these self-contained and isolated populations of relict fish, and it is noteworthy that about one per cent of Powan caught in Loch Lomond from 1951 to 1957 display a supernumerary (third) pelvic fin of variable extent. A similar malformation has been found in a small proportion of the Schelly living in Ullswater, and also in one Alpine coregonid species.

In Loch Lomond, commercial netting of Powan has been carried out during both world wars, largely by Irish crews experienced in the Lough Neagh fishery. No certain profits could be made, mainly because of the lack of a local market for the fish. Anglers are almost entirely concerned with sea and brown trout, and with salmon; and, of the waters around the loch, the greater part is under the control of the Loch Lomond Angling Improvement Association, whose origins as a co-operative fishery organisation date from 1860. In most years one to two hundred salmon are landed, several in the thirty- to forty-pound range, but it is significant that the majority of the fish are caught by a small number of 'regulars' among the many anglers frequenting the loch.

112

In the Glasgow area, and around all the larger towns of the West of Scotland, the activities of man have markedly affected the biology of the natural waters. By far the greater part of such human activities—dredging, damming, water abstraction, modified drainage and the rest—tends to reduce the productivity of the waters concerned, whether fresh, estuarine or marine. While much of this must be accepted as a by-product of economic progress, there remains one type of human activity which can never be justified—the pollution of natural waters. Throughout Britain, legal practice and educated public opinion have become increasingly unwilling to regard rivers and estuaries as merely providing cheap means of disposal for unwanted substances. As will be obvious, there is still serious pollution of waters in the Glasgow area. As elsewhere, two major types of pollution are involved: sewage wastes and effluents from various industrial processes. Unfortunately, the sequence of biological processes which can allow the waters of a river to recover from the effects of pollution with small amounts of raw sewage is in many cases reduced or prevented by concurrence of the second type of waste. Obviously, the concentration of the polluting waste determines the effect: small quantities of raw sewage or some other organic wastes may have merely a fertilising effect on a stream, bringing about a tendency to eutrophy. All greater concentrations will have adverse effects on the aquatic organisms, but various degrees of this can occur. The pollution may be such as to allow survival of most lower animals normal to the habitat though excluding the more sensitive fish. Greater concentrations may allow a limited fauna—worms, insect larvae and some leeches—all tolerant of low oxygen conditions. In still greater concentrations, the water will be dark, foul-smelling, thick with suspended matter, and lacking dissolved oxygen. No organism will survive other than a few bacteria and fungi. When pollution reaches this last stage it becomes of course of immediate concern to public health—and the first British legislation against river pollution dates from about a century ago, when cholera outbreaks were occurring in London. In many cases where a large village or small town discharges quantities of untreated or imperfectly treated sewage into an otherwise clean river the different conditions mentioned above can (in reverse order) be found downstream of the sewage outfall—a zone of foul, lifeless pollution, a zone of mild pollution with modified fauna and flora and a recovery zone with the fauna returned to normal except for the fish. This natural cleansing of the stream usually requires a few miles of distance, considerable aeration, and involves complex food chains of organisms (e.g. waste→bacteria→ protozoa→tubificid worms→midge larvae→fish, etc.). There is now no reason why any small town should discharge imperfectly treated sewage; there are several efficient biological treatments, including percolating filters and the activated sludge process, which will produce a final effluent pure enough to drink. As regards the Clyde river and estuary, the city of Glasgow has been treating much of its sewage effectively since the end of last century, though settled solids are conveyed by two hopper-vessels making daily journeys to dump them in the deep water off the south end of Bute. This dumping does not seem to have affected the marine bottom fauna of the area. Other inland towns such as Airdrie, Coatbridge and Paisley have utilised modern methods of sewage disposal since the 'thirties. Regrettably a number of towns on the Clyde estuary and on tributaries of the Clyde still make no attempt to purify their sewage. To sum up, the worst period of sewage pollution in the natural waters of the Clyde Area seems to have passed. Historically, the Clyde appears to have suffered little from large-scale pollution up to about 110 years ago, at which date salmon, sea trout and flounders were still being caught commercially at Govan, but over the subsequent fifty years the stream became increasingly filthy, and the gradual improvement to the present day can be taken as dating from the eighteen-nineties, when the first civic sewage works were completed at Dalmarnock. Turning to pollution with industrial wastes, the situation is presently worse. In this area almost every known type of industrial effluent is produced, and a considerable proportion discharged without adequate treatment into the waters of the area. For example, small quantities of exceedingly toxic substances are discharged, including salts of copper, lead and zinc from metal-plating, synthetic fibre and rubber processing; free chlorine from laundries and paper-mills; sulphides and cyanides from dye-works; and phenols and ammonia from gas and chemical industries; and further strong acids and alkalis from many of these. Less directly toxic but harmful in the large quantities which are discharged are the hot, de-oxygenated waters from various industrial coolers, washing slurries from coal-pits, and waste organic matter, not unlike sewage, from glue-works, paper-works, breweries, creameries and other food-processing plants. It is important to realise that the small amounts of the first class of industrial wastes mentioned above may have the most important biological effects: for example, very small traces of chlorine or phenols or copper are rapidly lethal to the organisms which were mentioned earlier as important in the natural purification of water from sewage or other organic waste. Thus, when occurring together, sewage waste and certain industrial effluents are synergic in their production of foul pollution. A bad example of combined pollution is the River Kelvin, which with its tributary the Allander Water receives waste from paper-mills, laundries and certainly some untreated sewage. Large amounts of organic matter are discharged in washing water from the processing of pulp in the paper-mills, and caustic soda is also discharged. Possibly both laundries and paper-works discharge some chlorine and ammonia. These chemicals kill off the bacteria and other organisms which could break down the organic material, which combines with the soda to form a soap. This, on slow-flowing stretches, forms a dirty scum on the surface, and wherever there is a small fall churns up into thick masses of evil-smelling soapy foam. It is unfortunate but probable that such foam will be visible in the Kelvin between the University and the Civic Museum and Art Gallery during this meeting of the British Association. However, even in the case of industrial wastes, it is such tributaries as the River Kelvin, the River Cart and the Calder Waters, rather than the River Clyde itself, which are badly polluted at present. The County Council of Lanark has been particularly active in improving the condition of the main river above Glasgow. The worst offenders, both as regards industrial and domestic wastes, are to be found on these tributary rivers, in the towns of the estuary, and on the River Leven (the outfall of Loch Lomond into the Clyde). Polluting matter in an estuary like the Clyde can be very persistent; sewage of say Langbank or Cardross goes downstream with the ebb, but much returns up-stream with the flow. Although the Clyde and its associated waters no longer support the fish they did in 1800, they are undoubtedly cleaner than they were in 1900. On the other hand, there are several threats to the health of the river from new pollutions: the domestic use of detergents, agricultural use of insecticides and weed-killers, and finally the possibility of radioactive wastes. But, if the legislation of 1951 is made effective in action, the activities of the worst offenders in the Clyde Area could be checked. Given another half-century of education and of urban improvement, a slight hope remains that the salmon, depicted in the coat-of-arms of the City of Glasgow, could again migrate under its bridges.

APPENDIX

A NOTE ON LAND ANIMALS IN THE CLYDE AREA

The distribution of the terrestrial fauna of the West of Scotland again reflects the topographical division into highland and lowland zones. Contrasts in both solid and drift geology are enhanced by markedly different agricultural utilisation of the two areas, and the disparate environments so provided support varying faunas.

Among the larger mammals, some species are distinctly more abundant in the highland region, including Red Deer (*Cervus elaphus*) and Roe Deer (*Capreolus capreolus*), the former going south and east of a line Helensburgh-Drymen only rarely and in winter, while the latter occasionally even penetrates the suburbs of Glasgow. As introduced species, Fallow Deer (*Dama dama*) occur in the Loch Lomond area, and Japanese Sika Deer (*Sika nippon*) in the Carradale district of Kintyre and elsewhere. Herds of feral goats (*Capra hircus*) are known from Holy Isle, Ben Venue and the Loch Ard-Ben Lomond areas; they are extremely wild and their horns show considerable reversion. There are, of course, great variations in all populations of the Mountain Hare (*Lepus timidus*), but well-established stocks occur in the Kilpatrick Hills and elsewhere, while the Brown Hare (*L. europaeus*) is common all round the Glasgow area. Rabbits (*Oryctolagus cuniculus*), once abundant, are presently (1957) greatly reduced in numbers, although in several places recolonisation by new stocks after myxomatosis has already occurred. The carnivores include: Otter (*Lutra lutra*), Fox (*Vulpes vulpes*), Stoat (*Mustela erminea*) and Weasel (*M. nivalis*), all more frequent in the northern and western parts of the region. A large proportion of the otters in the Clyde Area are essentially marine, fishing around the shores of the islands in the Firth, like the Cumbraes and Bute, or haunting the shores of the sea lochs. Neither Badger (*Meles meles*) nor Wild Cat (*Felis silvestris*) are really rare, though both are decidedly local and highland in distribution. Records of Pine Marten (*Martes martes*) within fifty miles of Glasgow are extremely rare. The Grey Squirrel (*Sciurus carolinensis*) is now abundant in certain, largely lowland, districts, but the Red Squirrel (*S. vulgaris*) survives in considerable colonies, particularly in coniferous woodlands in the highland region. Other common mammals include: Hedgehog (*Erinaceus europaeus*), Mole (*Talpa europaea*), Common Shrew (*Sorex araneus*), Pipistrelle, Daubenton's and Long-eared Bats (*Pipistrellus pipistrellus, Myotis daubentoni* and *Plecotus auritus*), House Mouse (*Mus musculus*), Short-tailed Vole (*Microtus agrestis*), Bank Vole (*Clethrionomys glareolus*), Water Vole (*Arvicola amphibius*), Long-tailed Field Mouse (*Apodemus sylvaticus*), and both rats (*Rattus rattus* and *R. norvegicus*).

Some of the birds occurring in the Glasgow area also reflect the Highland/Lowland dichotomy to some extent. For example, to the south-east of the Highland Boundary fault the Carrion Crow (*Corvus corone*) is common, while north and west it is almost entirely replaced by its close relative the Hooded Crow (*C. cornix*), which occurs in large numbers. Hybrid crows are not uncommon. Further, one would be best to go north and west into the highland zone to have a chance of seeing such birds as Golden Eagle (*Aquila chrysaetos*), Ptarmigan (*Lagopus mutus*), Red-throated and the rarer Black-throated Divers (*Colymbus stellatus* and *C. arcticus*), all of which reach the southern limit of their breeding range in Great Britain in this area. Other birds more at home in the highland part of the Clyde Area include Buzzard (*Buteo buteo*), Black and Red Grouse (*Lyrurus tetrix* and *Lagopus scoticus*), Ring-Ouzel (*Turdus torquatus*), Siskin (*Carduelis spinus*), Redstart (*Phoenicurus phoenicurus*) and Long-tailed Tit (*Aegithalos caudatus*). On the other hand, some more typical southern birds reach the north-west limit of their breeding range in the lowland part of the Clyde Area. These include Great Crested Grebe (*Podiceps cristatus*), Kingfisher (*Alcedo atthis*), Yellow Wagtail (*Motacilla flava*), Pied Flycatcher (*Muscicapa hypoleuca*), Hawfinch (*Coccothraustes coccothraustes*) and Goldfinch (*Carduelis carduelis*). In several districts near Glasgow bird populations have been markedly altered during the last twenty-five years by the extending coniferous plantations of the Forestry Commission. Early colonisers of the non-grazed hillsides include Short-eared Owl (*Asio flammeus*) and Hen Harrier (*Circus cyaneus*); while among the birds which usually breed in the growing forest are many finches and tits—especially Coal Tit (*Parus ater*), with Goldcrest (*Regulus regulus*), Long-eared Owl (*A. otus*), Jay (*Garrulus glandarius*) and Wood Pigeon (*Columba palumbus*).

Within the city of Glasgow, visitors will readily observe buildings favoured as roosts for the still-increasing flocks of the Starling (*Sturnus vulgaris*); and the prevalent architecture—tenements—undoubtedly suits the Swift (*Apus apus*), which breeds abundantly in many city districts. Throughout the city's parks and along the riverside the Lesser Black-backed Gull (*Larus fuscus*) is abundant. More interesting birds seen recently within the city boundaries have included Waxwings (*Bombycilla garrulus*) and White Wagtails (*Motacilla alba alba*) on passage, and, as solitary individuals, even Peregrine Falcon (*Falco peregrinus*) and Raven (*Corvus corax*). Ornithologists living in Glasgow, like those in other British cities, find the pools on a local rubbish dump attract birds of great interest. Among the rarities seen in recent years at a locality of this kind near Hamilton have been Red-necked Grebe (*Podiceps griseigena*), American Wigeon (*Anas americana*), Smew (*Mergus albellus*), and Glaucous and Iceland Gulls (*Larus hyperboreus* and *L. glaucoides*). Although the shores of the Clyde estuary never attract large flocks of wildfowl, there are several inland localities near Glasgow where winter migrants can readily be seen. The Clyde Valley above Bothwell Bridge, the low-lying ground at the south-east corner of Loch Lomond near the outfall of the Endrick Water, and the lochs and marshes of the Lochwinnoch area are well known to local watchers. Such species as Whooper Swan (*Cygnus cygnus*), Grey-lag and Pink-footed Goose (*Anser anser* and *A. brachyrhynchus*) occur with some regularity; and, more rarely, such species as Bewick's Swan (*C. bewickii*), Snow Goose (*A. hyperboreus*) and Canada Goose (*Branta canadensis*) have been recorded. Lastly, the rocky island of Ailsa Craig, lying in the entrance to the Firth of Clyde, may be visited by some readers of this book. It is famed as one of the breeding stations of Gannet (*Sula bassana*), and according to one source there were over 10,000 pairs in 1956. In recent years Fulmar (*Fulmarus glacialis*) have bred there, along with large numbers of Kittiwake (*Rissa tridactyla*) and Guillemot (*Uria aalge*), and smaller numbers of other seabirds.

116

Three species of reptiles occur in the area: Adder (*Vipera berus*), Common Lizard (*Lacerta vivipara*) and Slow-worm (*Anguis fragilis*), the first being more frequent in the Highlands. Frogs and toads (*Rana temporaria* and *Bufo bufo*) are abundant everywhere, and all three British species of newts (*Triturus vulgaris*, *T. cristatus* and *T. helveticus*) occur in certain ponds in lowland districts, the last of these being the common newt of the Highlands. Knowledge of the detailed distribution around Glasgow of some invertebrate land animals is scanty. As regards the over-all distribution of land snails, the highland boundary has little or no direct significance, the most important single factor being the occurrence of calcareous rocks and soils. To put it another way, an area of limestone in highland Argyllshire can, if other conditions are suitable, support almost all the species found in a 'good' lowland locality in the Midland Valley; and a lowland peat-moor in Ayrshire resembles, in its paucity of molluscan species, most highland moors. Such snails as *Helix aspersa*, *H. nemoralis*, *H. hortensis*, *Hygromia striolata* and *Helicella caperata* are among those more limited to calcareous localities, while such species as *Arianta arbustorum*, *Clausilia bidentata*, *Discus rotundatus*, *Oxychilus alliarius* and *Retinella nitidula* are ubiquitous through the West of Scotland. Three distinctly calciphile species, *Helicella virgata*, *H. itala* and *Cochlicella acuta*, are largely maritime in this area. A few species are tolerant of acid conditions to a considerable extent, including *Succinea pfeifferi*, *Cochlicopa lubrica*, *Vitrea crystallina* and *Vitrina pellucida*; but on typical moorland such slugs as *Arion ater*, *Limax marginatus* and *Agriolimax reticulatus* are the only common land molluscs. If only one species occurs, it is *Arion ater*. Thus, although no snail species can be regarded as typically highland or typically lowland, it is undoubtedly true that, as a result of the greater extent of calcareous rocks in that part of the area, very many land snails are both more abundant and more generally distributed in the Midland Valley east of Glasgow than in the highland regions to the north and west.

On the other hand, certain relatively common butterflies are probably more abundant in the Highland region, including Grayling (*Eumenis semele*), Large Heath (*Coenonympha tullia*), Green Hairstreak (*Callophrys rubi*) and Scotch Argus (*Erebia aethiops*). A close congener of the last, the Small Mountain Ringlet (*E. epiphron*), is the only truly alpine British butterfly, and occurs in the hills of western Perthshire to the north of Glasgow. Recent changes in distribution and status are known for some species. Rare before 1930, by 1948 the Peacock (*Nymphalis io*) had completed its spread through the Western Highlands and Islands, and is now well established. In contrast, the distribution of the Speckled Wood (*Pararge aegeria*) is of interest, since it now is found only within a limited area of the Western Highlands, though less than a century ago it occurred throughout Scotland. Finally, it is likely that several other groups of invertebrate animals are represented in the West of Scotland by both typically highland and typically lowland species.

It would be inappropriate to attempt here a full bibliography on aquatic biology in this area, but a few works are now quoted—most of them containing major lists of further references. No subsequent publication has replaced H. R. Mill's classic studies on the bathymetry and hydrography of the Clyde Sea Area (*Trans. Roy. Soc. Edinb.*, 1892-94, 36: 641-729; 38: 1-161). Further information on plankton productivity in sea lochs, and on the biology of *Calanus* and herring, can be sought in books and papers by S. M. Marshall and A. P. Orr (*Essays in marine biology*, Edinburgh, 1953; *The biology of a marine copepod*, Edinburgh, 1955; *J. Mar. Biol. Ass. U.K.*, 1927-39, 14: 837-868; 16: 853-878; 19: 793-828; 22: 245-267; 23: 427-455). Fishery data are given in the series of government reports (*Scot. Sea Fish. Statistical Tables* and *Rep. Fish. Scot.*). Biological work in Loch Lomond is reported in a book by H. D. Slack and others (*Studies on Loch Lomond, I*, Glasgow, 1957), and in papers by H. D. Slack and W. Russell Hunter (*Proc. Roy. Soc. Edinb.* (B), 1953-54, 65: 84-105, 143-165, 213-238; and elsewhere), and by A. C. J. Weerekoon (*Ceylon J. Sci.*, 1956, C, VII; N.S. 1: 1-94, 95-133). No general account of land fauna around Glasgow exists, but M. F. M. Meiklejohn and C. E. Palmar have regularly published records of rarer birds (*Scot. Nat.*, 1952-55, 64: 26-30; 65: 1-4, 115-119; 66: 65-69; 67: 65-71), and scattered papers on other faunistic records have been published in several journals (*J. Anim. Ecol., Proc. R. Ent. Soc. Lond., Ent. Mon. Mag., J. Conch., Glasg. Nat.,* and *Scot. Nat.*).

Any errors of fact or interpretation in the above account are entirely mine, but I am indebted to three colleagues: to Dr A. P. Orr of Millport Marine Station and Dr H. D. Slack of Glasgow University who have read the sections on marine plankton and on Loch Lomond respectively, and to Mr C. E. Palmar of Glasgow Corporation Museum who provided much information on birds. Further, I must thank Professor C. M. Yonge, C.B.E., F.R.S., for his continued counsel and for kindly reading the entire account, and, once again, my wife for her help at all stages of its preparation.

PREHISTORIC AND ROMAN TIMES

I. THE CLYDE IN PREHISTORY

HORACE FAIRHURST

Senior Lecturer in Geography, University of Glasgow

WHAT led to the initial colonisation of the sea lochs and islands of western Scotland, the ultimate fringe of the Old World, can only be a matter for speculation. They provided a remote environment where successive waves of settlement in prehistoric times seem often to have resulted in little more than peculiarities and late survivals to puzzle and distract the archaeologist. The cultural flotsam and jetsam cannot be disentangled easily, and the problems are apt to seem of local rather than European interest. Yet such an environment should be a challenge to clarify issues with experience from a wider field, and rigorously to select the significant from the incidental. Our basic knowledge remains quite inadequate in many respects for a general description, but the thrill of the unexplored still remains in large measure.

Within this western fringe, the Firth of Clyde played a dual rôle in early times. It led colonists moving northwards from the coastlands of the Irish Sea towards the heart of the Scottish Lowlands, but it also provided, as Sir Lindsay Scott suggested,[1] a sheltered route for further movement northwards. There were copper ores to be found around upper Loch Fyne and an easy crossing at the Crinan isthmus could have been utilised to reach onwards towards Loch Linnhe, the Hebrides and the Great Glen. The Island of Arran and the Crinan isthmus were strategically placed under such circumstances, and both were of outstanding importance in the early days of settlement.

Colonists from the North Sea coastlands soon found the easy route up the Tweed and over to the upper Clyde via the Biggar gap, which represented only a short portage for a canoe. Another possible route led to the upper Clyde basin from the Solway via Annandale. Two minor connections with the Ayrshire basin via the gaps at Lochwinnoch and Muirkirk were apparently established at quite an early stage. The lowlands of the Glasgow area thus begin to develop some degree of nodality at a remarkably remote period. Strangely, there is little evidence to indicate much transverse movement to and from the Forth. Only a low watershed intervenes, but in the present state of our knowledge this represented a zone of separation which justifies its use as a major boundary throughout prehistoric times.

Such problems of movement and also of the distribution of population would be easier to consider were there any clear indication as to the character of the natural vegetation. It is commonly assumed that forests were widespread over the lowlands; almost everywhere within our region, odd birch trees struggle up to at least 800 feet and much higher in sheltered places inland. Detailed studies of the pollen content of the peat bogs have no more than commenced, but already it seems that birch, alder and hazel were the main species and forest trees such as oak, elm and pine were subsidiary. Moreover, a distinct decrease in the amount of tree pollen has been traced in some places as far back, apparently, as the earlier days of settlement in the second millennium B.C.[2] Even if extensive openings had been made in the thickets and woodlands, occupation must long have remained patchy. More continuous settlement had to await not merely increasing numbers and further forest clearance but also an agricultural technique appropriate to cold heavy soils under damp climatic conditions. In general, it is noticeable that in the coastal areas few prehistoric sites occur much above 500 feet, but further inland in the upper Clyde basin, the inhospitable upland was not reached until well over 1,000 feet. The damp weather of the west seems mainly responsible for the lower limit of settlement.

The first colonisation as yet detected in our region came very late by European standards. It was not until the Ice Age was finally over and the last re-advance of the mountain glaciers in the Highlands was spent that a few scattered pioneers began to leave stone tools behind them—borers and scrapers to deal with hides and to make wood and horn implements. They were a hunting and fishing folk who merely collected what Nature gave in a harsh environment; the beach provided a perennial food supply and coastal sites were a common choice. Groups descended from the older Palaeolithic hunters and their Mesolithic successors were involved. Some reached the upper basin of the Clyde, possibly coming westward from the Tweed; others came from Ireland to leave the Larnian culture at Campbeltown. The antecedents of those at Ballantrae and Shewalton Moor in Ayrshire are more confused, and so are those of a little group at Woodend Loch just east of Glasgow.

The dating of these peoples has so far hinged on the problem of the '25-foot' raised beach—a marked feature around the Firth of Clyde—with which some of the tools have been found in association. These strand lines, when the sea reached as far inland as Glasgow, are thought to have been formed during the 'Atlantic submergence' which began perhaps about 6,000 B.C. Up-to-date methods involving Carbon 14 may in time give a more precise chronology.

As elsewhere in Europe, the arrival of people who possessed flocks and herds and practised primitive agriculture was a great landmark in prehistory. Just after the beginning of the second millennium B.C., a general ferment sent wanderers as far even as this fringe of the Old World. The evidence for these Neolithic invaders from the south is more tangible than for the earliest period and has been studied in more detail.

The characteristic site within the Clyde region is a huge and often elongated cairn covering a 'megalithic' burial chamber of great stone slabs. This is a long passage-like structure, divided into segments by cross slabs and capable of receiving several burials with accompanying grave goods. Similar megalithic chambers of 'Clyde-Carlingford' type occur in Northern Ireland. So far, evidence of the form of dwelling occupied at the time has remained elusive for the Clyde region, although a domestic site is believed to have been located at Townhead, Rothesay, and pottery has occurred elsewhere, as at Bishopton and at Knapper's Farm on the western outskirts of Glasgow. We are dependent almost entirely for indications of colonisation upon the tombs of the period. Figure 30 has been prepared in consultation with Mr J.G. Scott, and shows the distribution

120

locally. This is essentially coastal and western, with a penetration into the lower river basin as far as the Glasgow area. The upper Clyde Valley seems to have remained completely outside, though it was very quickly to be colonised by other farming folk. Mr Scott has suggested that land routes from the east may not have been neglected

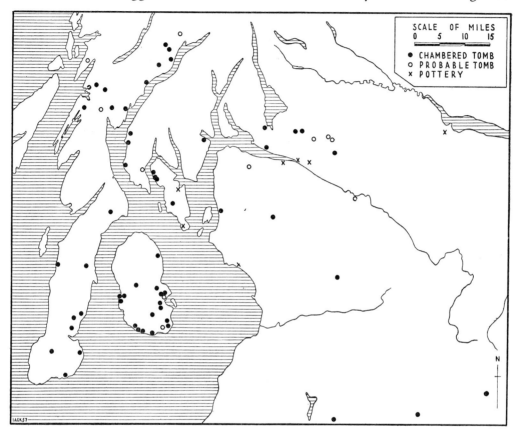

FIG. 30. The Distribution of Neolithic Sites. Material supplied by J. G. Scott is incorporated.

by the Neolithic immigrants and that a long barrow-like structure at Broadgate near Strathblane suggests Yorkshire affinities; he recalls the destruction of another barrow-like burial mound at Baldernock. Both sites lie in lowland country between Glasgow and the escarpment of the Campsies.

Perhaps before the last of the Neolithic farmers arrived, a fresh stream of colonists, coming ultimately from the Continent, began to affect especially the east of Britain. Once more the colonisation has been traced very largely through the resting places of the dead, though in this case a domestic occupation site has been found at Muirkirk on the eastern rim of the Ayrshire basin. The presence of the newcomers is attested by single burials which, in Scotland, occur in slab-lined cists (hard 'c') usually without any very noticeable covering cairn; they are accompanied by a large, decorated pot known as a beaker. It is tempting to think that Beaker folk arrived, via the Tweed, in the upper Clyde basin (Fig. 31) before the Neolithic settlers had penetrated so far; often the two cultures seem mutually exclusive. On the other hand, a scatter of beakers around the Firth, sometimes in the megalithic chambers, indicates another stream of immigrants coming by the older seaway along the west coast. Very few beakers have been found around Glasgow, which seems to preclude the Clyde as a major entry.

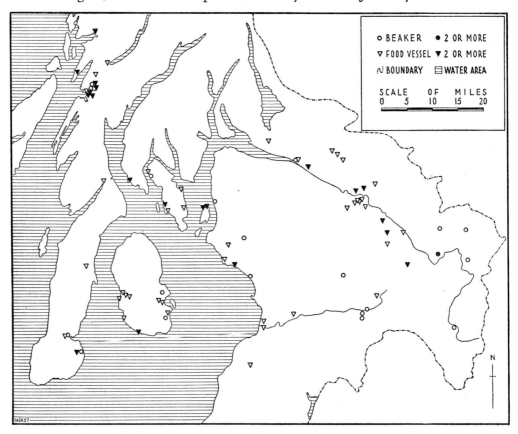

FIG. 31.   Beakers and Food Vessels within the Clyde region: from published data.

During the period of immigration which has just been considered, bronze was beginning to come into use; only slowly does it become at all common, and it was probably always expensive. Tin was a very rare ore, but copper was less difficult to obtain; it occurs in very small deposits in several localities within our region, and especially along upper Loch Fyne. Gold in small quantity also occurs in the upper Clyde basin, though the main source in the Bronze Age for ornaments appears to have been in Ireland. Not only the presence of gold ornaments but the character of the metal work generally indicates that contacts with Ireland were maintained; indeed, they are apparent throughout the whole prehistoric period. No one who has stood on the Mull of Kintyre and seen the complex alternation of land and water on all sides can wonder at the close connection.

By the Middle Bronze Age, perhaps about the middle of the second millennium B.C., the pre-Neolithic hunting folk and the immigrant farming and stock-rearing groups had merged into a population which left in the graves of the dead a type of pot known as a Food Vessel. In general, these Food Vessels have been found widely distributed over the lowlands of the central and southern parts of Scotland, but in the Clyde region in particular, the occupation appears to have been relatively intensive. The distribution, as plotted on Figure 31, is probably incomplete as regards published examples and others must have been destroyed in the past in great numbers. Apparently, however, the period of amalgamation had been accompanied by a distinct expansion of the settlement area over much of the lower Clyde basin and lowland Ayrshire. The distribution is essentially lowland, though alluvial flats or 'haughland' where flooding was likely were of course avoided; again, the low watershed between the Clyde and the Forth has yielded few examples. Around the Firth of Clyde, the Food Vessels occur in much the same localities as earlier sites, for settlement was restricted then, as now, to the narrow coastal lowlands within which the raised beach deposits frequently offered the most attractive soils.

By this time the ferment in Europe which had sent Megalithic and Beaker folk as far afield as the West of Scotland seems to have subsided, and for a period of many centuries there is little in the archaeological record to suggest large-scale invasion. Exotic implements have been found from time to time such as stone battle-axes (Chapelton, Lawfield, Whiteinch) and decorated bronze axes (Gavel Moss hoard) which indicate trade with the south, and gold ornaments suggest the continuation of Irish contacts; finds of blue paste beads, recalling the faïence beads of the Wessex culture, show a continuation of these activities at least until about 1350 B.C.

Much the same pattern of distribution would appear in a map of Cinerary Urns, some forms of which came into use rather early in the Bronze Age, but on the whole they were later than Food Vessels; locally, they may have survived for many centuries. Several varieties of Cinerary Urn may be distinguished, but there are no local peculiarities to record and the distribution shows no unusual concentration in the Clyde region. Our area continues as a rather characterless unit in a much wider culture-province. In the late Bronze Age, socketed axes and leaf-shaped bronze swords reached the Clyde apparently from the south, and these changes in the metal work clearly indicate contact with a wider sphere. On the whole, however, the evidence of occupation for the later Bronze Age is slender and not very informative. It scarcely suggests a population increasing at an ever-accelerating rate and vigorously developing the country which had been colonised so successfully in the earlier Bronze Age. This problem, however, is not local and we cannot linger over it.

Precisely when and by what means iron came into general use in this part of Britain is still obscure. The series of invasions, commencing at the close of the Bronze Age, which brought Early Iron Age folk from the Continent into South Britain, cannot as yet be shown to have affected the coast north of Scarborough (fifth century B.C.). On the other hand, a process of diffusion by wandering smiths could have made the cheaper iron tools available much further afield than the areas of actual immigration. It is fairly clear, however, that another period of ferment, with a vigorous movement into southern Scotland of refugees from the south, occurred a century or so before the Romans arrived. This seems to have involved aristocratic elements with a knowledge of fortification and of chariot warfare, who established themselves as leaders amongst the native population.[3]

The Roman Occupation, to be discussed later, was short lived, and even within the area marked off by the Wall from Forth to Clyde it did not revolutionise the native economy. Often, no clear-cut distinction can be made archaeologically between the 'Early' Iron Age and a 'Roman' or even 'Later' Iron Age. The problem is conspicuous

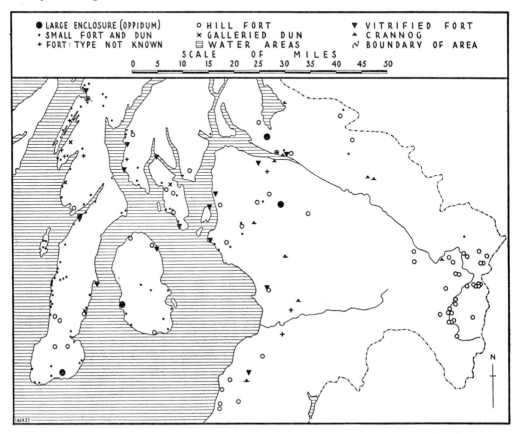

Fig. 32. Iron Age Sites within the Clyde region. Published data and some personal information are incorporated but the distribution is far from complete and the classification provisional.

in considering the characteristic native sites of the period; these are no longer the graves of the dead upon which we rely so much for evidence of Bronze Age occupation. As elsewhere in Britain, a new social organisation led to the construction of large numbers of fortified settlements; in Scotland, and especially in our Clyde region, these assume a complexity and profusion which is not encountered over much of England. Moreover the period of occupation may be prolonged, in some cases, well into medieval times.

The Iron Age settlements vary in form from enclosures several acres in extent, through rather smaller hill forts, often with multiple ramparts and ditches, to tiny fortified homesteads. Figure 32 shows the distribution for the Clyde region in so far as is possible from published material, extensive use of the Six-inch Ordnance Survey map and some personal observation. The complete absence of inventories by the Royal Commission on Ancient and Historical Monuments for any of the counties concerned

124

makes virtually impossible any claim to be comprehensive. Argyll has been especially difficult; the country is very rich in small duns, but there is almost a dearth of published surveys. The recently established Mid-Argyll Society is making rapid progress in that area, and the Kintyre Society has much unpublished material in its possession. Of the sites shown on Figure 32, only a very few have been excavated, and the majority of these were investigated many years ago without the production of adequate reports.

An important distinction can be made within the Clyde region between the western coastlands where the sites rarely occur above about 700 feet, and the upper Clyde basin where the upper limit of settlement is very much higher and the whole lies above 700 feet. This change in the distribution between east and west is, however, not peculiar to the Clyde region; partly it is a reflection of contrasting environmental conditions as between a rather drier, sunnier east and a damp west with much low-lying cloud. But cultural differences seem also involved.

In the century or so before the arrival of the Legions in A.D. 80, the hill country of South-East Scotland from the Lothians to the county of Dumfries came to form the tribal territory of the Votadini and the Selgovae. Within the whole of this area there are very numerous examples of hill forts which are believed for the most part to date back to the Early Iron Age; they are not large by southern standards, but are often provided with multiple defences.[4] The close distribution extends westwards to include a remarkable cluster around the upper Tweed, extending over into the upper Clyde basin. Characteristically these forts within our region are placed on eminences over-looking the lower levels of the basin, or on hill tops; while most of the area lies above 700 feet some of the sites are as high as 1,400 feet. At this altitude, the winters are rather bleak, but there is relatively well-drained alluvial land on the terraces by the rivers, and the steep but smooth hill slopes are well covered with grass and heather. A considerable population of farming folk found the area congenial and either dwelt within, or utilised as strong points, these numerous hill forts.

Below Lanark the sites rapidly become scarce in comparison, and the same is true of the uplands forming the watershed between the Clyde and Ayrshire. Slopes are often gentle, and natural drainage is not so good as in the Southern Uplands, while boulder clay becomes widespread in the lowland country. Around Glasgow, Iron Age sites are remarkably scarce. Long and intensive cultivation and the highly industrialised and urbanised nature of the area offer one obvious explanation, but under natural conditions, poorer drainage and cold clay soils with much woodland may not have attracted invaders from outside.

This restriction of colonisation from the South-East to the upper Clyde basin might recall the distribution of the east-coast type of beaker during the earlier period of ferment. In the coastlands of the Firth, the distribution of the sites on Figure 32 is reminiscent of the Neolithic. There is a scatter in the low ground along the Firth and a penetration eastwards via the Lochwinnoch gap and the Clyde itself, to the slopes of the Kilpatricks and the Campsies. This sub-region in general links with the west coast of Scotland and Northern Ireland in an Atlantic Iron Age of different complexion from that of the South-East. The Firth seems to have been acting again as a corridor for colonising movements along the western seaboard. This Atlantic Iron Age was of considerable complexity and seems to have continued into times which were historical in many parts of Britain.

The western sites include occasional examples of the larger hill forts characteristic of the South-East, and also of the 'vitrified' forts. The latter were for long an archaeological puzzle, but it is now known that they resulted from the destruction by fire of ramparts built of stone and revetted with timber beams. Such vitrified and timber-revetted forts are not all of one type. One group seems to have been erected in eastern Scotland by immigrants from the sea, but our western examples involve a movement again by sea, but apparently from the south. Dunagoil in the Island of Bute was excavated many years ago and is the most famous type site, but two periods of occupation are involved; the fort may have originated not long before the Roman Occupation. The Meikle Reive, a fort on the scarp of the Campsies to the north of Glasgow, appears as an eastern outlier from this group; in excavations recently by the Glasgow Archaeological Society, pottery similar to the Dunagoil ware was found, but the earliest fortifications were replaced by a later series of ramparts and ditches.

Even larger forts, in the form of villages or oppida, sometimes occur in this western sub-region, but are comparatively rare. Carman above Alexandria and Walls Hill in southern Renfrew are good examples. The latter has recently yielded Dunagoil ware, but medieval pottery was also discovered.

By far the most numerous sites in the west are the very small 'forts' and stone-built duns which are in fact no more than fortified homesteads. They appear to be the local equivalent of palisaded homesteads of Early Iron Age type such as Little Woodbury in the south, or those which air photographs have revealed in the lowlands of eastern Scotland, or the raths of Ireland. While some may date to pre-Roman times, other duns continued to be occupied periodically until late medieval or even modern times. The same is true of the crannogs, which are homesteads built on an artificial island in some shallow loch or marsh. These were common in Northern Ireland, Galloway and in the Clyde and Ayrshire basins; one at Bishop's Loch just east of Glasgow yielded Dunagoil ware, another at Langbank where the Clyde begins to widen provided a bone comb of the second century A.D., while Roman objects were found in yet another at Hyndford Bridge near Lanark.

Perhaps the character of the physical environment along much of the west coast helps to explain the profusion of small sites. The good land is so restricted that dispersed settlement in isolated farmsteads is the obvious adaptation; stone for a defensive wall is easier to obtain than stout timber for a stockaded enclosure. The local distribution of stone-walled duns shows, however, that other factors are involved. The duns occur commonly in Argyll, Arran and Bute, but to the east of the Firth there is a small group in northern Ayrshire, another in Wigtown and an extension eastwards around the slopes of the Kilpatricks and the Campsies as far as the Forth. Excavated examples have yielded Roman glass and pottery in fragments, and they have generally been ascribed to the period of the second century A.D.

A number of well-known duns, which have been excavated, throw more light on the complexity of this Atlantic Iron Age. They have cell or gallery structures within the well-built stone wall and sometimes a stairway leads to the wall head. Dunburgidale in Bute, Kildonan in Kintyre and Druim an Duin and Ardifuar in the Crinan area are examples of this. To some extent these features recall the circular broch towers of the far north. The latter occur sporadically as far south as Tiree and Lismore on the west, with very doubtful outliers indeed in Wigtown, but do not extend into the Firth of Clyde.

On the east, there is a scatter of broch sites south to the Tweed, with two outliers from this direction at Coldoch on the upper Forth and at Calla in the upper Clyde basin. The pre- or post-Roman date of these outliers is disputed and the galleried duns and allied structures provide a difficult dating problem also. Several have yielded fragments of Samian ware—which may well have bedevilled the chronology of the period in the West of Scotland; an Irish pin of the seventh century A.D. from Kildonan may give a truer reflection of the age and affinities of some of these duns. The establishment of the Dalriadic kingdom of the Scots in Argyll in the late fifth century is probably no more than a historical record of the cultural continuum which had long embraced both South-West Scotland and the adjacent parts of Northern Ireland.

Ptolemy's Geography indicates that by Roman times a people called the Damnonii occupied the area around the mouth of the Clyde, though the limits of their territory are unknown. Archaeologically, the lowlands of the Glasgow area appear rather as a no-man's-land; the hill forts become rare below Lanark, while the Atlantic Iron Age culture barely penetrates. Which intrusive group represents the Damnonii it is difficult to say. A not inconsiderable element may have survived from the Bronze Age, sufficiently numerous to withstand to some extent the flux and reflux along the western coastlands, and to stem the Selgovae and Votadini to the south and east.

The withdrawal of the Legions from Scotland late in the second century was followed by a very long period for which the written records are so fragmentary that 'dark ages' may be said to last almost until the Union of Scotland in the eleventh century. In this shadowy period a British kingdom dimly emerges in Strathclyde; the fact that it survived for so long argues for some political coherence and successful organisation as well as a population of some magnitude. As of old, the eastern frontier must have lain somewhere near the low watershed between Clyde and Forth; the upper Clyde basin was for the most part lost to the Angles in the east at an early date. Across the carseland and mosses along the Forth lay the land of the Picts. In what is now Argyll, the Scottish kingdom of Dalriada flourished and extended into the upper Forth by the sixth century; the capital lay on the Crinan isthmus at the fortress of Dunadd. Strathclyde's capital was a very similar site at Dumbarton Rock, situated as far inland as sea-going ships could penetrate, overlooking a haven, and just below the lowest ford on the Clyde at Dumbuck (Pl. VII). Both forts appear to belong to the type Stevenson recognised as 'nuclear' from the site at Dalmahoy near Edinburgh.

Such excavations as those at Buston crannog in Ayrshire (many years ago), at Dunadd itself on various occasions and at several other duns in the coastlands of the Firth have shown something of the archaeology of the period in the west. Several early ecclesiastical sites have also been examined, including the King's Cave in Arran with its spirited animal carvings and riders on horseback, and quite recently, St Ninian's chapel in Bute dating to the fifth-sixth centuries. Within Strathclyde itself, however, evidence of occupation has been most elusive. Apart from Dumbarton Rock, a 'Dark Age fortress' has been recorded high above Fintry at Dunmore on the north side of the Campsies; the Meikle Reive and the vitrified fort at Ardwell near Bowling on the Clyde may have been reconditioned. But otherwise there is little to add and one can only surmise that a dispersed population was characteristic whose isolated farmsteads have been completely obliterated by over a thousand years of ploughing and the extensive building of modern times. An experimental plotting of the early burghs, monasteries and churches of the thirteenth century quite clearly suggests that the population of the time was well established in the lowlands on a pattern closely followed until the days of the Improvers and the Industrial Revolution. Apparently, therefore, one must look to an earlier period in the 'dark ages' of the first millennium A.D. for the formative period of the settlement pattern—and ponder anew the problem of the sparsity of the Iron Age sites in the lower Clyde Valley.

From the end of the eighth century the west coast was persistently raided by the Northmen, and in the course of time a sporadic settlement occurred. Scandinavian place-names appear to indicate an important influence on the western shores of the Firth, but as yet there is little evidence of permanent occupation in the archaeological record. Graves have been found, but no forts can be attributed specifically to the invaders. At King's Cross in Arran, a Scandinavian ship burial was discovered just outside a small stone dun; the stones outlining the hull are still visible on the site.

Within Strathclyde itself, only one Norse burial has been recorded, at Bridge of Fruin near Loch Lomond. The kingdom was less exposed to the raiders because of its inland position, and Strathclyde may owe its survival into the eleventh century to the preoccupation of its stronger neighbours with constant Norse attacks. In conclusion, it is interesting to note that there is a small cluster of sites in the lower Clyde lowlands where a number of free-standing stone crosses show Norse influence. They form almost the sole surviving ecclesiastical remains for the period, except for a collection of hog-backed tombstones at the Old Church, Govan.

In so short a survey as this it has seemed more important to indicate the extent of the field of study in the West of Scotland and its peculiar characteristics rather than to concentrate upon any finer points of detail. A coherent account of the occupation of the area from period to period is not yet possible. Much may have been destroyed for ever in the densely populated Glasgow area, and how far our distribution maps indicate even the palest reflection of past ages remains so much guess-work. Such problems loom large in Strathclyde itself, but in many ways the coastlands of the Firth offer a more promising field of research, to which attention continually turns. So often the evidence is either confused or elusive, and the satisfaction of a story well told must await a long period of intensive research.

II. THE ROMAN PERIOD

Anne S. Robertson

Dalrymple Lecturer in Archaeology, University of Glasgow

The name Clota—Clyde—first appeared in Roman literature, as far as we know, towards the end of the first century A.D., when the historian Tacitus, in his biography of his famous father-in-law Agricola, wrote thus of Agricola's campaigns in North Britain: 'The fourth season (i.e. of A.D. 81) was spent in securing the districts overrun, and had the courage of our armies and the glory of the Roman name allowed it, an ultimate frontier-line would have been found within Britain itself. For Clota and Bodotria, being carried far inland by tides from opposite seas, are separated by but a narrow strip of land. This isthmus was now strengthened by fortified posts, and the entire sweep of country to the south was occupied, so that the enemy were pushed back as it were into another island.'

Although Agricola recognised the strategic importance of the Forth-Clyde isthmus, he himself did not use it as a frontier, but as a temporary halting place before a further advance northwards which brought him, in A.D. 84, to the site of his victory over the Caledonians at Mons Graupius. Agricola's posts on the Forth-Clyde isthmus were therefore of a temporary character, probably defended by no more than a palisade and a ditch or ditches, and linked only by a road. They were apparently evacuated when Agricola and his field army were withdrawn from Scotland after the battle of Mons Graupius. The 'sweep of country to the south' was not, however, abandoned at the same time. Recent excavation has shown that on the contrary Agricolan forts in South Scotland were given a more permanent character, and were held by the Romans until about A.D. 100. Till then, it seems, Agricola's scheme for the complete conquest of Caledonia continued to appear a practical possibility, and his forts and roads into Scotland were accordingly kept in commission.

These roads followed the two main natural routes from the south. One was by way of the Tweed and Lauderdale to the Forth; the other ran up Annandale and on to Clydesdale. Roman forts, enclosed by ramparts and ditches, and dated by the pottery and coins found in them to the late first century A.D. (or the Flavian period), have been identified along both these routes, and also on a cross road linking the two main routes by way of the upper Tweed and running on westwards past a fort near Loudoun Hill, in Ayrshire. From there, the cross road probably continued to a harbour on the Ayrshire coast (Fig. 33).

In constructing these and other lesser roads in South Scotland, the Romans set out deliberately to isolate the Lowland tribes, with whom they had already come into contact by trade or by campaign. The Selgovae, who probably owed much of their obdurate resistance to the stiffening provided by exiled warriors from the south, were enveloped and kept in their place by the two main northward routes, and by the forts on these routes and between them. The Votadini to the east seem to have resembled the Selgovae in their occupation of hill forts and farmsteads, but to have differed from them in their more peaceful, co-operative relations with the Roman invader. There was probably little resistance, either, from the Damnonii, living in small and widely dispersed homesteads of varying character in the Clyde basin and in Ayrshire. The Novantae, however, of Galloway and south Ayrshire provoked strong countermeasures. It is generally agreed that it was their territory which was involved when Agricola, in A.D. 82, 'having crossed over by the first boat, subdued tribes hitherto unknown in many successful engagements, and established garrisons in that part of Britain which looks towards Ireland'. Aerial photography has recently revealed several new Roman camps and forts in Dumfriesshire and Kirkcudbrightshire, two of which, at Dalswinton and at Glenlochar, have since been proved by excavation to date back to the Flavian period.

There is much less certainty about the scene of Agricola's sea-crossing, if indeed it ever took place at all, for the text of Tacitus is here corrupt and unreliable. The most likely suggestion is that he transported troops across the Solway to expedite the penetration and subjection of the territory of the Novantae. A less likely, although very attractive, suggestion is that Agricola crossed the Firth of Clyde from a presumed harbour on the Ayrshire coast to explore Kintyre and the Western Isles. Certainly the names of a number of the islands and their inhabitants were known to the early second-century geographer Ptolemy.

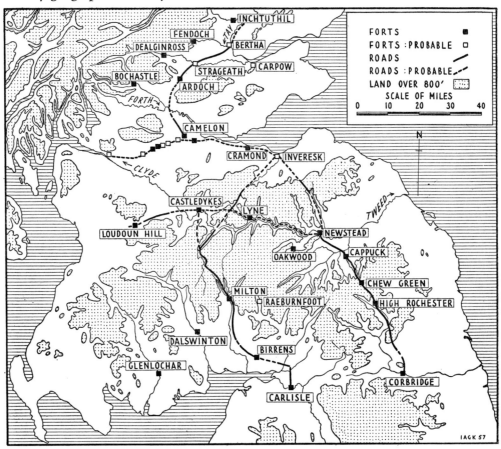

FIG. 33. Roman Roads and Sites in the Flavian Period.

In the interval between the end of the Flavian occupation of Scotland about A.D. 100 and the Antonine campaigns of about A.D. 142 which culminated in the building of the Antonine Wall from Forth to Clyde, there appears to have been some movement and shifting of population in the Lowlands, particularly perhaps in the west. The Lowlanders had become accustomed, during the Flavian period, to acquiring Roman coins, pottery, bronzes, etc., and it would not be surprising if, when their immediate source of supply was withdrawn from them about A.D. 100, they followed it south. At any rate, so much unrest was there on the northern frontier of the Roman province that in A.D. 122 a permanent barrier, Hadrian's Wall, was begun from the Tyne to the Solway. The Lowland reaction to this was sharp and aggressive, and in A.D. 142 a Roman army, under Lollius Urbicus, governor of Britain, once again invaded Scotland, moving rapidly northwards along the two main routes, until the troublesome North

Britons were driven back to a safe distance from a new frontier line, the Antonine Wall (Fig. 34). As a result of this campaign, a large number of irreconcilables were conscripted from the Lowlands and were transported to the German frontier.[5]

The Antonine Wall ran from Bridgeness on the Forth to Old Kilpatrick on the

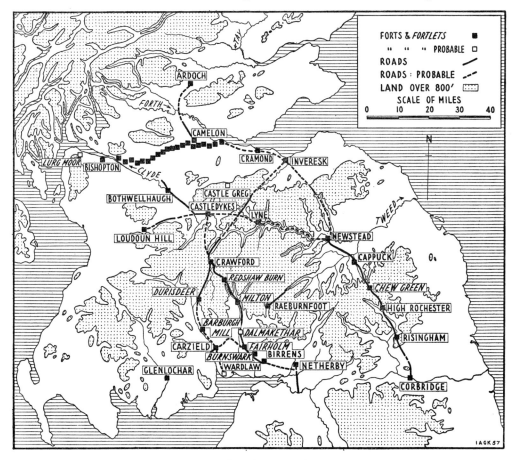

FIG. 34. Roman Roads and Sites in the Antonine Period.

Clyde, and for the greater part of its length it clung to the southern slopes of the 'isthmus valley', with a clear view across the valley to the threatening hills on the north. It was built mainly of turf, standing on a stone foundation about fourteen feet wide, and it had a great ditch, about forty feet wide and twelve feet deep, on its north side, and a military way running alongside it to the south. There were nineteen forts set at two-mile intervals along the Wall, most of them occupying sites previously selected by Agricola in A.D. 81, and there were smaller posts at certain intermediate points. A unique feature of the Antonine barrier is its series of distance slabs or legionary tablets, each recording the length or distance of the Antonine Wall that had been completed by a certain working squad of legionaries. (See Plate XX.)

The occupation of the Antonine frontier line called into existence twenty or thirty other forts and fortlets strung along a network of roads which covered South Scotland and apparently penetrated as far north as Perthshire (Fig. 34). The duty of garrisoning the Antonine Wall forts and the other forts and fortlets fell mainly, if not entirely, on units of the non-citizen troops, the auxiliaries, who were more lightly armed and more expendable than the legionaries.

The Antonine road system re-used the surviving framework of the Flavian period, but with variations and additions which reflect unmistakable changes in native population and behaviour, especially in the west. Over the people of Dumfriesshire there was clamped down a grid of roads, forts and fortlets or signalling posts. The Romans clearly had information about a threat to peace from this area during the Antonine period which is not yet in the hands of the modern archaeologist. We can only speculate that there had been some movement of population into this district since the end of the first century A.D. Lower Clydesdale, too, featured in the Antonine system. A Roman road ran down the Clyde valley from Castledykes near Lanark past Bothwellhaugh towards a point, as yet undetermined, near the western end of the Antonine Wall.[6]

On the western sector of the Antonine frontier, also, the Romans displayed an acute and energetic grasp of local conditions. A harbour was established for the reception of supplies at a point below Old Kilpatrick, probably at Dumbarton (as well no doubt as a harbour on the Ayrshire coast, possibly at Irvine). A fort was built at Old Kilpatrick, and a fortlet or watch-post two miles to the east at Duntocher, probably for the organisation of patrols along the dangerous ground facing the Kilpatrick Hills. Thus control would be maintained over the restless, resentful natives to the north while the building of the Antonine Wall was proceeding from the Forth westwards to the Clyde.

A harbour on the Clyde below Old Kilpatrick might also have accommodated a small naval squadron, charged with the task of keeping the Firth free of enemy craft. Attempts by North Britons to land on the south bank of the Clyde and to outflank the Wall were also provided against by the construction of a fort at Whitemoss Farm, Bishopton, and of a fortlet on Lurg Moor above Greenock. This fort and fortlet were probably only two links in a chain of Roman stations along the Renfrewshire coast but the others still await discovery.

The Antonine system in Scotland was maintained in operation, although not without disasters and vicissitudes, for forty or fifty years, before it was given up by the Romans either about A.D. 186 or about A.D. 196. Hadrian's Wall then became once more the northern frontier of the Roman province of Britain.

During the Antonine occupation of South Scotland, as during the Flavian period, much Roman material passed from Roman into native hands, either by legitimate or by illegitimate means. Nor was there a one-way traffic only. The addition of civilian annexes to so many of the Antonine forts in Scotland, and the discovery in or near Roman forts of native objects, or of objects which betray the presence of women and children, prove that native material, some of it in human guise, infiltrated into the heart of the military areas.

In the years A.D. 209-11, the emperor Severus carried out campaigns against the Caledonians north of the Forth, and also came into conflict with the Maeatae, a tribe who lived near the Forth-Clyde line. South-West Scotland does not appear to have been affected by Severus' campaigns. As a result of these campaigns, however, a Roman

132

protectorate seems to have been established in the Scottish Lowlands, which lasted until almost the end of the Roman occupation of Britain in the early fifth century A.D.

Till then, Scotland, and not least the South-West, received a fairly steady stream of Roman coins, pottery and other manufactured articles. Nor was this the only contribution made by the Romans to Iron Age life after the Roman occupation of Scotland ended. The elaborate Roman road system must have continued to offer convenient routes to travellers for centuries to come, and the massive forts and other Roman works must have been a familiar feature of the Dark Age landscape, as they are indeed a feature of our present-day landscape. The Antonine Wall in particular stood firm century after century, serving, if not as a barrier, at least as a boundary, march or trysting-place.

To the south of this boundary, in the early fifth century A.D., executive power seems to have devolved on native princes. The native genealogies record two lines of such princes, one ruling near the east end of the Antonine Wall, and the other at Dumbarton near the west end. Each line used Romanised names, and, apparently, sub-Roman or Roman titles. It was one of these princes, Ceredig of Dumbarton, who, in the first half of the fifth century A.D., received a letter from St Patrick objecting to a slave raid Ceredig had made on Ireland, with the implication that it was un-Christian and un-Roman conduct. So tenaciously did Roman traditions outlast Roman power in South-West Scotland!

1 Scott, W. Lindsay. The Colonisation of Scotland in the Second Millennium B.C. *Proc. Prehist. Soc.*, 1951, N.S. 17.

2 Durno, S. E. Pollen Analysis of Peat Deposits in Scotland. *Scot. Geogr. Mag.*, 1956, 72 (3).

3 Piggott, S. 'The Archaeological Background' in *The Problem of the Picts*, edited by Wainwright, F. T. Edinburgh, 1954.

4 A distribution map was published by Professor S. Piggott in *Scientific Survey of South-eastern Scotland*. British Association, Edinburgh, 1951.

5 Macdonald, Sir George. *The Roman Wall in Scotland*, Oxford, 1934.

6 Miller, S. N. *The Roman Occupation of South-West Scotland*, Glasgow, 1952.

THE CITY AND BURGH OF GLASGOW

1100-1750

George S. Pryde

Professor of Scottish History and Literature, University of Glasgow

AFTER the long twilight of the British kingdom of Strathclyde and the Celtic monarchy of united Scotland, in which the church and community founded by St Kentigern no doubt lived on in the obscurity of almost total darkness, Glasgow emerges into the bright, full light of historical record in the twelfth century. The fairly ample state of our knowledge of the subject is the happy result of the survival of the episcopal register of charters and other deeds [1]—a fortunate condition shared by only three others of the thirteen medieval dioceses of Scotland—Aberdeen, Brechin and Moray. The document-ation thus preserved permits us to trace, in some detail, the origins and development of the distinctively dual character of medieval Glasgow: it was both a city and a burgh from the earliest, or nearly the earliest, epoch of the use of such terms. Though other bishops' seats (most notably Kirkwall, Dunkeld and Old Aberdeen) later acquired this double status, only St Andrews enjoyed it, like Glasgow, from the first phase of the feudal monarchy, and, to the medieval mind, these two stood, as to dignity and respectability, in a class by themselves.

CIVIC AND MUNICIPAL ORIGINS

Scottish practice in the middle ages, much like that of England, tended to confer the term 'city' on a cathedral town only if it were deemed worthy of the title, and this meant, as a rule, some form of municipal incorporation, or at least a size, importance and physical appearance worthy of such an honour. (The style was quite inapplicable to Iona or Lismore, and it was denied to Whithorn, to Fortrose and—until a late date—to Dornoch.) Thus local use and wont, the granting or withholding 'on the ground' of a title which might well be bestowed, for example, in papal bulls as a mere matter of 'common style', may serve as a useful, practical check, an indication of the prosperity and consequence of an urban community.

Glasgow owes its reconstitution as a bishopric to David I, who, while still as 'earl' in charge of South Scotland on behalf of his brother, Alexander I, caused an investigation to be carried out by a local jury into the history, privileges, functions and temporalities of the episcopal see (c. 1115). The result of the inquiry was to secure the endowments of the church and to pave the way for its physical restoration; the rebuilt cathedral by the banks of the Molendinar was dedicated in 1136, and David I, as king, was only the first of many monarchs to grant lands, rents and churches to the bishopric. (See Plate II.)

Documents of the reigns of David I (1124-53) and his grandson, Malcolm IV (1153-65), yield no evidence as to any Scottish 'city', but the middle years of William the Lion are more fruitful. Papal Bulls of 1172 and 1187 refer in turn to Glasgow and St Andrews as each a city (*civitas*), and, since one was soon to become a burgh and the other already was one, it is clear that the dignity was well deserved.

The idea of the Scottish burgh was a direct importation from England, a borrowing and adaptation of the concept of the Anglo-Saxon and Anglo-Norman 'borough', which was itself linked with the Continental institution of the free town. On the political side, like the castle and the sheriffdom, the burgh was part of the feudal reorganisation of the kingdom and was intended to strengthen the rule of law and the principle of local responsibility to the central government. On the economic side, trading and marketing privileges, extending to defined monopolies in the making, buying and selling of goods, provided for the accumulation of commercial wealth and, indirectly, of Crown revenue. Glasgow was not in the first 'wave' of the Scots burghs: David I, their founder, had eighteen burghs holding from himself and also, towards the end of his reign, licensed the creation of two burghs of the Church—St Andrews, dependent on the bishop of that see, and Canongate, having the abbot of Holyrood as its superior. The western city was therefore not among Scotland's first twenty burghs, but had to wait until the second major series of 'erections'.

By a charter that can be dated to the years 1175×1178, William the Lion granted Bishop Jocelin and his successors a burgh (*ut burgum habeant apud Glasgu*), with a weekly market on Thursday. It was, though a bishop's burgh, endowed from the start with all the liberties and customs of the king's own burghs. Further, the charter took the burgesses into the king's firm peace *per totam terram meam in eundo et redeundo* and forbade, under forfeiture, any disturbance or injury to them or their goods. Later charters by King William conferred the right to hold an annual fair (*nundinas*) as freely as any that were held in the king's burghs, and amplified the grant of king's peace by extending it to all who came to the fair, remained there, and went from it, as long as they did what they justly ought to do according to the assize of his burghs and kingdom —that is, paid their customs and other duties.

Thus twelfth-century Glasgow was hailed by the Pope as a city and by the king as a burgh; but, remembering that bulls and charters might be permissive grants of privilege rather than factual statements, proofs of the grantor's goodwill rather than the grantee's condition, we do well to check their terms against what is known from other sources about the actions of the townsfolk at this time. As it happens, we are tolerably well supplied with materials for such a cross-check.

CONDITIONS IN THE TWELFTH AND THIRTEENTH CENTURIES

From the fact that Glasgow, at all stages reputed to be Scotland's second diocese in rank and wealth, was restored and re-dedicated, with full episcopal status, in 1136, it is a reasonable, indeed an inescapable, inference that the town-dwellers must have increased sharply in numbers about that time. A cathedral called for a substantial establishment of clergymen and it also needed the services of tillers of the soil, small crofters, fishermen and sundry craftsmen; under the shadow, so to speak, of the great church many secular pursuits could with advantage be conducted. This reality un-doubtedly underlay the foundation of the burgh in the eleven-seventies, and yet it is clear that the process of founding the burgh must be regarded, in the case of Glasgow as in several others (*e.g.*, St Andrews, 1140×1153, Ayr, 1203×1206, Dumbarton, 1222, and Dingwall, 1227), as having a strong physical element: the build-up was in some sense rather like that of one of our 'new towns'. This is the conclusion that we must draw from a charter (dated 1179×1199) whereby Bishop Jocelin granted the monks of Melrose a 'toft' or burghal holding, *quod Ranulfus de Hadintune edificauit in prima edificatione burgi ad opus domus de Melros*: [2] thus, among the new settlers, the monks were given the favour of a 'town house'.

For thirteenth-century Glasgow, we have glimpses of municipal administration and urban life; while we should be glad to have fuller information on these topics, it remains true that Glasgow is as well documented as any early Scottish burgh, and much better than most. The preservation in sundry ecclesiastical chartularies of land deeds and property transactions is itself an indication of the growing importance to society at large of the western city and of accommodation therein; and these deeds incidentally shed some light on the place and the people. One document, for example, which can be dated 1268 at the latest, records the sale of a burgage and mentions Bryce the baker,[3] while the witnesses to a gift of land to the Church in 1270 include Roger the skinner, Geoffrey the dyer and William the fuller, all of them burgesses of Glasgow.[4] The usual burghal crafts were thus taking root from an early date. The record of another sale of a burgage (this time in the Fishergate) contains, under the year 1285, our first reference to Glasgow bridge.[5]

These proceedings, carried out *secundum legem burgorum*, or *secundum consuetudinem civitatis nostre*, show that general burghal law and practice were fully operative in Glasgow. Three head courts were held in the year (at Yule, Easter and Michaelmas), when the whole community—the *cives* or *burgenses*—were expected to attend. An inquest or jury of twelve or more burgesses was sworn to declare the law and establish the facts in a stated case or dispute, but there was as yet no standing council. Here, as elsewhere, the chief magistrates were indifferently termed *prepositi* or *ballivi*. The normal restrictions on the disposal of a burgage were observed—poverty and need must be proved, the tenement must be thrice offered to the next of kin at head courts, and security must be given for the payment of the king's rent or ferme.[6] A sasine was declared to have been given in 1293 *per intol et vttol* ('entry-penny' and 'ische-penny') *super solum vt moris est*. And the common seal of the city or burgh was in use from 1268, generally, though not always, being reinforced by the seal of the bishop's official. Clearly there was here a legal *persona*, an indwelling and trading fellowship with a communal life and a corporate sense.

RELATIONS WITH NEIGHBOURING BURGHS

Our documents contain hints about the growth, and more especially the southward march, of the city. The old centre, the original Glasgow 'cross', stood at the junction of the Castle-gate to the north, Drygate to the east, High Street to the south, and Rottenrow to the west, and in this quarter there are mentions of the Blackfriars' place, on the east side of High Street (1246), and of the bishop's castle and his palace, as separate structures (1258). Here, too, the cathedral (the re-building of which is said to have been begun by Bishop Jocelin, 1175-99) was completed, with a wooden spire that was later replaced in stone, about 1280. But expansion took the houses down the hill to the south, to form a new 'Glasgow cross', where the streets eventually called Trongate and Gallowgate ran east and west, and High Street and Saltmarket followed a north-south line towards the new bridge over the Clyde. The western arm of the new cross, under its earlier name of 'Sanct Thenew's [St Enoch's] gate', soon became only less noted than the upper reaches of the High Street for the number and fame of its religious foundations: towards the end of the thirteenth century, or early in the fourteenth, we hear of Our Lady chapel, St Thenew's chapel, and the chapel of St Thomas the Martyr, all in that thoroughfare. And yet the main significance of the southward extension is economic: it was the desire for a commercial outlet to the river and the sea that brought the traders, fishermen and craftsmen down to the Clyde (see Fig. 3).

While Glasgow was, and indeed has remained throughout Scottish history, the only city of the West, it had several rivals and troublesome neighbours among the burghs. Three miles up the River Clyde and on the opposite, or left, bank lay one of David I's own burghs, Rutherglen. Its slight seniority as a burgh to Glasgow has led many romantically disposed chroniclers and commentators to imagine a wide and dramatic contrast between the flourishing, all-powerful up-stream 'royal burgh' and the huddle of miserable wattle-and-mud cottages clustering, as a mere 'burgh of barony', at the foot of the cathedral. The terms, when applied to the twelfth century (or even much later), are wildly anachronistic, and the picture is wholly apocryphal. Such indications as we have point to Rutherglen having a short lead in the early middle ages, which was wiped out in the later. Its burgh ferme, for example, was £13 per annum, compared with Glasgow's sixteen merks, or £10, 13s. 4d.

If it was Rutherglen's proximity, rather than its antiquity or importance, that rendered it an embarrassing neighbour, it was their strategic position—on the seaward side—that made awkward rivals of two others. Six miles down the Clyde, on the left bank, was Renfrew, which, though also one of David's burghs, had been granted to the FitzAlans, ancestors of the royal Stewarts. And fourteen miles downstream from the episcopal city lay Dumbarton, which was erected as a king's burgh by Alexander II in 1222.[7] Against the excessive claims of two of the three that king issued warnings. In 1226 the bailies and serjeants of Rutherglen were forbidden to take toll or custom in the town of Glasgow: these should be levied only at Shettleston cross, as was the ancient practice (*sicut illa antiquitus capi solebant*). In 1243 the Dumbarton bailies were instructed not to interfere with the Glasgow burgesses, who were to be as free to trade in Argyll, Lennox and throughout the kingdom as they had been before the king caused any burgh to be founded at Dumbarton. (See Plate VII.)

These early conflicts had a protracted sequel. Interburghal strife, usually over trading rights, continued throughout, and indeed survived, the middle ages. James II in 1450 ordered the men of Renfrew and Rutherglen to desist from impeding passage to and from Glasgow market, and from taking tolls within the barony. Following a dispute over a French ship in the Clyde in 1469, a decree declared Dumbarton to have been wrong in preventing the Glasgow burgesses from buying wine from the foreigners, and forbade such misconduct in the future. An indenture of 1499 set forth an agreement between Glasgow and Dumbarton to respect each other's equal rights on the Clyde, while the year 1542 brought another decree directing Renfrew and Rutherglen to allow merchandise to proceed peacefully to Glasgow. Fourteen years later these three burghs actually agreed to collaborate for the removal of the ford and the sandbanks at Dumbuck, where huts were built for the accommodation of the workmen; the transaction, futile as it was in effect, is of interest as the first fumbling attempt towards the deepening of the Clyde.

THE LATER MIDDLE AGES

The fourteenth and fifteenth centuries brought modifications, but no substantial changes, in the internal administration of the city and burgh. In 1397 Robert III, by a precept under the privy seal, authorised the changing of the date of the weekly market from Saturday to Monday; it is not known when the original Thursday market had been abandoned. In 1447 a burgh mill, built by the bishop on the Molendinar burn, was acquired by negotiation and purchase.

The bishop's control over his burgh remained, however, real and strong. In the story of its rise and progress, the charter of regality of 20 April 1450 has been hailed as a memorable achievement, a landmark on a long road. Nineteenth-century historians, misreading its terms, thought that the town became a burgh of regality in 1450, with improved status and rights—it 'was placed nearly on a level with neighbouring royal burghs', and 'elevated . . . one step in rank and dignity'.[8] This view has been accepted uncritically by more recent writers,[9] but is not borne out either by the terms of the document or by its historical context. By his charter James II conveyed to the bishop and his successors the city of Glasgow, the barony, and Bishop Forest 'in free regality' (*in liberam puram et meram regalitatem*). The grant of regality (involving almost the whole of the rights of the Crown in administration and justice) was in favour of the bishop, and the only material change lay in *his* acquisition of a superior jurisdiction. The city was *not* made a burgh of regality—a term, incidentally, which is very nearly confined to post-Reformation times, and which, in any case, is little more than a legal refinement, implying no real distinction from, no higher rights than, a burgh of barony.

The truth of the matter becomes even clearer in James III's charter of 15 July 1476, defining the bishop's regality jurisdiction and re-stating his right to appoint provost, bailies and serjeants, and in James IV's permission to the bishop to have a tron, or weighing machine, in his burgh (4 January 1490-1). In the two last-mentioned charters, Glasgow is called city or burgh of the bishopric (*civitas seu burgus episcopatus*)—the true medieval style or form, to which modern commentators would do well to pay heed, for it might have saved much avoidable heart-searching in the recent past, when local historians anxiously endeavoured to reassure themselves, on entirely wrong grounds, as to the absence of a stigma of inferiority in Glasgow's municipal status. Since the terms royal burgh, burgh of barony and burgh of regality are, at the earliest, fifteenth-century accretions, and since the distinctions that they ultimately implied were slow in developing, the labour of excusing medieval Glasgow for having a bishop instead of the king as overlord was, however ingeniously argued, wasted effort.[10]

Three events of the fifteenth century served to enhance, in an outstanding way, the fame, dignity and appearance of the city. At an unknown date, but probably about 1410, the thirteenth-century wooden bridge over the Clyde was replaced by a handsome stone bridge of eight arches, and this structure, offering the only convenient crossing of the river, brought trade and traffic to and through Glasgow, besides making a good impression on visitors. Next, on 7 January 1450-1, a bull granted by Pope Nicholas V,

138

on the urging of James II at the instance of Bishop William Turnbull, founded the University of Glasgow. As this subject is separately dealt with in this volume, and as its significance for the town and townsfolk is self-evident, there is no need to elaborate the point here; but the words of the preamble are worth noting, for there is much to suggest that they were no empty compliment to the city—'where the air is mild, victuals are plentiful, and great store of other things pertaining to the use of man is found'. The third event turns on another papal bull, or rather on two of them. In 1472 St Andrews had been elevated to an archbishopric, and the advancement of the rival see was resented in Glasgow. Bishop Robert Blacader induced James IV to champion his claim to equal status, the Scots Parliament in 1489 lent the project its enthusiastic support,[11] and on 9 January 1491-2 Pope Innocent VIII promoted Glasgow to the coveted archiepiscopal rank, with the dioceses of Dunkeld, Dunblane, Galloway and Argyll as suffragans (Dunkeld and Dunblane being later transferred to St Andrews province and the Isles to Glasgow). The parallel with Canterbury and York was noticed at the time, and, as in England, the existence of two metropolitans led to jealous bickering and unseemly strife, which, in time, was to rouse the scornful mirth of John Knox. While it is obvious that, if Scotland had to have two archbishoprics, the choice of Glasgow was right and indeed inevitable, while, too, the move furthered the good repute and attraction of the western city, the sad truth is that the arrangement exaggerated the already top-heavy form of the ecclesiastical establishment of Scotland and increased the tendency to starve the parochial clergy in order to make a brave show at the higher levels.

Some interesting if less dramatic improvements in the city's amenities during the century preceding the Reformation may be mentioned. The grammar school or high school, situated on the west side of the High Street, is recorded in 1461. It was supported by the burgh and, as was usual in such circumstances, enjoyed a local monopoly: in 1494 one David Dunn, a priest, was forbidden to hold his school in Glasgow and to teach grammar, since he had not been licensed by the burgh. The patronage of the school was the subject of a dispute between the cathedral and municipal authorities in 1508; at that time, or not long after, the burgh won control. Apart from the College buildings, the city's late medieval foundations included religious houses—Greyfriars to the west of the High Street and St Kentigern's in the Fields, outside the East port— hospitals for the indigent and impotent—St Nicholas, the fifteenth-century forerunner of Glasgow's oldest secular building, Provand's Lordship, and another at Stablegreen in the north of the built-up area—and a few superior domestic buildings, such as the episcopal palace and the Lennox town-house, in which Darnley was to spend his last Christmas (1566).

The government of the burgh may have progressed *pari passu* with the beautification of the city, though without leaving much in the way of positive evidence: the surviving burgh records, or town council minutes, begin only in 1573.[12] There are hints—no more—of a strengthening of the authority and self-reliance of the municipality, as such, in the period between the mid-fifteenth and mid-sixteenth centuries. The year 1453 bears record of 'an honourable man, John Stewart, the first provost that was in the city of Glasgow'. A royal letter of 1492, confirming the city's privileges, was addressed not to the bishop, but to the burgh. We have seen that the burgh contrived, early in the sixteenth century, to make good its claim to exercise the patronage of the grammar school. In 1510-11 the ecclesiastical and municipal authorities were in dispute over judicial matters: the town's statutes forbade appeals to the courts of the Church if the cases could be settled in the burgh court. The Church insisted on its right to an appellate jurisdiction, but still the bailies fined a man eight shillings for contempt of court, his offence consisting of appealing to the archbishop. The logical outcome of these developments was seen in 1560, when the last Roman Catholic archbishop, James Beaton, fled to France, taking with him not only the cathedral ornaments but also the early records of the bishopric, city and university. The provost and town council, in the absence of the superior and of any directions from him, proceeded themselves to the election of the two bailies.

TRADE AND FINANCE IN MEDIEVAL GLASGOW

In these transactions we can sense a growing maturity and confidence, a flexing of the municipal muscles. This is confirmed by the accepted estimates (they are nothing more, though reasonable enough) of the city's population: it was reckoned to be about 1,500 in the year 1450, and no less than 4,500 in 1560. Glasgow's increasing reputation as an ecclesiastical and educational centre contributed to this expansion, but her commercial advance is also significant. In the fourteenth century Scottish trade was concentrated in the eastern ports. Berwick, until its loss in the English wars, led all the others, Edinburgh and Aberdeen came next, and then Dundee, Perth, Linlithgow, Haddington, Montrose, Cupar and Stirling.[13] Very little commerce entered or issued from any western ports, which had only a few small fishing-vessels: Glasgow's imports and exports probably passed through Linlithgow by way of an overland journey. Of thirty-nine burghs listed in the Exchequer Rolls of the years 1366-74 as contributing to the taxation levied for the payment of David II's ransom, Glasgow stood no higher than twenty-third.

Foreign commerce began to look up in the fifteenth century. The first Glasgow merchant on record is William Elphinstone, who about 1420 was exporting salmon and herring to France, and importing brandy and salt. The Clyde shore and the many burns leading to it were useful for beaching small boats, but the condition of the river severely limited Glasgow's trading possibilities. Nothing over six tons could negotiate its shallows, so that sea-going vessels had to be met and off-loaded onto lighters ('gabarts') in the Firth; alternatively, the city merchants were driven to use the port of Irvine.

Despite all difficulties, some commercial progress was achieved. The earliest complete and surviving 'stent roll' or tax roll of the Scottish burghs belongs to the year 1535 and it gives a fair picture of the relative wealth and importance (and consequently of the commercial prosperity) of the leading towns, then numbering forty-two, about the close of the middle ages. The first nine places all went to burghs on the eastern sea-board, but Ayr was tenth and Glasgow eleventh. It is noteworthy that, just as in the fourteenth century, burghs other than those holding from the king were liable for payment of the ransom levy, so now the places that were stented as burghs were by no means confined to the royal burghs: besides Glasgow, St Andrews, Brechin, Arbroath, Dunfermline, Kirkcaldy and Dysart were all subject to the normal tax laid upon the burgess estate.[14]

Out of these seven non-royal burghs selected to share the burden imposed on the third estate, the three that were episcopal cities were associated more or less closely,

140

from the fourteenth century, with parliamentary proceedings and all three are duly recorded in the rolls of Parliament as being represented there during the medieval period—St Andrews for the first time in 1456, Brechin in 1479 and Glasgow in 1546. And, although the personnel of the burgess estate in Parliament and of the burghs' own meetings in Convention were not identical, they were nearly so, and the same argument—that of financial competence—was equally powerful in each case. Thus, despite its title, the Convention of Royal Burghs, from its first meeting in April 1552, had Glasgow and some others among its enrolled members. Clearly medieval Glasgow lost nothing in the way of dignity and privilege, or of the duties that went with these, through its dependence on the bishop or archbishop of the diocese; it would probably be truer to say, bearing in mind the recourse of people and the economic activity attracted by the presence of cathedral, college, schools and churches, that on balance the western metropolis was the gainer through being *civitas seu burgus episcopatus*.

MERCHANTS HOUSE AND TRADES HOUSE

If salmon and herring formed the main exports from the medieval city, it follows that the bulk of the woollen and leather manufactures, and still more of the sundry metal, stone and wooden products, were intended for disposal in the home market. Still, in accordance with the social and economic notions of the time, the output of such articles called for both state direction and local regulation; and Glasgow's period of industrial organisation, following general lines laid down elsewhere a little earlier, stretched from 1516 to 1605.

To the medievalist the natural division of the burgesses was into merchants or wholesalers, the exporters and importers, on the one hand, and, on the other, the craftsmen, who were either handworkers and artisans or else petty retailers and shop-keepers. Between them, too, jealousy and conflict of interest were regarded as inevit-able. The merchants, organised in their merchant guilds in the larger burghs (though not in Glasgow) from the thirteenth century, viewed it as a point of honour to despise and depress the lowly craftsmen. Since the voice of the burgess estate in Parliament was in effect the voice of the merchants, statutory law reflected their scornful and dictatorial attitude towards their humbler brethren, and a series of acts passed between 1424 and 1555 virtually forbade as conspiratorial any endeavours of the craftsmen to combine in incorporations or to elect their own deacons. In 1556, however, the crafts' right to organise was formally recognised by the Regent, Mary of Guise. This was a privilege which had already been assumed in practice in several of the burghs, despite all statutory prohibitions: the Edinburgh Cordiners, for example, were constituted as a lawful incorporation in 1449, the first to be so recognised in Scotland.

In Glasgow a seal of cause, the local deed of incorporation, was granted to the Skinners (including furriers and glovers) in 1516; the Tailors followed in 1527, the Weavers in 1528, and the Hammermen (including blacksmiths, goldsmiths, lorimers, saddlers and other sub-crafts) in 1536. Masons, Bakers and Cordiners or Shoemakers were all incorporated by 1559, and, between the Reformation and the close of the sixteenth century, five others were organised—the Coopers, the Fleshers, the Bonnet-makers, the Barbers and Surgeons (forming one combined, if to our minds anomalous, craft), and the Wrights. About the year 1600 (or very soon thereafter), two others appeared to give Glasgow a total of fourteen crafts—the Maltmen and the Gardeners. (Edinburgh also had, and has, fourteen incorporations, but not the same fourteen. The Goldsmiths, Furriers and Waulkers formed separate crafts in the capital, while the Maltmen, Gardeners and Dyers did so in Glasgow. Dundee, Perth and Ayr had each nine crafts, others fewer.)

Though an informal merchants' society was in existence by 1569, Glasgow had no merchant guild and no dean of guild; nor was there a deacon convener of the crafts. In 1595, the Convention of Royal Burghs criticised this failure to follow 'the comely order of other free burghs' and recommended a decent reform. As had been done in the cases of Edinburgh (1583) and Aberdeen (1587), disputes between merchants and craftsmen were referred to a body of arbitrators whose decreet would serve as a final settlement. The aims were to prevent unfreemen usurping burgesses' privileges, to avoid 'mutual controversies and civil discords', and to ensure conformity to 'other weill reformit burghs'. The outcome was the Letter of Guildry (1605), one of the basic documents of Glasgow's corporate life, studiously moderate in tone and so sensibly devised as to create, between merchants and craftsmen, a degree of harmonious co-operation probably unknown elsewhere in Scotland. Besides appointing a dean of guild and a deacon convener, each with a place on the town council, it opened guildry membership on equal terms to both 'ranks'. Each of these 'callings' maintained its own decayed brethren, widows and orphans in a hospital that was often styled its 'house', and this term came, in the course of the seventeenth century, to be applied to the 'rank' itself in its entirety. Thus evolved Glasgow's unique institutions of the Merchants' House and the Trades House, as the two halves of a truly integrated guildry. Burgh reform in 1833 and the abolition of exclusive trading privileges in 1846 transformed these bodies into their latter-day state of being purely social and charitable organisations, though the dean of guild and deacon convener still retain their *ex-officio* places on the town council.

GLASGOW A ROYAL BURGH

Apart from the flight of the archbishop, the destruction of the monasteries, and the romantic and traditional account (which may have some truth) of the salvation of the cathedral at the hands of the craftsmen, the Reformation brought changes to the status and powers of the municipality. It did not at once make Glasgow a royal burgh, but it made this an ultimate possibility. Though the old Church, with which the city had been so closely associated, had fallen, there was still, until 1690, an archbishop, real or titular, of the reformed faith, and he, as superior, was entitled to the annual burgh ferme of sixteen merks. He also claimed the right to nominate the burgh magistrates, or, if he did not, this was done by the bailie of the regality, whose office, from 1596, became hereditary in the ducal family of Lennox. These vested interests delayed and beclouded the formal promotion of the burgh.

Not till 1587 do we find the new term, burgh of regality, applied to Glasgow. In 1596, following Edinburgh's 'Black Saturday 'riot (17 December), when the king, in deep anger and real or feigned fear for his life, threatened to move the capital, he actually approached Glasgow, but, being offered the city fathers' service without any monetary contribution, he did not pursue the matter, and a chastened Edinburgh was very soon restored to grace. In 1605 a move was launched to give Glasgow free elections, without

142

reference to the superior's rights. An act in this sense, drafted in 1606, was defeated by the Lennox faction. In 1611, however, a new charter declared the city to be a royal burgh, with a full legal claim to its own burgh lands or 'royalty', but reserved the archbishop's right to nominate the magistrates. A confirming charter by Charles I in 1636 not only reserved the regality rights of the Duke of Lennox and the sixteen merks due as burgh ferme to the archbishop, but also provided that an additional sum of twenty merks (£13, 6s. 8d.) be paid each year to the Crown.

The anomaly of dual, or even triple, superiority did not finally disappear until 1690. In the time of the Troubles, with episcopacy in eclipse, the Scots Parliament or Cromwell gave Glasgow full power to elect its own magistrates, but after the Restoration of 1660 the archbishop, or Lennox as his bailie, exercised his right to name the provost, and sometimes did so very badly, by choosing, for example a bankrupt man or one who was not a member of the council. As in other burghs, the year of the Revolution, 1689, saw the magistrates elected by a poll of the burgesses, but a new royal charter and Act of Parliament of 1690 gave the town council power to choose the magistrates, and thus brought Glasgow into line with the normal practice elsewhere.[15]

In the years between the Reformation and the Revolution the government of the burgh came to follow a fixed pattern or 'sett'. The provost was, until 1609, usually a neighbour laird like Stewart of Minto or Elphinstone of Blythswood, but thereafter a statutory requirement insisted that he be an 'actual resident burgess and trafficker'. Meanwhile the two bailies of medieval usage became three by the fifteen-nineties, and the council usually chose, in addition, the treasurer, master of work and water-bailie (to attend at the riverside, collect dues and prevent the improper dumping of ballast). The number of the councillors varied, sometimes reaching as high as thirty-three, but from the early seventeenth century it was twenty-three—twelve merchants and eleven craftsmen—and, a little later, twenty-five (thirteen and twelve from the two 'ranks'). The town clerk was much the most important of the paid officials, but there were also a law-agent or procurator, sometimes a town surgeon, always the town herds, minstrels and officers or serjeants, and, of course, the city ministers and schoolmasters.

For ministers and teachers, stipends had to be found, and the town council in a burgh like Glasgow, while co-operating with the kirk sessions, was the chief paymaster. Moreover, there were the 'common works' to be maintained, commissioners' expenses in Edinburgh to be met, wine and banquets to be supplied to the town's friends, magistrates' fees and the officers' wages to be defrayed. Expenses were heavy and constantly rising, and the treasurer had the delicate task of continuously forcing up the revenue with the least possible resort to 'stenting' or taxation, which, while barely tolerated to meet a parliamentary grant, was bitterly resented for local purposes. From £569 Scots in 1573-4, the total revenue rose to £4,492 in 1610-11. Burgess-entries, petty customs, feu-duties and annuals helped to swell the amount, but the great money-raiser was the town mills (to which the burgesses were 'thirled'). Besides the original mill on the Molendinar, a second mill on the Kelvin (the site of which was later occupied by Clayslaps mill) was acquired in 1577, and two others (Partick and Wester Craigs) were secured in 1608. By 1692 the burgh mills were bringing in £5,300 per annum towards a total revenue of £16,900. The big items of expenditure were then £7,000 for the stipends of six city ministers and three teachers, £5,000 for the common works, and £2,500 for fees and wages of all kinds.

Certain investments in property made by the seventeenth-century city fathers enhanced the real wealth and financial stability of the burgh. In 1649, acting on behalf of the city itself, of Hutcheson's Hospital, and of the Trades House or Hospital, the town council bought the barony of Gorbals, on the south side of the river, from Sir Robert Douglas; the price, £80,000 Scots, was high for those days, and bespeaks an affluent community. Linningshaugh, lying to the east of the royalty, and representing the beginnings of the present (or New) Glasgow Green, was acquired in 1662, the large and valuable estate of Provan, to the north-east, in 1667, and an area to the west—Meadowflat and Ramshorn, including the site of the later George Square—in 1694.

COMMERCIAL EXPANSION

Between 1550 and 1750 Glasgow naturally played some part in the political and ecclesiastical affairs of the nation. Queen Mary's final defeat, on 13 May 1568, took place at Langside, then outside the city, but now well within its bounds. The epoch-making General Assembly of November 1638, which abolished episcopacy and precipitated the Bishops' Wars, met in Glasgow, where some of its members found the prices of accommodation excessive. It was in 'the Laigh Kirk' (or crypt of the cathedral), where the Barony congregation worshipped, that Zachary Boyd, in October 1650, denounced to his face Oliver Cromwell, then on a brief visit to the city; the English general is said to have taken the subtle revenge of treating the railing minister to three hours of prayer at dinner. The city was a centre of the Covenanting opposition to the policies of Charles II and James VII. Its member in the Scottish Parliament stood out against the Union in the debates of 1706-7, though it remained loyal and indeed patriotic during the Jacobite rising of 1715. Walpole's malt tax of 1725 produced the Shawfield riot, when the local member's house was wrecked, but Glasgow's Hanoverian principles were not in doubt: the citizens had no difficulty in resisting the blandishments of Charles Edward, short of popular Lowland support as well as of money and clothing, in December 1745.

It is in other ways that these two centuries were memorable for the development of Glasgow: its economic advance, based on the enterprise and skill of its inhabitants, is truly remarkable. The population, estimated to have been about 4,500 in 1560, reached 7,644 in 1610, rose to 11,943 in 1688, and to 12,766 in 1708. Its expansion brought it up to second place in size, behind Edinburgh alone; and the same is true of its ranking in the burghs' stent-roll, which was revised periodically by the Convention in order to include new creations, to ease the burden of decayed towns, and to increase the quota of the more prosperous. From eleventh place in 1535, Glasgow reached ninth in 1557, seventh in 1578, sixth in 1587 and fifth in 1591, at which stage only Scotland's 'big four' —Edinburgh, Dundee, Aberdeen and Perth—stood higher. By 1635 it was sharing fourth place with Perth, but in 1649 Perth dropped back to fifth, paying £4 out of every £100 of tax imposed on the burghs, and leaving Edinburgh (at £36), Dundee (£7), Aberdeen (£6, 13s. 4d.) and Glasgow (£6, 10s.) in the first four places. The next revision, in 1670, carried Glasgow (£12) clear above Aberdeen (£7) and Dundee (£6, 2s.) to take second place to Edinburgh (£33, 6s. 8d.)—a ranking that was to hold good for a long time.

In the realms of commerce and finance, Glasgow was now beginning to outstrip its old rivals of the Clyde region, but strife and bickering continued throughout the sixteenth and seventeenth centuries. The causes of conflict were numerous and varied. Rutherglen and Lanark, with their predominantly landward interests, objected to, and tried in vain to evade, Glasgow's right to exact the petty custom of 'ladle' on corn coming to its market. Renfrew, depending more and more on its herring fisheries, resented the city's impost on all herring brought across Glasgow bridge. The riparian burghs combined from time to time to oppose the use, by Ayr and Irvine, of small nets that caught the herring fry and so ruined that industry. Above all, Dumbarton, strategically situated and claiming a monopoly of 'adventure trade' arriving in the river between the mouth of the Kelvin and Loch Long, aroused the enmity of the Glasgow merchants, and there were recurrent complaints of the Dumbarton men luring away Dutch and French ships destined for Glasgow.

Despite their mutual animosities, all the royal burghs were agreed in trying to suppress 'unfree trade', whether by port or creek, fair or market, and it was from this direction that the next major threat came. The Renfrewshire laird, John Shaw, had his town of Greenock erected, in 1635, into a burgh of barony, although Glasgow, Dumbarton and Renfrew (Pl. X) opposed the plan. The danger to Glasgow, whose merchants had to rely on off-loading and lighterage, was obvious, but the answer was not found until Charles II's reign. Meanwhile, we have a picture of Glasgow's condition in 1656, in the report compiled by Thomas Tucker, a Cromwellian official. Glasgow's twelve ships included six of 100 tons or more, and this meant that Glasgow now stood second to Edinburgh's port of Leith as regards shipping, and ahead of Dundee, Kirkcaldy, Montrose and Aberdeen (see Fig. 36). Her customs revenue was exceeded only by that of Leith and of Bo'ness (the port for Stirling and Linlithgow, and the centre of the coal and salt trades). Her exports comprised coal, herrings and plaiding, while she imported wine, brandy, salt, pepper and prunes from France, iron and timber from Norway, Dutch goods by way of Bo'ness, hides and skins from the Highlands, and occasional cargoes of oranges and lemons from the Barbadoes. Her growth, said Tucker, would be assured, 'were she not checqued and kept under by the shallownesse of her river'.

That great and undeniable disability was soon tackled in earnest. In 1662 the first quay was built at the Broomielaw (hitherto only a 'shore' without facilities), but already a more ambitious scheme was afoot. At Newark bay, some nineteen miles down the river and three miles above the upstart port of Greenock, the city fathers resolved to build a seaport and landing-stage for their own sea-going ships. Land was bought there in 1667 and developed so rapidly, with houses, stores, a quay and a sea-wall, that 'Newport Glasgow' was opened in 1668. The results of this enterprising move were immediately beneficial. The American and French trade grew up, alongside the Baltic and Dutch. Glasgow's first cargo of tobacco from Virginia (along with sugar, ginger and logwood) is recorded in 1674, and others followed in 1677, 1681 and 1691—all this despite England's Navigation Acts prohibiting such 'carrying trade' with her colonies. And in 1675, when a Greenock ship brought wine, brandy and salt (all 'staple wares') to the Clyde, the cargo was seized and, after a Court of Session case, confiscated. (For Glasgow's merchants, 'fair trade' principles clearly worked only in one direction!)

The 'State and Condition' of the Scots burghs were reported to the Convention in 1692, when each vied with another in depicting its poverty, in order to obtain financial aid or at least relief from taxation. Thus much must be discounted from Glasgow's mournful tale of empty houses, falling rents, decayed trade and the highly prejudicial competition of such flourishing places as Hamilton, Paisley and Greenock. Exports and imports were valued annually at £205,000 Scots, or about £17,000 sterling, while the consumption of wine, brandy and malt was at a high level, and the shipping figures still show Glasgow clearly in second place to Leith. Glasgow, it is true, suffered when total disaster overtook Scotland's grand project of rehabilitation through the Darien Company; but the losses were shared with the entire nation, and it is at least pleasant to record that, in September 1707, the city received, from the 'Equivalent', the sum of £2,114 to recoup her lost investment. Not less agreeable is the end of the story (stretching over nearly five centuries) of commercial strife with Dumbarton. Provost Anderson, of Glasgow, agreed with Provost Smollett, of Dumbarton, in 1700 to renounce any right to dues from the other town's ships; Dumbarton undertook not to claim the first offer of 'adventure' ships in the river, and Glasgow paid the smaller burgh £3,000 as compensation.

A VIGOROUS AND LIVELY COMMUNITY

In industrial, as in commercial, affairs seventeenth-century Glasgow was progressive and enterprising. It is true that the traditional monopolies and craft restrictions were retained, the council insisting, for example, on all vendors of produce using the town's tron (1675), and doing their best to suppress suburban coopers (1691). Alongside such archaic attitudes, however, a new spirit was stirring. The Drygate had its cloth factories, run by Robert Fleming and his partners (1638) and by an English clothier, Samuel Pitchersgill (1650). George Anderson's printing press started in 1638, coal-pits were being worked in the Gorbals in 1655 and 1680, and, after the great fire of 1652 (which Cromwell called 'this sad dispensation from the hand of an angry God') and the resultant anxiety about dangerous trades, four candle-factories were set up in the fields west of the city, to give a new street-name, the Candleriggs (1658).

After the Restoration new ventures blossomed forth. The Glasgow Fishing Company, having a Dutch partner, skilled in curing, was formed in 1667. A 'soapery', using blubber brought in by whaling-ships, opened in 1673. A sugar refinery, the first of several, was started in 1675; duty-free rum was a valued by-product and Glasgow soon became the Scottish centre of this trade. The Old Green was leased in 1696 to a rope-work company, and a glass-works, manufacturing both glass bottles and window glass, was established just north of the Broomielaw in the year 1700. Bustling activity and a willingness to experiment were the key-notes of the time.

Besides sponsoring economic advances, the magistrates and town council, from the time of the Reformation onwards, took what was for those days a broad view of their social duties. They co-operated with the kirk session to set up new charges (including the Barony, 1595), and provided and maintained new buildings. They appointed and paid the master and the reader of the grammar school, but were quite ready to license smaller and less ambitious 'adventure' schools; thus in 1663 no fewer than sixteen persons were authorised to 'keip and hold Scots schooles within the toune'. In 1681, to help the masters of the College to keep good order, they forbade billiard-tables between the Cross and 'the Wyndheid', in which district they would be a temptation to young

146

scholars. Although police measures were primitive, the council did enrol a 'watch' from time to time, to suppress night-walkers and vagrants. New public wells also made their appearance, and periodic gestures were made in the direction of a sanitary policy by prohibiting the throwing of 'fuilyie' or 'muck' on the streets and ordering the seizure of untethered swine. The occasional visitations of the deadly 'pest' or plague called for sterner measures. Ports were closed, back-dykes built up, the watch doubled, contacts with infected towns forbidden, and suspects isolated on the Gallowmuir; happily, however, the epidemic of 1645-8 proved to be the last.

In poor relief the usual pattern of administrative devices holds good in Glasgow. It was hoped, rather than expected, that the ordinary church collections would suffice for the worthy but impotent poor, while the strong and idle got compulsory labour at a workhouse or cloth mill. Begging was frowned upon, though from time to time permitted to those natives who had their 'tokens'. The city was, however, very early in the field with a 'poor's rate': in 1638 an annual stent of £600 was imposed to provide outdoor relief for all deserving cases. Other assessments followed, and in 1697 a committee was appointed to establish additional almshouses and to levy up to 1 per cent of all incomes for the use of the poor.

Although the council were strict enough on Sunday observance, with bans on drinking, shopping, slaughtering or working, they welcomed new amenities and new skills. The Dundee 'calsaymaker' (paviour) was borrowed in 1578, under strict promise of return. An apothecary and a haberdasher were licensed in 1654, two Edinburgh bakers were brought over in 1656 to bake wheaten bread, and Alexander Thom got permission in 1678 to reside and exercise his art of 'architectorie and measonrie'. The city's first fire engine, built after the great conflagration of 1652, was delivered in 1657. A town's post, with a weekly wage, appears in 1660, the first hackney-coach and the first coffee-house are recorded in 1673, and a stage-coach began in 1678, running to Edinburgh every Monday and returning on Saturday, at a fare of eight shillings sterling in summer and nine shillings in winter. Newsletters and gazettes were being received regularly during the reign of Charles II.

EFFECTS OF THE UNION

The Union of 1707, though opposed by Glasgow's member, brought great opportunities in the bigger markets opened to it, and more especially in the lawful access afforded to the profitable transatlantic traffic with the American colonies. Though some little time elapsed before the economic fruits of Union could be garnered, Glasgow merchants were not slow to recognise that their city was now on the right side of the map. The most gainful branch of commerce was in tobacco, which, in the form of snuff, was in great and growing demand throughout Europe. First chartering and then owning their ships, suffering a slight check in the seventeen-twenties through English jealousy (or familiarity with Scottish sharp practice), but surviving to forge ahead in the next decade, the men who came to be known as Glasgow's 'tobacco lords' challenged the traders of Bristol and London.

The highly speculative and lucrative days of the tobacco trade were to come only after mid-century, but there is clear evidence that, long before then, the Glasgow men had secured a large share of the exotic and monopolistic traffic, and that their enterprise

147

had greatly benefited the city's shipping in general; for, whereas in 1692 the local fleet had comprised fifteen ships (only four of them of 100 tons or over), eight lighters and part-shares in four other large ships, there were in 1735 sixty-seven vessels, aggregating no less than 5,600 tons, and of these one-third traded to America. The rapid advance of the city is also apparent from the sharp increase of its population: Webster's unofficial census of 1755 puts it at 23,546, but (as the compiler himself warned) that figure referred to a few years previously and was an under-estimate.[16]

New industries were stimulated by successful commerce, some of the products serving as return cargoes for the tobacco ships. Holland cloth, lawns, checks, incles (linen tape), linen prints, thread and knitted stockings were all being manufactured in the first half of the century, as were shoes, saddles, gloves and various forms of metalware; and many of these went to the plantations.

In other ways the innovations are likewise noteworthy. Glasgow's first newspaper, the *Courant*, was launched in 1715, though it was only to survive for two years; it was followed in 1729 by the more durable *Glasgow Journal*. The city's oldest purely charitable institution, the Buchanan Society, was founded in 1725, and the even more famous Glasgow Highland Society began in 1727. Physical expansion forged ahead. In the west end, King's Street and Princes Street were laid out in 1724, and buildings soon appeared along their routes. Thanks to the initiative of John Orr of Barrowfield, the first of what was to become a ring of suburban villages took shape—Calton to the east in 1731, Anderston to the west in 1735, each forming a weaving community set apart from the city itself.

The new Town's Hospital, facing the Clyde just west of the old Glasgow bridge, won the ecstatic encomium of the first of the many local historians, John McUre: it 'exceeds any of that kind in Europe . . . resembling more like a Palace, than a Habitation for necessitous old People and Children' (1733). The printing press of the Foulis brothers, started in 1741, and its admirable editions of the classics, brought the city a new kind of fame.

As the half-century drew to a close, the record reveals a strange mingling of the old and the new, and we seem to sense (doubtless with retrospective wisdom) intimations of the vast changes impending. In 1748 the town council, judging the constitution to be open to the objection of 'having a tendency to continue the government of the city in a particular set longer than may be for the public interest', resolved that four councillors out of the thirty-one (two merchants and two craftsmen) should retire each year and make room for four others—scarcely a Draconian remedy for the ancient practice of self-election! In 1749 the East and West Ports were taken down; before long, two well-known inns would appear at the sites—the Saracen's Head in the Gallowgate, the terminal for the Edinburgh coach, and the Black Bull in the Trongate, the great meeting-place for Glasgow's Highland community. Under the year 1750 John Gibson, the second and one of the best of the city's historians, notes a decay of the old-time frugality. Wealth was increasing, the first of Glasgow's banks were just being founded, fashionable clothes and furnishings were coming in, wheel-carriages were finding favour, assembly rooms and a play-house catered for luxurious tastes, new streets were being opened and elegant houses being built, of stone instead of wood. There is a familiar ring about the chronicler's final comment on the changing scene—'In vain did the clergy . . . declaim against this change of manners'.

1 *Registrum Episcopatus Glasguensis*, ed. Cosmo Innes, pubd. in 2 vols. by Bannatyne and Maitland Clubs 1843.

2 *Lib. de Melros*, i, 36-7; *Nat. Mss. Scot.*, i, no. XLII.

3 *Reg. Epis. Glasg.*, i, 197-8. In the *Tabula* the deed is mis-dated 1280-90: Master Reginald de Irewyn, one of the principals, was dead by 1268: *ib.*, 178-9.

4 *Ib.*, 181.

5 *Reg. de Passelet*, 399-401.

6 Besides those already mentioned, sales of burgages are recorded in or about 1283 (*ib.*, 382-7), about 1290 (*Reg. Epis. Glasg.*, i, 198-200), and in 1295 (*Reg. de Neubotle*, 144-5).

7 The date is 8 July 1222 (8 Alex. II), not 1221, as is usually stated. Its terms are known from a confirming charter of 1609: *R.M.S.*, vii, 190.

8 Pagan, J., *Sketch of Hist. of Glasgow* (1847), 5, 8; Crawfurd, G., *Sketch of Trades House of Glasgow* (1858), 7; *cf.*, Macgregor, G., *Hist. of Glasgow* (1881), 54-6.

9 Renwick, R. and Lindsay, Sir J., *History of Glasgow* (1921), i, 209; Mackenzie, W. M., *The Scottish Burghs* (1949), 78.

10 See especially, for passages that are quite needlessly apologetic about such matters, Marwick, Sir James, *Early Glasgow* (1911), 4, and Murray, David, *Early Burgh Organisation in Scotland*, i (1924), 148-50.

11 *A.P.S.*, ii, 213.

12 A volume of extracts from the records, covering the years 1573-1642, was published by the Burgh Records Society in 1876. This was, in effect, the first of eleven volumes, coming down to 1833: the project was completed in 1916.

13 There are tolerably full records of the great custom receipts for the years 1327-33 and again for 1366-1376: *E.R.S.*, i, between pp. 74-83 and 420-7, and ii, between pp. 254-5 and 470-84. (My ranking is a compound of the two sets of returns.)

14 *Recs. Conv. R. Burghs*, 514-15.

15 *Charters . . . of Glasgow*, ii, 236-40; *A.P.S.*, ix, 153-4.

16 *Scottish Population Statistics* (Scot. Hist. Soc., 1952), 9, 29 and note 1.

INDUSTRIAL AND COMMERCIAL DEVELOPMENTS

TO 1914

JOHN B. S. GILFILLAN
Lecturer in Scottish History, University of Glasgow

AND

H. A. MOISLEY
Lecturer in Geography, University of Glasgow

VIEWED in its regional setting, medieval Glasgow would scarcely seem the most likely of burghs to rise to a position of dominance in the economy of the West of Scotland. That the ecclesiastical burgh of Bishop Jocelin should attain such a distinction would certainly have appeared incredible to the inhabitants of the older, 'king's burghs' of Rutherglen and Renfrew; and equally so to those of Dumbarton, the ancient and strategically situated capital of Strathclyde, created a burgh by Alexander II some forty-seven years after Glasgow received its charter. But despite the keen rivalry, and apparently superior geographical position of some of her neighbours on the Clyde, the quiet cathedral city of St Mungo was soon to be numbered among the leading burghs of Scotland. By 1535 Glasgow stood eleventh in taxable importance among the Scottish burghs, and before the close of the sixteenth century she attained fifth place, eclipsing all her rivals in the west, being exceeded only by Edinburgh, Dundee, Aberdeen and Perth. In 1611 Glasgow became a royal burgh and by 1670 it was the second city in Scotland, yielding pride of place to Edinburgh alone. It was only after the union of the Scottish and English Parliaments in 1707, however, that the West of Scotland really 'came into its own'.

Initially trade, and particularly foreign trade, was the basis of Clydeside's economic development, with political and geographical factors exerting potent influences. Against the geographical disadvantage of a western situation in the pre-Union period, when Scotland's trade was mainly eastward with continental ports, the Glasgow region possessed one incomparable asset—the Clyde. Its value to the region lay originally in the Firth rather than in the river itself, which was navigable by only the smallest of boats beyond Dumbarton. The Firth, however, with its numerous bays and sheltered sea lochs, was such as to encourage navigation and sea-borne trade from the earliest times. In one of the many prehistoric dug-out canoes discovered in the silt of the Glasgow area since 1780 a plug of cork was found which has been regarded as indicating an early trading connection with Spain. More advanced techniques of shipbuilding may have been learned on Clydeside from the Romans, whose galleys possibly rode at anchor beneath Dumbarton Rock, and the Roman influence would undoubtedly extend the horizon of local traders. Even in the more open waters beyond the sheltering arm of the Kintyre peninsula the characteristics of the western seaboard, with its outer island barrier and heavily indented coastline, are such as to encourage coastal navigation and trade by even quite primitive vessels. By the sixth century the coracles of the Celtic monks of Ireland were sailing in these waters and penetrating far northwards up the Scottish coast. Communication between the Clyde and Ireland had been established even earlier, by the time of St Patrick (whose traditional birth-place is on Clydeside near Bowling), and from the date of the founding by Irish immigrants of the Scots kingdom of Dalriada, about 500, regular trade with the north-east Irish coast was probably instituted. In medieval times communications with the Highlands and Islands were gradually developed, the perils of rounding the Mull of Kintyre in winter being avoided by dragging the boats across the narrow strip of land at Tarbert which separates Loch Fyne from the sheltered Sound of Jura. Full advantage was thus taken of the protected waters and safe anchorages afforded by a broken coastline.

The upper Firth of Clyde and its sea lochs afford many deep-water anchorages (Pl. V) of which the most important is the 'Tail o' the Bank' off Greenock, which marks the junction of deep lochs and shallow estuary. For some sixty miles the approaches, whilst ample for navigation, are sheltered from all directions. In this respect the Firth of Clyde contrasts with the Mersey, with its notorious Outer Estuary or Bay, and compares favourably with any English Channel port and with the Thames. Even the approaches to the Bristol Channel ports are far more open. As to fog, at least the Clyde is no worse off than Liverpool and London; and the tidal range is less than at any other major British port (Table X).

London Bridge	23 feet	Bristol	45 feet
Liverpool	32 feet	Greenock	12 feet
Southampton	15 feet	Glasgow	13 feet

TABLE X. Tidal Ranges at Ordinary Spring Tides.

The estuary above Port Glasgow is physically quite different from the sea lochs. Whilst the latter were formed by glaciers eroding deeply into the solid rock, the former is cut almost entirely in loose material—clays, sands and gravels—deposited either by ice, by running water, or in the shallow sea which entered the Clyde basin in immediate post-Glacial times. Consequently, whilst the natural channel of the tidal river was wide, shallow and full of islands and shoals, the same material, forming its bed, was easily removed when the need arose.

Man was not slow to take advantage of this extensive and sheltered arm of the sea, particularly since, apart from its use for trade and commerce, it contained a valuable natural resource in its fish, especially herring and salmon. Trade was for long restricted by law to the burghs, but fishing was carried on from many other places too, amongst which were a number of small Renfrewshire settlements which were later to become the ports of Greenock and Port Glasgow. The early royal burghs farther down the Firth, such as Rothesay, Irvine and Ayr, whilst they had better access to open water, were less advantageously placed than the burghs on the upper reaches of the Clyde as regards overland communications. Their immediate hinterlands were restricted, as was their access to the rest of Scotland. Of the up-river burghs, Dumbarton held a unique position, standing as it did at the junction of sea routes with land routes from the north, west and east, which here had to make the crossing of the Leven. Its Rock, a volcanic plug, commanded the estuary and the Vale of Leven, affording a remarkable defensive site. Dumbarton claims to have been the capital of the ancient kingdom of Strathclyde, and its situation was certainly significant from earliest historic times. Later, in the fourteenth century, King Robert the Bruce lived in the nearby castle of Cardross; he and other Scottish kings built or equipped ships here. In the eighteenth century Dumbarton was still an important staging point on the route from Edinburgh and Glasgow to Inverary (in the High Street the Dukes of Argyll maintained a town house). Artillery, the bridge over the Leven (erected about 1765) and finally modern road and rail transport have robbed the site of its strategic value—besides which there is no longer need to guard the entrance to the Lowlands from incursions by Highlanders or sea-borne Viking raiders. Nevertheless, the Sovereign, when visiting the county, still calls at Dumbarton Castle to be handed the keys. (See Plate VII.)

Until the eighteenth century Dumbarton's merchants shared with those of Glasgow in the trade of the Clyde. Glasgow was not accessible to sea-going vessels, but it had the better hinterland, being fifteen miles farther inland, and situated at the lowest bridge of the Clyde. Sea-going vessels could put into Dumbarton, but there are also frequent references to such vessels discharging, presumably into river craft, at Inchgreen (near Greenock), Newark (Port Glasgow) and 'Port of the Rig'. Smaller vessels also discharged at Kilpatrick and some even reached Glasgow, contending with many sandbanks on the way.

Glasgow was not alone in suffering from the unsatisfactory nature of its river. Dumbarton was repeatedly inundated and constantly eroded from the rear by a great meander of the Leven. Irvine was troubled by severe silting. Renfrew suffered the remarkable misfortune of losing its port altogether when, in the seventeenth century, a great flood caused the Clyde to abandon the channel beside the town in favour of one on the north side of King's Inch. As early as 1556 it is recorded that the people of Glasgow, Renfrew and Dumbarton erected huts at Dumbuck, about a mile up the Clyde beyond Dumbarton, and each worked six weeks in turn in an attempt to remove the ford and sandbanks. This co-operation indicates the importance to the Dumbarton merchants of access to the inland market; their trading rights were of small value in the restricted local hinterland of the burgh. In 1600 an Englishman, Smyth, was consulted as to the clearing of the river, and in 1612 we hear of chains and cables being prepared in Glasgow in order to remove large stones at Dumbuck. Timothy Pont's surveys about this time show the large number of islands in the channel; burgh records abound with references to fords and sandbanks. No precise record of the nature of the channel is available until the mid-eighteenth century, but, from the soundings then carried out (Fig. 35), it seems likely that, even at high water, a depth of no more than three or four feet was to be relied on, at any rate above Renfrew. At Dumbuck, Erskine, Renfrew and even above the Kelvin junction near Glasgow Bridge the river was readily forded at low water.

Meanwhile Glasgow was beginning to flourish, although the seventeenth century was to close, as it had opened, under a cloud of economic depression. Early attempts to

152

Pl. IX.
NORTH-WEST
GLASGOW,
from University
Tower

West-end stone-
built terraces.
Kelvin gorge
hidden by trees,
right middle
distance, with paper
mill chimney,
centre. Town en-
closed by Kil-
patricks, left, and
Campsies, right,
separated by Strath-
blane with High-
land hills beyond.

Annan, Glasgow

Pl. X.   GREENOCK, looking up the Clyde estuary

Residential west-end in foreground, Town Hall tower and urban centre on right. Main harbour area projecting into river in middle distance, hiding Port Glasgow beyond. Dumbarton Rock centre distance and Kilpatrick Hills on left.

Pl. XI. GOUROCK AND THE UPPER FIRTH OF CLYDE, from the east

Railway pier and terminus station right centre, approach line blocking access of town to west side of bay. Road-metal quarry in volcanic plug on left. Dissected Cowal plateau beyond; Dunoon extreme left; Holy Loch right centre.

Pl. XII.
PAISLEY, from the
south

White Cart River
in foreground; old
mill beside rapids
on left. Paisley
Abbey (twelfth
century) top right;
Town Hall centre.
Open spaces result-
ing from recent
clearance of decayed
nineteenth - century
tenements.

The Scotsman

establish new industries on Clydeside—for example, woollen manufacture—were initially unsuccessful, but following the Restoration in 1660 several important developments took place. In 1667 five ships were fitted out for whale fishing, and in the same year soap manufacture was begun—the foundation, perhaps, of the West of Scotland's chemical industries. At the same time another important industry was started—sugar-refining, itself an outcome of overseas trading. There were developments, too, in tanning, rope-spinning, and the weaving of woollen and linen cloths. In 1663 a quay had been built at the Broomielaw, where it had long been the practice to unload small

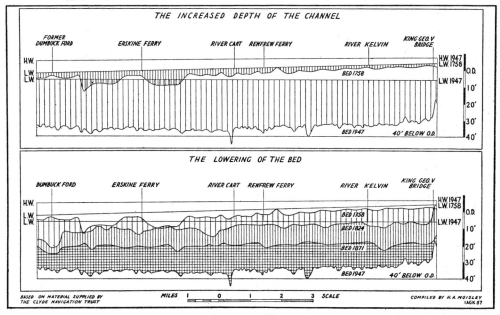

FIG. 35.   The deepening of the Clyde, 1758–1947.

boats, but the increase in trade and shipping made it desirable to have better facilities downriver. Both the burgh of Dumbarton and the Superior of Easter Greenock and Cartsburn refused to make land available, so in 1668 Glasgow acquired a site at Newark, in the parish of Kilmacolm, where the bay had long been one of the anchorages for vessels unloading into small boats. Here Glasgow began building a harbour where ships could discharge on to a quay, and in 1676 feus began to be let for houses. Thus a new settlement, Newport (later Port Glasgow), began. In future, it was ruled, all Glasgow merchants were to use Glasgow or Newport and no other 'port, harbour or creek'.

Clyde trade was not, however, confined to Glasgow, despite the decay of Dumbarton and Renfrew. Greenock had been made a burgh of barony in 1635, and Greenock men and ships engaged in trading as well as in the herring fishing; by 1675 there were complaints from Glasgow that Greenock merchants were infringing the staple of the royal burghs by handling salt, brandy, tanned leather and wine. Greenock was not lightly to be held down, and further complaints that its growing trade was prejudicing that of the royal burghs (mainly of Glasgow) are recorded. By about 1683, however, Glasgow was purchasing warehouses in Greenock. Perhaps by then there was sufficient

153

trade to keep Newport fully occupied. These warehouses, formerly the storehouses of the Royal Fishery Society, were used for tobacco, but, in 1691, they were sold and the regulation regarding Newport was re-enacted.

The increase in trading in the seventeenth century should not be exaggerated. The ports of the west coast still lay outside the busiest streams of trade, which were across the North Sea to Holland, Germany and the Baltic (Fig. 36). But almost all the shipping

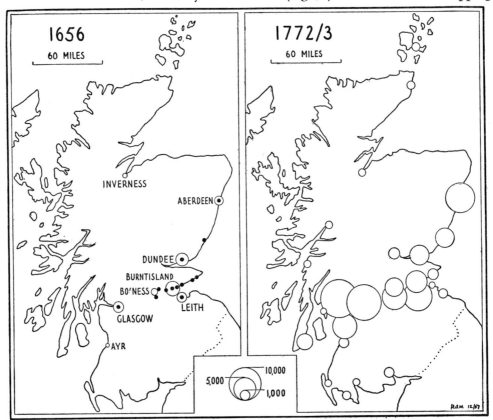

FIG. 36. The Shipping of Scotland, 1656 and 1772/73.

Circles are proportionate to tonnage of shipping belonging to each *head* port. *Note:*—on the 1656 map, all individual ports, including member ports, having more than 100 tons are marked with black dots. The symbol for Dundee is only approximate.

of the west was concentrated on the Clyde, north of which there was not even a customs port; in 1656 the Commissioner had remarked that these parts were 'destitute of trade and inhabited by ancient Scots or wilde Irish'.

THE TOBACCO ERA

The Act of Union, in 1707, brought about a fundamental change in the position of the West of Scotland. North American and West Indian trade was now open to Scottish merchants on equal terms with those of Whitehaven, Liverpool and Bristol. On the Clyde, experienced and enterprising merchants were available to seize the opportunity. Hitherto their trading had been confined mainly to France, Holland and the Baltic, where they were at a disadvantage compared with their east-coast rivals. Now from being something of a back door to Scotland, the Clyde became a main entrance. The change could not have very rapid consequences; a fleet had to be acquired and manned, markets for colonial goods had to be developed, and sources of manufactured goods had to be explored in order to obtain outgoing cargoes. The whole of Scotland was desperately short of funds to start such enterprises. Nevertheless, it was not long before English merchants were complaining of unfair competition—a sure sign of Scottish success.

Glasgow's only industries of importance at the beginning of the eighteenth century were sugar-refining and soap-making. The first of several 'sugar-houses' had been erected in the city in 1667; the whaling company had a blubber factory at Greenock, where its ships were based, and a 'soaperie' in the Candleriggs. As yet the textile industry was comparatively insignificant, but it rested on a solid foundation of local skill and only awaited the stimulus of the Union to bring it into prominence. Linen, which had been made in Glasgow on a modest scale since the Commonwealth period and was already acquiring some celebrity in the home market, formed the basis of a new export industry—the supply of clothing for the colonists and their slaves. Daniel Defoe, writing within twenty years of the Union, noted the importance of linen in Glasgow's economy: 'they make a very great quantity of it and send it to the plantations as their principal merchandise'. He was impressed also by Glasgow's manufacture of muslins, 'which they make so good and fine that great quantities of them are sent into England and to the British plantations, where they sell at a good price'. The weavers of the West of Scotland thus early established a reputation for skilful workmanship in fine textiles—an accomplishment which was to stand the region in good stead when its tobacco trade collapsed later in the century.

As early as 1674 there is evidence of an interest in Virginian tobacco on the part of Glasgow's merchants, but such trade as they had with the English colonies in America at that period was, of course, only small and surreptitious. After the Union of 1707 the trade developed fairly rapidly, although the vessels employed were at first chartered from English ports, chiefly Whitehaven. Largely as a result of the severe financial losses suffered in the Darien disaster, it was not until 1718 that a Glasgow-owned tobacco ship crossed the Atlantic—and this was a small vessel of only 60 tons, built at Greenock. The early success of the Glasgow tobacco traders, despite such crippling disadvantages, in their competition with English merchants, was attributed by the latter to fraudulent evasion of customs; but, by the Scots, to the simplicity and frugality of their trading methods. The merchants of London, Bristol, Liverpool and Whitehaven combined together to crush the Scottish trade; after an official enquiry in 1721, however, the Lords of the Treasury declared that the complaints were groundless, and that they arose 'from a spirit of envy, and not from a regard to the interests of trade or of the King's revenue'.

By 1723 there were twenty or thirty ships engaged in the trade from the Clyde, and four years later, according to Defoe, the Glasgow merchants were sending 'near fifty sail of ships every year to Virginia, New England, and other English colonies in America'. For the first—and not the last—time in her history Glasgow was profiting from the fact that she was situated considerably nearer to America than were her English

155

rivals. Defoe records that Glasgow vessels were often 'at the Capes of Virginia before the London ships got clear of the Channel', thus saving a month or six weeks on the whole voyage. It was not until about 1735 that the Clyde finally triumphed over southern competition and interference; thereafter the development of the tobacco trade was phenomenal. Resident agents were appointed in the colonies and methods of trading (originally a system of barter) became more complex: in forward dealings whole crops of tobacco were often purchased before they were even planted, and princely fortunes were rapidly amassed. Thus arose Glasgow's first commercial aristocracy—'the tobacco lords', whose scarlet cloaks, gold-headed canes and pompous air as they paraded the Plainstanes were long to be remembered in the city. This period is still commemorated by many street names, such as Glassford Street, Oswald Street, Virginia Street and Jamaica Street.

Some indication of the activity in the Clyde when the tobacco trade was beginning can be obtained from the customs records of the period. Fortunately the practice of letting the customs to a tacksman ceased about this time; official collectors and 'waiters' were appointed. A few details from their ledgers will illustrate the nature of the trade of the Clyde in the early seventeen-forties (Table XI).

The discrepancy between the number of vessels entering from, and the number departing for North America and the West Indies is accounted for by the fact that some vessels made 'triangular' voyages, calling at European ports before finally crossing the Atlantic in the low latitudes of the north-east trade winds. Tobacco and salt herrings, for example, were taken to European ports, and wine was picked up at Madeira on the outward voyage. Rum, sugar, ginger and 'cotton wool' were obtained in the West Indies, and here, and in North American ports, a great variety of manufactured goods were unloaded—iron pots, linens, woollens, stockings, handkerchiefs, shirts, shoes, lead shot, cutlery, saddlery, earthenware, candles, chains, beer and also salt herrings. Finally, although the period is rightly known as the tobacco era, large quantities of naval stores and other goods were brought back with the tobacco. In addition there was a small fleet of vessels engaged solely in European and Irish Sea trade; many of these brought in provisions and goods, notably textiles, for re-export, and it is worth noting (see Table XI) that there was some division of interest between Greenock and Port Glasgow. The former had far more of the Irish and European trade than the latter and, whilst at first Port Glasgow had the lion's share of the American trade, Greenock's share grew rapidly as time went on. Port Glasgow, despite its foundation by and for the merchants of Glasgow, appears never to have had many vessels solely in the European trade, and before the end of the tobacco era it was to yield pride of place to Greenock even in that staple commodity.

This trade changed little in character until the outbreak of the American War of Independence in 1775, but it greatly increased in volume. With this increase came an ever-growing fleet of Clyde-owned vessels: by 1772 the Clyde owned 56 per cent of Scottish foreign-going shipping, a remarkable change since 1656 (Fig. 36); more than three-quarters of this—over 23,000 tons—belonged to Greenock and Port Glasgow, representing a twenty-five-fold increase in eighty years. Thereafter progress was to be less rapid. A remarkable feature in this period is the much more rapid increase of trade and shipping in Greenock than in Port Glasgow. This was accounted for partly by the increasing activity of Greenock merchants, trading in Greenock-owned vessels, and

156

partly by the tendency of Glasgow merchants more and more to use Greenock as a port and, very often, to take shares in Greenock ships. One can only presume that there just was not room at Port Glasgow, either in the harbour or warehouses, for all the traffic. The harbour at Greenock, first formed about 1707, was considerably larger than that at Port Glasgow and, in addition, there were several small piers. The latter were, however, probably used by the herring fishing boats, of which there were about three hundred

	Greenock	Port Glasgow
NUMBER OF VESSELS ENTERING FROM:		
North America	36	43
West Indies	3	17
Europe	79	21
Ireland	19	36
All Ports	137	117
NUMBER OF VESSELS CLEARING FOR:		
North America	34	24
West Indies	17	12
Europe	81	60*
Ireland	22	18
All Ports	154	114
TOBACCO (thousands of lbs per annum):		
Entered	3,380	4,824
Cleared	2,392	3,728
IRON ENTERED (tons):		
Swedish	894	69
Russian	45	28
Other	5	23

TABLE XI. Extracts from the Custom Port Books, Glasgow, September 1742—September 1744.

* Many of these vessels were ultimately bound for North America.

in the seventeen-seventies. Thus it is not surprising that schemes to improve the navigability of the Clyde, and so to bring more trade to Glasgow, were in the air, as was a plan to cut a canal to the Forth. Smeaton sounded the river (Fig. 35) in 1755, but nothing more was done until 1768 when John Golborne, of Chester, advised the construction of jetties or 'wing-dams' such as are seen on the Rhine today. These forced the water into a narrow channel, increasing its speed and erosive power. 'Ploughs'—rather like huge rakes—were pulled to and fro across the bed to assist the process. In this way navigation of the channel by small boats was made more reliable, but there was still no question of ocean-going vessels reaching Glasgow; even quite small boats required several tides to get up, lying aground at each low-water.

By this time more than half the tobacco trade of Britain had become concentrated on the Clyde: 49,000 of the 90,000 hogsheads imported into Great Britain in 1772 came to Glasgow. There were then some thirty-eight firms in the business, many of them dealing in vast sums annually. Smollett tells us in *Humphry Clinker* that one merchant, John Glassford, alone owned twenty-five ships and traded for above half-a-million sterling a year. By its nature the tobacco trade brought great wealth to a comparatively small number of individuals, its value to the region as a whole lying not so much in its immediate effects as in the accumulation of commercial experience that was to encourage industrial development. It was very much an entrepôt trade, the tobacco arriving in the Clyde being almost all re-exported to France, Holland, Germany, Italy and Norway. There it was consumed mainly in the form of snuff. The 'farmers general' of the French Customs were the principal purchasers. In 1771, 46 million pounds of tobacco came to the Clyde, and of this quantity nearly 44 million pounds were re-shipped abroad. In addition to naval stores and timber of all kinds, whale oil, bar iron (over 1,200 tons in 1771), and flax seed were being imported from the colonies. From the West Indies came rum (178,000 gallons in 1771), sugar (47,000 lbs), cotton (59,000 lbs), mahogany, coffee and many other commodities. The old-established trade in Madeira wine, loaded on the westbound leg of the 'triangular voyage', also continued.

In return, a wide variety of goods, mostly manufactured, were exported to the Americas. The ramifications of this kind of trade were enormous. On the one hand we find Clyde merchants setting up their own stores and agents in the colonies, and operating their own colonial-registered coasting vessels there. At the other end of the line, so to speak, these same merchants encouraged and developed manufactures of all kinds in and around the Clyde basin. The most important of these was the linen industry, which employed large numbers of weavers in town and country districts alike and which in turn led to the development of bleachfields and printworks. It was the existence of this substantial population of skilled textile workers, particularly weavers, that was to enable the Clyde basin to take up cotton manufacture so rapidly after 1780. As well as linen there was silk-gauze—introduced to the Paisley district from London about 1760—and sewing thread, also a Renfrewshire specialty. It was in the old mansion house of Bargarran in Renfrewshire that the Scottish thread industry was born. Christian Shaw, daughter of the Laird of Bargarran, had gained notoriety in her girl-hood as the originator of the Renfrewshire witch-hunt of 1697, but in later years she won a more commendable fame as the originator of 'Bargarran Threed'—a fine sewing thread equal, if not superior, to the Dutch variety, from which it was copied. Her mother and sisters helped in the manufacture and young women in the neighbourhood were initiated into the art as the demand for the thread increased, so that eventually the Bargarran household became the centre of quite an extensive and profitable industry. Friends of the family assisted in spreading the fame of the product far and near, and soon the 'ounce' or 'nun's thread' of Bargarran became widely used and its manufacture began to be imitated in other districts. Paisley became the chief centre of production,

158

having ninety-three thread mills by 1744 and one hundred and thirty-seven by 1791. An iron industry was also established about this time. The Smithfield Company, for example, set up workshops in Glasgow about 1732 and in 1738 erected a forge, rolling and slitting mill on the River Kelvin at Partick (Fig. 37). Also in Glasgow was Moses McCulloch, Gallowgate, an ironfounder whose firm survives today at the same address. Farther down the Clyde, at Old Kilpatrick, the Dalnottar Ironworks was

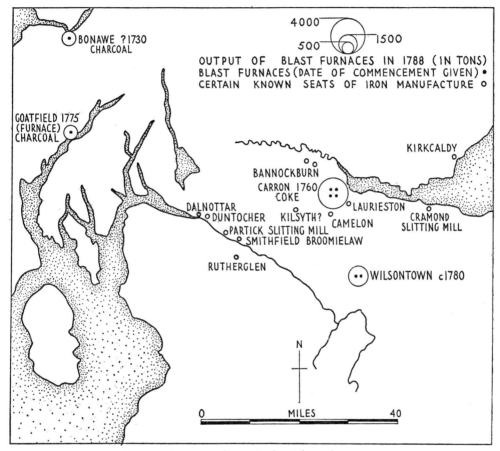

FIG. 37. Iron manufacture in the eighteenth century.
In addition coke blast furnaces were also started near Glasgow (at Clyde Ironworks), at Omoa, and at Muirkirk, about 1788; commencing dates for charcoal furnaces are by no means certain.

started about 1769, and the same company erected mills at Duntocher a little later. Such works provided some of the iron goods—nails, hardware, shovels, etc.—for the colonial trade; in addition, the Glasgow merchants bought from the ironworks and domestic nail-makers established around the Forth (Fig. 37). Pottery in Glasgow and glass manufacture in Glasgow and Dumbarton were similarly established, and, like the ironworks, stimulated the demand for coal. Tanning, the making of leather goods and the weaving of 'incles' (tapes) were amongst the other manufactures developed as a direct result of the colonial trade. By 1771 the West of Scotland could boast a favourable trade balance of home-produced exports, amounting to half-a-million pounds sterling. The figures (in thousands of pounds sterling) were: imports, £1,386; re-exports (chiefly tobacco), £1,354; home-produced exports (chiefly linen), £503. The value of textiles alone, exported from the Clyde in 1771, was £450,000. Thus the need to supply outward cargoes for the tobacco ships had stimulated the growth of local manufacturing industries, which in their turn were to broaden the basis of the Clyde's overseas trade and form a bulwark against subsequent depression.

It was somewhat ironical that in the very year, 1775, of the American revolt, Golborne and his son should receive from Glasgow £3,900 and a silver cup for their successful work on the river. Although the revolt brought about the sudden downfall of the tobacco lords—by 1777 only 295,000 pounds of tobacco were imported—trade was to recover remarkably quickly. Whilst some merchants were ruined and their American properties confiscated, others had already secured great fortunes and acquired estates in the West Indies; much capital amassed in tobacco trading had also been invested in the new industries producing goods for home and overseas. Further funds were now freed, sugar, textile and shipping interests were greatly expanded and, by 1791, the West of Scotland had practically recovered its 1771 level of prosperity.

This recovery, the most significant feature of which was a virtual doubling of production for home consumption, owed less to the mechanical developments of the Industrial Revolution than might be supposed; it was based rather on the spirit of commercial enterprise fostered in Glasgow earlier in the century and exemplified, for example, in the founding of the city's Chamber of Commerce—the first in the British Isles—in 1783. Philosophically accepting the loss of their American markets, Glasgow's merchants turned their eyes again towards Europe and established trading agencies in London and Ostend. Even before the American War was over, Golborne was again called in. And, meanwhile, Glasgow had achieved legal status as a port. The Forth and Clyde Canal, begun in 1768, was within three miles of Glasgow when the war began. Nevertheless, in 1777 a basin was made at Hamilton Hill and, the town having undertaken to provide a 'proper house at a moderate rent' for the Revenue Officer, 782 feet of quay were declared 'a lawful place for the shipping and unshipping of goods'. Adam Smith was one of the Customs Commissioners who signed the declaration in 1779. The first foreign vessel recorded was a French one, carrying wine. Work recommenced in 1786 and the canal was opened to the Clyde in 1790. Thus, within a few years of the collapse of her tobacco trade, Glasgow was in a position to push her commercial frontiers in new directions. A second, fundamental change in her 'space-relations', comparable to that of 1707, had been accomplished.

THE PREDOMINANCE OF TEXTILES

It was fortunate for Clydeside that just when a new industry—cotton—was born, the region possessed both the capital and the skilled labour resources necessary to develop it. The reserves of capital derived from the colonial trade, and the reserves of skill accumulated in the making of fine linen and silk, enabled Glasgow's *entrepreneurs* and artisans to turn quickly to this new exotic industry, despite the relatively high degree of economic organisation it called for. Unlike the linen industry, with its slow evolution from the 'domestic' to the 'factory' system, cotton spinning was mechanised from the very beginning in Scotland. The initial mechanical inventions were developed in

160

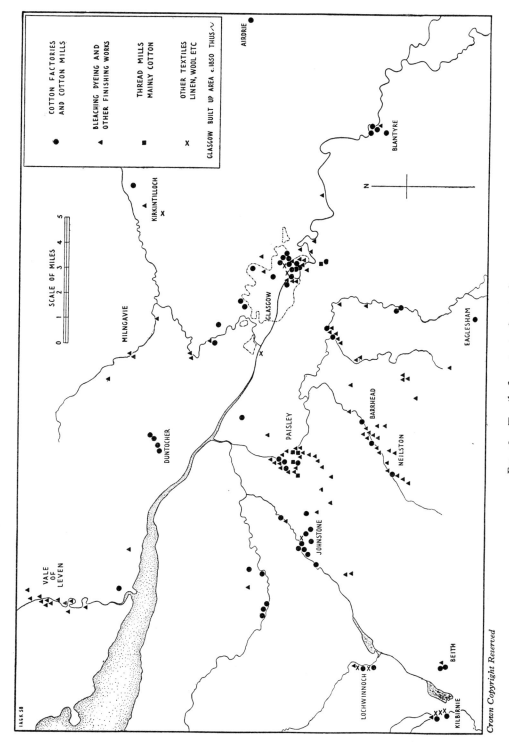

Fig. 38. Textile factories in the 1850's.
Based mainly on the First Edition of the O.S. Six-inch map.

L

England between 1769 and 1775, and it was some three years later when the first effective cotton-spinning mill in the West of Scotland was established at Rothesay. It was quickly followed by others, at Anderston, Barrhead and Johnstone for example, their sites being determined primarily by the availability of water power—the country-side round Glasgow abounded in swift-flowing streams.

Between 1787 and 1834 the number of cotton mills in Scotland increased from nineteen to a hundred and thirty-four, and by the latter date almost all of them lay within twenty-five miles of Glasgow. Many were founded in more outlying districts in the early stages of the industry's expansion, but apart from a few large mills, such as those at Catrine in Ayrshire, Ballindalloch in Stirlingshire, and Deanston and Stanley in Perthshire (all founded in the seventeen-eighties), the industry became localised mainly in Lanarkshire and Renfrewshire (Fig. 38). Its rapid growth is illustrated by the figures of raw cotton imports to the Clyde: between 1775 and 1790 the annual weight of cotton imported rose from 137,000 pounds to over one-and-three-quarter million pounds, and by 1810 was not far short of ten million pounds. Cotton was now Scotland's leading industry and it almost entirely displaced linen and silk in the west. The value of the Scottish cotton industry's annual output by 1814 was almost £7m., or about four times that of the linen industry.

In view of the tremendous output of yarn from the spinning mills, the hand-loom weavers' position was initially an enviable one. These craftsmen, who worked at first mainly in their own homes, were employed either by the great mill-owners or, more usually, by middle-men known as 'manufacturers': merchants who bought the yarn, employed the weavers as piece-workers, and marketed the finished cloth. The system had its origins in the eighteenth-century domestic linen industry, and continued to be the common form of organisation in the cotton industry until the eighteen-forties. Many of the villages in the surrounding countryside originated at this period as weaving settlements. So profitable were the activities of these 'manufacturers' that many of them became large factory-owners themselves: thus Glasgow's 'tobacco lords' were succeeded by a new aristocracy of 'cotton kings'—David Dale, of the New Lanark mills, the Monteiths of Anderston, the Finlays and Buchanans of Catrine. It was the age of the 'self-made' man, of whom David Dale was one of Glasgow's more pleasant examples. The son of a small shop-keeper in Stewarton, Ayrshire, he began life as a herd-boy, and then entered the linen trade. By 1783 he had attained such prominence in the commercial life of Glasgow that, despite his humble origins, he was appointed vice-president of the city's newly established Chamber of Commerce. Its president and founder, Provost Patrick Colquhoun, was in contrast a member of the merchant aristocracy of the tobacco period, who had been brought up in affluent circumstances. David Dale's acceptance into what had been virtually a hereditary hierarchy was more than a personal triumph: it marked the birth of a new line of 'merchant princes' in Glasgow and the passing of an era. Some thirty years later even the office of Provost was to be attained by a weaver's son—Henry Monteith. His father, James Monteith of the Anderston Mills (founded in 1780), and David Dale were among those Glasgow manufacturers who invited Arkwright, the inventor of the spinning frame, to visit Glasgow in 1783—a year which marks not only the end of the American War but also Scotland's full entry into the Industrial Revolution. Arkwright was associated with Dale in the founding three years later of the New Lanark cotton mills, which by 1793 were the largest of their

162

kind in Britain. Their 1,300 workers included paupers from various parishes in Scotland, and orphans—more fortunate than most factory children—whose diet, clothing, accommodation and secular and religious training were carefully supervised by Dale. After the famous social reformer, Robert Owen, became his son-in-law and took over the mill, New Lanark was internationally known as a model of industrial welfare. Many of the schemes usually credited to Owen, however, were originated by Dale.

Such benevolent paternalism was a feature of the early stages of the Industrial Revolution, when dependence on water power led to the siting of factories in the open country and the creation of often entirely new village communities, whose welfare was felt to be the personal responsibility of the mill-owner. This close relationship between employer and workers tended to be obscured with the concentration of the factories in urban areas following the introduction of steam power, which made rapid headway in the early nineteenth century. The competitive conditions of the Napoleonic War period, the existence of a labour surplus in the towns, and the suitability of the newer textile machinery for operation by women and children, all contributed to a worsening of the situation. With the extended use of steam engines, too, the 'dark Satanic mills' of the towns cast their shadows over the surrounding countryside, lengthening shadows which reached out even to the cottages of the hand-loom weavers. There were vast numbers of these domestic workers in the small towns and rural areas around Glasgow: by 1791 as many as 15,000 weavers working for Glasgow 'manufacturers' were to be found within an area extending from Girvan in the south to Stirling in the north, besides many more in the villages of the south-west. The hand-loom then reigned supreme, but early experiments in power-loom weaving were being made in Glasgow before the end of the eighteenth century—in one of which the motive power took the unusual form of a large Newfoundland dog operating a treadmill. But although forty primitive power-looms were in operation in a Dunbartonshire mill (at Milton, near Bowling) in 1794, and 200 similar looms were installed in John Monteith's factory at Pollokshaws in 1801, it was not until 1806-7 that the practicability of power-loom weaving was convincingly demonstrated, at Catrine in Ayrshire. Six years later the number of power-looms in Scotland had grown to 1,500 and although initially they were used only in weaving the coarser types of cloth their scope of application steadily widened. Between 1820 and 1829 their numbers swelled from 2,000 to 10,000 but as late as 1834 they were unknown in Paisley, a last stronghold of fine hand-loom weaving. Even there, however, their penetration was not long delayed: by 1838 one hundred and twelve power-looms were at work in Paisley.

In the latter year there were over 51,000 weavers in south-west Scotland, of whom all but 2,400 were producing cotton or mixed cotton and silk fabrics. Since 1815, however, the position of the plain weavers had drastically deteriorated, particularly in Glasgow and the smaller surrounding towns. The advent of the power-loom was not the only cause of their downfall: lack of organisation and overcrowding of the craft by unskilled labour were also responsible. The earnings of hand-loom weavers, which had been as high as thirty or forty shillings a week at the beginning of the century, were reduced by 1840 to about seven shillings and sixpence for first-class muslin weavers and four shillings and sixpence for less skilled craftsmen. They survived only at the extremes of their trade: the labour of the low-grade weaver became so cheap that he was sometimes employed in preference to machinery on certain work, while the top-ranking craftsmen, such as the Paisley shawl weavers, could produce specialised work with which machines could not compete. Even the Paisley shawl, alas, met its doom with the introduction of cheap *printed* imitations which killed its reputation as a fashionable, luxury product.

Fabric printing, dyeing and bleaching were by this time firmly established industries in Renfrewshire and Dunbartonshire. These branches, which owed their development mainly to the requirements of the cotton industry, were destined to outlive their parent, the chief area of their survival being the Vale of Leven in Dunbartonshire. The first stimulus to the erection of bleachfields had come from the linen industry. From 1727 onwards the laying out of new fields was encouraged by the Board of Trustees for Manufactures, which gave grants of £50 per acre toward the capital cost. £2,000 were distributed by the Board in 1729 among various Scottish bleachfields, the most extensive of which was that of Dalquhurn in the Vale of Leven, covering twelve acres. A second bleachfield in Dunbartonshire, at Cameron on Loch Lomond, also received a grant from the Board of Trustees in the same year. At both the Dalquhurn and Cameron fields, Dutch bleachers were employed at first to instruct the natives, for in the early eighteenth century the art was little understood in Scotland. Indeed, for many years considerable quantities of goods were sent from this country to be bleached in Holland, and it was not until about the middle of the century that Scottish bleachers began to compete successfully with their Dutch rivals. The concentration of the industry in the Vale of Leven was due primarily to the suitability of the water supply, Loch Lomond forming an unfailing natural reservoir of exceptional purity. Its outlet, the River Leven, not only afforded an abundant supply of water free from lime and other minerals, but also provided a convenient means of transport between the bleachfields and the Clyde, being navigable by lighters during part of the year. In Renfrewshire the River Cart performed a similar function, many of the fields being close to Paisley—the centre of weaving. A copious supply of water was of paramount importance in the early days of the bleaching industry when the entire process was dependent on natural agencies: the cloth was spread out on the grass fields, which were sheltered by beech hedges and intersected by narrow canals or trenches, from which the water was gathered in long ladles and sprinkled over the goods several times each day. In 1781 the Presbytery of Dumbarton was greatly perturbed by reports from some of its Kirk Sessions that the 'watering of cloth' was being performed in the Vale of Leven bleachfields even on the Sabbath. In introducing a seven-day week in defiance of Sabbatarian protests the bleachwork proprietors were endeavouring to reduce the lengthy period occupied by the natural bleaching process. About eight months of exposure to the action of air, sunlight and moisture were necessary; because of climatic conditions the work could be carried on during only part of the year, so that seasonal labour had to be employed. The bleachfields relied largely on the Highlands for a supply of workers, great numbers travelling south annually at the beginning of summer and returning to their homes for the winter months. Indeed this employment of seasonal Highland labour continued beyond the middle of the nineteenth century in connection with Turkey Red dyeing, many of the Highlanders eventually settling in the district.

In the latter part of the eighteenth century, however, the art of bleaching was revolutionised by the introduction of chemicals, which greatly speeded up the process and gave a new stimulus to development. Dr Roebuck's discovery of the use of vitriol

164

in 1749 reduced the bleaching period from eight to four months, and following the French chemist Berthollet's demonstration of the bleaching properties of chlorine in 1785 the old open-air process was gradually superseded by artificial methods. Within two years of Berthollet's discovery chlorine bleaching was tried out at Clober Field in Dunbartonshire, on the suggestion of James Watt, who is thus credited with the introduction of the process to Great Britain. The profitable results achieved at Clober led to similar experiments elsewhere, and the chlorine method was perfected with the introduction of chloride of lime—'bleaching powder'—by Charles Tennant, of St Rollox, in 1799. As the chemical process accomplished in a few hours what had formerly taken weeks or even months, and was independent of climatic and seasonal changes, its adoption resulted in an immediate expansion of the bleaching industry and a corresponding development in the associated trades of dyeing and printing. By the beginning of the nineteenth century there were more than sixty bleachworks in the Clyde basin, all using bleaching powder. Consequently, the fields were little used and returned to cultivation. As the century advanced, the preparation of cotton rather than linen cloth for dyeing and printing became the predominant concern of the bleachfields, and the three industries of bleaching, dyeing, and calico-printing tended to become integrated.

The art of fabric printing had been introduced into Scotland as early as 1738—twenty-six years before it was begun in Lancashire—but although large printworks were founded in 1742 at Pollokshaws it was not until the close of the eighteenth century that it became firmly established as a leading industry of the Clyde Valley. Its development was retarded at first by artificial restrictions imposed to protect the woollen industry. After 1774, however, a variety of factors combined to favour the industry's growth, the most notable of which was the rise of the Scottish cotton manufacture. It is significant that many of those responsible for the establishment of the early printfields had connections with the colonial merchant houses. Time-saving developments in bleaching processes, and in printing techniques—such as Thomas Bell's invention of cylinder printing in 1785—also contributed greatly to the industry's expansion at the end of the eighteenth century.

While the suitability of the water in Renfrewshire and the Vale of Leven was ultimately responsible for the localisation of calico printworks, it was not the initial attraction. Economic considerations formed the principal motive, for in the immediate vicinity of Glasgow wages were high, whereas an undeveloped rural area offered an almost unlimited supply of cheap labour. Thus William Stirling, son of a tobacco merchant, and his partners, whose original printworks were situated at Dalsholm on the Kelvin, decided to remove to Cordale in the Vale of Leven about 1770, finding 'the price of labour at Dalsholm unsuitable for their purpose'. By the early nineteenth century as many as seven different companies were engaged in calico-printing in Dunbartonshire alone, paying upwards of £40,000 annually in excise duties; in Renfrewshire, a further £10,000 per annum was paid. Further expansion came in the second quarter of the century with the introduction of Turkey Red dyeing, which was to become the great specialty of the Vale of Leven. The process had been first brought to Scotland at the end of the eighteenth century by a French dyer from Normandy, who successfully established it at the Glasgow works of Henry Monteith & Co. Its initial development was slow, the dye being at first applicable to thread and yarn only, but after 1810 it was gradually extended to piece goods or cloths, achieving immediate popularity because of the remarkable brilliance and durability of the colour. Turkey Red dyeing was begun in the Vale of Leven in 1827 at Croftingea; other bleachfields quickly followed suit. A tendency towards integration was becoming apparent throughout the industry, and by 1840 the three processes—bleaching, dyeing and printing—were generally being carried on simultaneously in the same factories. The development was bilateral, for while printworks had extended their operations to embrace bleaching and dyeing, many of the original bleachfields had found it profitable, having adopted Turkey Red dyeing, to begin printing their own cloth themselves. The bulk of the trade was now concentrated in eleven works in the Vale of Leven, controlled by nine firms, which were to show remarkable resilience to the periodic crises confronting the industry in subsequent years. (See Figure 38.)

DEVELOPMENTS ON THE RIVER

Hand in hand with the tremendous development of manufactures in the closing years of the eighteenth century went a recovery of trade, which led in turn to a recovery in shipping (Table XII). By 1787 the tonnage belonging to the Clyde was almost 60 per cent greater than it had been at the height of the tobacco trade, and double the figure to which it had fallen in 1783. Particularly significant at this time, as may be seen from the Table, was the eclipse of Port Glasgow by Greenock, where many improvements

Year	Glasgow	Port Glasgow	Greenock
	tons	tons	tons
1772–3	—	10,100	15,700
1783	—	7,600	9,600
1787	—	11,500	28,100
1810	2,600	13,100	40,000

TABLE XII. Tonnage of Shipping (excluding fishing boats) registered on the Clyde.

Sources: 1772-3, P.R.O. Customs, 17.
1783, Cleland: *Annals of Glasgow* (1816).
1787, B.M. Add. MS. 38429.
1810, Chalmers: *Caledonia*, III (1824).

to the quays and harbours were followed in 1818 by the opening of a magnificent new Custom House. Whilst many of the ships on the Greenock register belonged entirely to Greenock merchants, Glasgow firms such as Stirling, Gordon & Co., Buchanan, Steven & Co., and others, also had vessels there—and these were amongst the largest belonging to the Clyde.

166

The fleet thus established was made up partly of second-hand vessels bought from other ports, partly of prizes, and partly of newly built vessels. The Clyde could boast of a tradition of shipbuilding extending back to the days of Robert the Bruce and James IV, both of whom had used the banks of the Leven for the construction or repair of vessels, but this early promise was not fulfilled. In the late eighteenth century Dumbarton's staple industry was glass manufacture, and neither there nor elsewhere on the Clyde was shipbuilding of great significance. Boat-building, of river craft and fishing boats, had long been carried on, and Scott's of Greenock trace their origins to the early years of the eighteenth century; but before the American revolt Clyde shipping had been built mostly in North American or English ports. The great demand for ships after the war, and the loss of American sources (for only British-built ships, or prizes, qualified for British registry), stimulated the local industry. In the seventeen-eighties, about 3,000 tons of locally built vessels were added to the register each year, although the largest vessels—over 200 tons—were almost all obtained from other ports. The significance of the local industry may be judged from the make-up of the 1787 register (Table XIII).

This boom was short-lived. In the period 1799-1806 only about 1,500 tons a year were built, although about 9,000 tons were added to the registers each year. By this time large vessels built in Nova Scotia and Quebec figure prominently, as do those built in English ports, and prizes. But the registers do not tell the whole story: there was, in addition, a vast fleet of small boats trading and fishing in the sheltered waters of the

Place of Building	All vessels	Those built in 1787
	tons	tons
River Clyde	16,800	3,400
Other West Scotland	4,000	800
East Scotland	2,300	300
England and Wales	6,800	1,300
North America	4,100	50
Prizes, made free	8,100	—

TABLE XIII. Tonnage of Shipping owned on the Clyde, in 1787, according to place of building.

Source: MS. Registers, H.M. Customs.

river and Firth. These boats, and the many carpenters who built and repaired them, were to nurture Clyde shipping and shipbuilding.

Meanwhile other events, which were to determine the industrial and commercial geography of the Clyde basin for years to come, were taking place. Whilst Greenock improved its harbours and gained an ever larger share of Clyde shipping, Glaswegians pressed on with the improvement of their river. Having seen what the Golbornes had

167

been able to achieve, their aim now was not merely to add the Clyde to the long list of British 'inland navigations' but to bring at least the smaller sea-going ships into the city itself. From 1799 to 1826 Telford and Rennie were repeatedly advising on the work required. The original dykes were made more regular and, over long stretches, their ends were joined by a training wall or 'long dyke', thus reclaiming many acres of land. As early as 1806 Rennie proposed a wet dock in Glasgow, but it did not materialise. It was easier to extend the quays, on both banks, downstream. The increasing use of the canal basin at Port Dundas as a seaport for European trade, and of the river quays for Irish and coastal trade, led in 1808 to the admission of Glasgow as a port of registry. Many of the early registrations are of vessels plying to Europe from Port Dundas. By 1815 small foreign-going vessels were reaching the city by way of the Clyde, too, and in that year Glasgow became a head-port, no longer subordinate in any way to Greenock (which had by now displaced Port Glasgow as the head-port for customs). The legal quays extended to about 1,800 yards—900 on the canal and 900 at the Broomielaw. The Custom House at the Broomielaw was built in 1837. Its modest style and size still afford a marked contrast with those of its contemporary at Greenock. By the eighteen-thirties, vessels of up to 250 tons readily reached the Broomielaw. The channel had been reduced to no more than 150 feet wide in places, but a depth of seven or eight feet was available, even at low tide. Greenock was beginning to be neglected by the smaller vessels, though she still had virtual monopoly of ocean-going ships.

The success of Henry Bell's steam-boat in 1812 was followed in the eighteen-twenties by the development of steam tugs and dredgers. These could deal in a manner hitherto undreamed of with the two chief obstacles—adverse winds and lack of depth—so far preventing the full growth of Glasgow as a port. Thenceforth further deepening did not have to depend on the maintenance of a narrow channel, nor did passage of large sailing ships to Glasgow depend on favourable winds. There seemed to be no reasonable limit to the size of vessels for which the channel could be adapted. Consequently an ambitious scheme for a three-hundred-foot channel with a minimum depth of twenty feet was drawn up by David Logan, engineer to the Trustees of the Clyde Navigation. This was approved, with little modification, by James Walker, the London civil engineer, and was incorporated in a Parliamentary Bill which became law in 1840. The 'lines of improvement' so laid down have formed the basis of all subsequent work—a tremendous tribute to the vision and foresight of Logan. It was estimated that, to obtain the required width and depth, four-and-a-half million cubic yards of stone and clay would have to be excavated and a further three million removed by dredging. Springfield cotton mill—one of the largest in the city—Parkholm printing works and Wingate's engine works were amongst the properties which were to be bought and demolished.

Much of this work was carried out in the eighteen-forties and -fifties, but the ambition of a twenty-foot minimum depth proved difficult to attain. The increasing volume of trade persistently over-reached the capacity of the quays; vessels frequently had to berth three or four alongside one another, causing much delay and trouble. So demands for increased berthage pressed heavily on the resources of the Trustees: a wet dock had been authorised in 1840, but it proved easier to make temporary timber wharves, downstream, later to be replaced by masonry. Thus the length of the quays was more than doubled between 1840 and 1858, when it reached 4,400 yards. By this time a minimum depth of eleven feet at low water had been attained. Further major development by dredging had been inhibited since 1854, when the channel at Elderslie reached solid rock, and this obstacle was to delay the work for many years.

COAL AND IRON [1] AND SHIPS

Coal had been mined in the Clyde Valley at least as early as the sixteenth century, and by the first quarter of the seventeenth, primitive mining was an established industry in the Lanarkshire parishes of Bothwell, Cambuslang, Carluke, Lesmahagow and New Monkland. A small coastal and Irish trade in coal had been established from the Clyde, but Lanarkshire coal met competition from that shipped coastwise from Ayrshire, even at Greenock. In the eighteenth century, the iron, pottery and glass manufactures established for the colonial trade increased the local demand for coal. Thus John Dixon laid a wooden tram-road from collieries at Knightswood to the Clyde, to facilitate the supply of coal to his glassworks at Dumbarton, and when he opened 'coal-works' at Little Govan he similarly laid a tram-road to the Clyde at Springfield. The Monkland Canal, opened in 1790 (Fig. 39), was primarily intended to increase the supply and reduce the price of coal in Glasgow. By the junction with the Forth and Clyde Canal at Glasgow it gave the Lanarkshire coalfield direct access to the sea. Nevertheless, the remarkable development of coal-using industries in the Glasgow area continued to absorb the greater part of the output and shipments remained quite small.

The iron industry, in particular, demanded more and more coal. A measure of its progress may be obtained by comparing the annual imports of bar iron into Scotland in the middle of the century—about 1,500 tons—with the 6,000 tons which were imported in 1798. With increasing demand came increased prices. This, in turn, led the ironmasters to seek means of producing their own bar iron. Bloomery sites, of uncertain age, are still identifiable on the hills of Argyll and Bute (Fig. 42), though they probably represented a negligible production of iron. Charcoal blast furnaces had been established at Goatfield (Furnace), Loch Fyne, about 1770, and beside Loch Etive at Bonawe, by about 1750 (Fig. 37). These were exotic growths, using local charcoal to smelt Cumberland and Lancashire ore, the products being shipped back to England—though Bonawe is said sometimes to have smelted Ayrshire haematite. In the Forth basin the Carron Company—suppliers of iron goods to Glasgow merchants—had set up coke furnaces about 1760 to smelt local coal-measure ore and, in 1774, a company of Leith iron merchants, Wilson's, set up a foundry near the Lanarkshire-Midlothian border, taking advantage of local coal. About 1780 they erected a blast furnace here to make their own iron; a second furnace followed in 1787. In the same year the Cramond (nail-makers in Midlothian), the Dalnottar and the Smithfield Companies joined forces to make iron at Muirkirk in the hills on the Ayrshire-Lanarkshire border. Here, also, coke blast furnaces were soon at work and a foundry was established. In 1786 the Cramond Company set up the Clyde Ironworks on the outskirts of Glasgow to make iron for their Cramond works (Fig. 37). Thus the establishment of iron smelting was essentially an extension of an industry which had developed during the tobacco era.

Further developments were slow. Amongst the industries which grew up on the banks of the Monkland and Forth and Clyde Canals were several iron foundries. A company which had one of these set up blast furnaces at Shotts in 1802 to make their

169

own iron. About the same time the Dixon family, who had the Dumbarton glassworks and collieries in Govan, set up the Calder Ironworks near Coatbridge. Meanwhile, stemming initially from the mechanisation of the textile industry—the first steam engine in Glasgow to be used for cotton spinning was installed at Springfield, on the north bank of the Clyde, in 1792—and stimulated after 1812 by the development of steamboats, mechanical engineering was rising into prominence in Glasgow. It is easier to account for the success of the city's cotton weavers than to explain the rapid pre-eminence attained by the Glasgow engineer. Here there was no tradition of acquired skill and, indeed, the Scots had been more remarkable for their ingenuity in filching

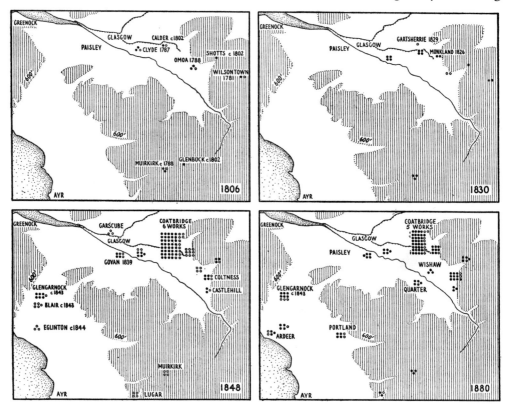

FIG. 39.   Blast furnaces in the West of Scotland, 1806, 1830, 1848 and 1880.
Furnaces *not* in blast are shown by open circles; the dates of commencement of the various furnaces are given; the Monkland and the Forth and Clyde canals are shown.

the inventions of others in the eighteenth century than for the display of any mechanical aptitude of their own. Even James Watt's notable invention in 1765 was the result of an attempt to improve an English machine and brought no immediate benefit to Glasgow but rather to Birmingham. Most of the early textile machinery was brought from England, and it was in maintaining and repairing it that Glasgow's first mechanics learnt their craft. They proved industrious apprentices and soon displayed an aptitude for modifying and improving the inventions of others. Glasgow became famous for its 'millwright engineers' and by the early nineteenth century there were several firms making textile machinery, the proprietors in many cases being themselves cotton manufacturers. Such firms and those making steam engines provided a local market for the as yet small, but growing, iron industry.

The manufacture of pig-iron was beginning to show some signs of concentration on the coal and iron-ore field of the Monkland parishes, even at the beginning of the century, and the construction of railways converging on the Monkland Canal at Coatbridge further emphasised this tendency which is clearly evident from the maps (Figs. 39 and 40). It was in the same district that Mushet first discovered the blackband

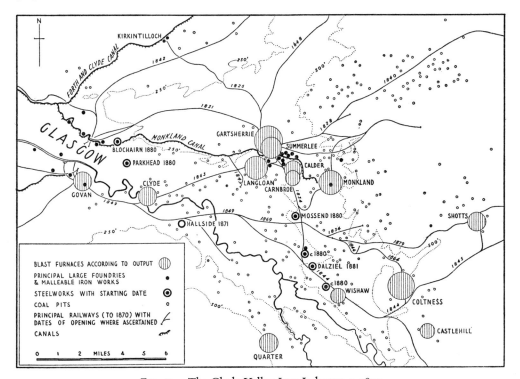

FIG. 40. The Clyde Valley Iron Industry, c. 1875.

Symbols for blast furnaces are graded according to estimated output at each works. At Coatbridge the number of furnaces *in blast* in 1880 was: Gartsherrie 12; Summerlee 6; Langloan 7; Carnbroe 3; Calder 4. The works at Monkland had 8 and the rest 5 each, except Wishaw and Castlehill which had 2. See also Figure 39.

ores, a discovery which was of little consequence until 1828 when Neilson patented an 'improved application of Air to produce Heat in Fires, Furnaces and Forges'—the hot blast. By 1835 almost every ironworks in Scotland had it and were said to be saving some five tons of coal for every ton of iron made. Blast furnaces sprang up like mushrooms. At Coatbridge the Bairds' new furnaces at Gartsherrie, blown in about 1830, were followed by many others (Fig. 39). Most of them congregated around Coatbridge, but Glasgow itself got an illuminating reminder of its new source of wealth with the lighting of 'Dixon's Blazes' at Govan in 1839. Much of the iron was shipped as pig, coastwise or overseas. A depression followed, but several factors soon led to a further phenomenal increase. About 1840 Neilson's patent expired; iron began to be applied to shipbuilding, and simultaneously came the enormous demand created by railway development, which reached its maniacal peak in the mid-'forties. Lanarkshire produced 426,000 tons of pig-iron in 1848, and in Ayrshire, where blackband ores had now been discovered,

Place of Building	All vessels		Steamers	
	1834–35	1850–51	1834–35	1850–51
	tons	tons	tons	tons
Wear	23,000	44,000	—	—
Tyne	4,500	4,900	—	350
Clyde	3,600	12,500	560	5,300
Thames	3,200	3,200	215	500
Mersey	3,000	3,100	150	100
All U.K.	71,500	112,700	1,180	6,270

TABLE XIV. Annual tonnage of merchant shipping, according to place of building, 1834–35 and 1850–51.
Source: Lloyd's Registers, 1836–37 and 1852–53.

a further 60,000 tons were made. The West of Scotland was rivalling the English Midlands and South Wales in the iron trade; the era of heavy industries had begun.

The launch of Henry Bell's *Comet* from Wood's yard at Port Glasgow in 1812 opened a new era in Clyde shipbuilding and, at the same time, revolutionised local communications. She was, according to the (perhaps incredulous?) clerk who registered her, 'a square stemmed carvel full-built passage boat with a Cock Pit, being furnished with a steam engine by which she sails'. This engine, of three horse-power, was made by John Robertson, a Glasgow mechanic. The sheltered estuary and Firth of Clyde, with its abundant short-range traffic, was an ideal proving ground for early steam vessels which were soon plying to Rothesay (1815), Campbeltown (1816), Belfast (1818) and Liverpool (1819). The *Comet* herself, fitted with a larger engine, ventured into more open waters in 1819 to inaugurate a West Highland service to Fort William via the Crinan Canal. By this time Clyde-built steamers were plying on the Thames and Mersey. In 1830 James Naismith patented his improved engine and the following decades saw great developments. According to Lloyd's Register (as distinct from the Registers kept by the Customs authorities), in 1835 more than half the tonnage of steamships built in Britain was built on the Clyde, although, otherwise, the Clyde was a minor centre of shipbuilding (see Table XIV). By the middle of the century the Clyde, whilst by no means rivalling Sunderland, had apparently overtaken all other centres. In 1818 Thomas Wilson had launched an iron boat, the *Vulcan*, on the Monkland Canal near Glasgow and, in 1831, an iron steamer—Neilson's *Fairy Queen*—was launched in Glasgow. Whilst the Clyde was not the sole pioneer of iron ships, the fortunate coincidence of a rapidly growing iron industry and a developing skill in marine engineering was soon to have remarkable results: in 1850-51 three-quarters of the tonnage of iron vessels built in Britain came from the Clyde—and most of them were steamers (Table XV). In the adoption of screw propulsion, too, the Clyde soon took the lead but wooden sailing vessels were not neglected, even in Glasgow itself (Fig. 41).

Place of Building	Iron hulls		Screw propulsion	
	1847–48	1850–51	1847–48	1850–51
	tons	tons	tons	tons
Clyde	1,050	6,070	460	4,360
Tyne	760	1,190	1,020	310
Wear	—	—	—	—
Thames	360	660	490	—
Mersey	650	110	—	—
All U.K.	2,870	8,020	2,000	4,870

TABLE XV. Annual tonnage of merchant shipping,
according to place of building, 1847-48 and 1850-51.
Source: Lloyd's Registers, 1848, 1849, 1851, 1852.

This was not all. Not content with pioneering the new building methods, Glasgow firms helped to finance the introduction of the new types of vessel, both in home waters and overseas. In 1839 Glasgow and Liverpool interests joined forces in founding the Cunard Company, to provide a regular steamer service to North America. The contract for the hulls and engines of the first four vessels was entrusted to one of the partners, Robert Napier of Glasgow. The wooden hulls were constructed under his supervision by four different builders. With the success of these vessels Clyde shipbuilding really came into its own.

EXPANSION OF IRON, STEEL AND SHIPBUILDING

The greatly expanding use of iron in Britain and overseas resulted in a tremendous growth of the Scottish iron smelting industry. Between 1848 and 1870 production rose from 200,000 tons to 1,206,000 tons. By the second half of the century the industry was dominated by large concerns, usually with interests in coal and ironstone mining as well as in smelting and other branches; their control was directly centred in Glasgow. Whereas earlier the emphasis had been on cast iron, for which 'Scotch Pig' was peculiarly suited, after 1840 production of malleable iron expanded rapidly to fulfil the demands of railways and iron shipbuilding. Since the days of the colonial trade, when small malleable-iron works had been producing wrought iron goods from imported bar iron, this side of the industry had become moribund. Its revival in 1836 necessitated the importation of English labour, but from 1840 growth was rapid. Puddling furnaces and rolling mills were set up, almost all either in Coatbridge near the blast furnaces, or in Glasgow beside the canal or railways (Fig. 39). Although by 1853 about 136,000 tons of malleable iron were being produced in Scotland—and output continued to expand until the early 'eighties—this branch of iron production remained less important than in other parts of Britain. Moreover, as Table XVI shows, neither the cast-iron nor the malleable-iron trade ever consumed anything approaching the total output of Scottish blast furnaces; much was disposed of by coastwise shipments and foreign exports especially to America.

Date	Total production	Used in Scotland		Exported		
		Foundries	Ironworks *	Coastal	Rail	Foreign
1846	c. 600	200	80	193	?	119
1856–60	926	165	160	278	?	267
1868–70	1,141	249	198	237	26	367
1878–80	961	166	161	188	31	338

TABLE XVI. Distribution of Scottish pig-iron (thousands of tons).

* i.e. malleable-iron works; the figures are not the total production of malleable iron, which was 237,000 tons in 1878-80.

Source: Meade, Coal & Iron Industries, 1882.

In the eighteen-eighties the malleable-iron industry began a decline, initiated by the replacement of wrought iron by steel—a change which took place very rapidly. At the same time, production of local ores, which in any case were not suitable for the acid steel processes, fell rapidly; even when basic processes were developed ore still continued to be imported, for the best local seams were by now exhausted and what was left was expensive to extract. Thus increasing competition at home and abroad, growing dependence on imported ores and—rather as in the cotton industry—failure to keep abreast of technical progress, gradually had their effect. On the other hand, steel manufacture went forward at a great rate. The Steel Company of Scotland had established the first Siemens open-hearth furnaces at Hallside in 1871 (Fig. 40). Other steelworks were opened in the Motherwell area—the most notable being Colvilles (Dalziel, 1880), which had previously been a malleable-iron works. The long-established Blochairn Ironworks, on the banks of the Monkland Canal, and the Parkhead Forge, newly acquired by William Beardmore, were both converted in 1880. In the main, the ironmasters of the Coatbridge district were unwilling to change and Motherwell became the centre of the new industry, with Glasgow itself not far behind. In 1885 the output of steel was 241,000 tons; by 1892 it had about doubled and by 1914 it reached almost 1·5 million tons. But much of the pig-iron used was now made from imported ore—about 1·8 million tons were brought into the Clyde in 1913, by which time only

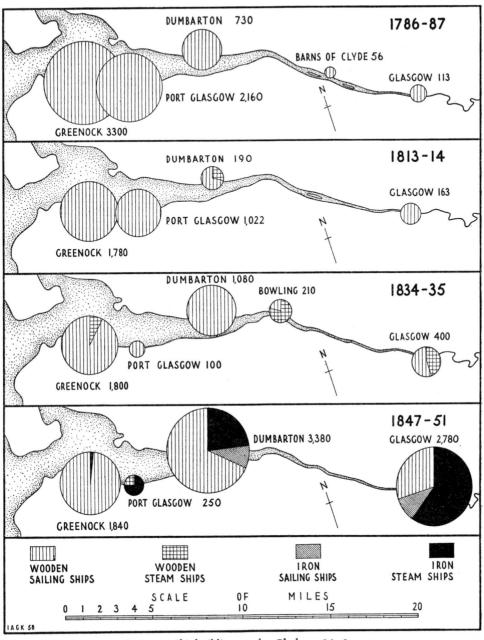

FIG. 41. Shipbuilding on the Clyde, 1786-1851.
Figures are tonnages built annually, to which circles are proportionate.
Sources: 1786-87 and 1813-14, Official Registers.
1834-35 and 1847-51, Lloyd's Registers.

about 600,000 tons were mined in Lanarkshire. Moreover, some of the steelworks used imported pig-iron. Thus the steel industry was by no means as firmly rooted in local raw materials as had been its predecessor. Its inland location, whilst convenient for coal supplies, added carriage to the cost of ore, a factor which was to become more significant as time passed.

	Sail		Steam	
	Wood	Iron	Wood	Iron
	tons	*tons*	*tons*	*tons*
Glasgow	690	120	170	1,800
Dumbarton	2,310	290	—	790
Port Glasgow	50	50	—	140
Greenock	1,750	—	—	20

TABLE XVII. Average annual tonnage of shipping built and registered at Lloyd's, 1847-51.

Source: Lloyd's Registers, 1848-52.

It was the demands of Glasgow owners as much as the growing reputation of Clyde-built steamships that contributed to the rise of Clyde shipbuilding in the second half of the nineteenth century. Indeed, as Table XVII shows, building of wooden sailing ships was more important than that of iron steamships at the middle of the century. Dumbarton seems to have been the first point of growth, though the old-established industry at Port Glasgow and Greenock still continued (Fig. 41). By the 'sixties, Glasgow, having established itself both as a centre of small iron steamship construction and as a deep-water port, began building sailing vessels in large numbers, for as yet steamships were not well suited to the longer trading routes on account of their voracious coal consumption. But the fame and subsequent prosperity of the Clyde-built ships were to stem from the development in Glasgow of marine engines and iron hulls. Several of the most famous firms originated as millwrights or ironfounders and later took to building their own hulls. The Napiers, David of Camlachie and his cousin Robert, J. & G. Thomson, and John Elder & Co. (now Fairfields) all originated in this way. On the other hand, Stephens, now of Linthouse, were builders of wooden sailing ships on the east coast who, seeing the remarkable increase of shipping on the Clyde, moved in to help supply the demand and to adopt the new techniques.

Until the late eighteen-seventies steel, though superior to iron, was little used for ships. It was regarded with distrust largely owing to the difficulty of obtaining really reliable plates and bars. Both an improvement in quality and a substantial reduction in price were necessary before it could be generally adopted; the inventions of Siemens and of Thomas and Gilchrist were decisive. But technical developments alone were insufficient to dispel the doubts of conservative builders; men of vision, having the courage to experiment with the new material and to stake their reputations on the out-

176

come, were required to smooth the way for the cautious and the sceptical. Such pioneers were found on Clydeside in John Elder, James and George Thomson and—most notably—William Denny. It was the latter who, in 1879, launched the *Rotomahana*, the first ocean-going steamer to be built of mild steel. He was tireless in his advocacy of the new material, expounding its advantages and capabilities in papers read before professional societies and institutions. Of the 18,000 tons of steel shipping launched on the Clyde in 1879, nearly half came from his yard. By 1889, 326,000 tons of steel shipping were launched whilst that of wood and iron had dropped from 157,000 to 9,000 tons. This was a development unequalled in any other shipbuilding area. These developments were paralleled by others in the field of marine engineering. Improvements in the quality of steel about 1878 led to vital developments in boilers and engines. As long as boilers had to be of iron—and to satisfy the Board of Trade and Lloyd's they had to be of exceptionally thick iron—little progress toward higher steam pressures and economy of fuel was possible. The first 'water tube' boilers were not a success and A. C. Kirk, of Napiers, who attempted to develop a triple expansion engine in the 'seventies was temporarily thwarted for this reason. In 1874, boilermakers still had great distrust of steel, but improvements during the next four years led to its adoption not only in hulls but also in boilers. Its use enabled the safe limit of steam pressure to be raised and thereafter the development of marine engines in power and efficiency was remarkable. This was the death knell of the sailing ship, even in the distant grain and tea trades.

The close interrelation of iron and steel-making, shipbuilding and marine engineering was reflected in an increasing tendency towards integration among Clydeside firms in the latter part of the nineteenth century. As early as 1851 the inconvenience of sending hulls away from Dumbarton to be engined elsewhere led Peter Denny to form a partnership with John Tulloch, a Greenock engineer, and John McAusland, of Dumbarton, in order to establish local engine works in the town. Until 1868 several of the engines they built were for other shipbuilding firms, such as Caird & Co., of Greenock, Barclay Curle, and Tod & McGregor, but thereafter they concentrated on serving their parent yard. In 1854, three years after the opening of Denny's engine works, the Dennystown Forge was erected in Dumbarton—an establishment comparable to the Lancefield, Govan, and Parkhead Forges in Glasgow, and the Clyde Forge in Greenock. This enterprise was closely associated with the shipyard and engine works, two of its original four partners being James Denny and John Tulloch. The interconnection between the partnerships was maintained in after years, and eventually in 1918 the shipyard and engine works were combined into a private limited company, William Denny & Brothers, Ltd. Following the adoption of steel in shipbuilding, a development in which, as we have seen, the Dennys were pioneers, an open hearth furnace for the production of steel castings was added to the Dennystown Forge; by the close of the nineteenth century it was in a position to supply practically anything in forged steel and iron required by the shipbuilding and engineering industry. The integration of steel production with shipbuilding and marine engineering was seen in a more spectacular form in 1899 when John Brown & Co., the great Sheffield steel firm, acquired the Clydebank Engineering and Shipbuilding Works. The Clydebank company was itself the successor of J. & G. Thomson, engineers (1846) and shipbuilders (1851), of Finnieston and Cessnock Bank. Another notable example of the conjunction of steel-making with shipbuilding was provided by William Beardmore, the nucleus of whose empire was the Parkhead Forge, which had been established in 1842 by Robert Napier. About 1860 it was taken over from Napier by his son-in-law, William Rigby, in partnership with Beardmore. Meanwhile the shipbuilding firm of Robert Napier & Sons, of Govan, had been formed in 1853, and it too passed into the control of Beardmore's in 1900, whereupon they established a new shipyard on an extensive site at Dalmuir, downstream from Clydebank.

By the late nineteenth century other branches of engineering had also become prominent on Clydeside. Some, such as the manufacture of pumps of all kinds, electrical engineering and instrument making, were related to existing local industries, especially shipbuilding. Others, such as locomotive construction, had a local history at least as old as that of iron-steamship building and, like marine engineering, owed their origin to the enterprise of millwrights and engineers employed originally in connection with the textile industries. Indeed, at first specialisation was not the rule. The millwright, James Cook of Tradeston, for example, besides looking after textile machinery, made engines for early steamships and, eventually, specialised in sugar machinery. All these depended heavily on overseas markets; almost two-thirds of the locomotives built in the Glasgow area at the end of the century went for export, and so did much of the sugar machinery. Supplies of raw materials, skilled labour and port facilities soon attracted industries from other parts. One of the three locomotive firms which became the North British Locomotive Co. had migrated from Manchester. About 1870 the American firm of Singer commenced making sewing machines in Bridgeton; soon they were building a huge new factory at Clydebank, for which another American firm, Babcock and Wilcox, supplied and installed the boilers. Babcock and Wilcox, in their turn, began manufacture on Clydeside, first in the Singer factory and later at Renfrew and Dumbarton. Thus, by the end of the century, the age-old connection with America was appearing in a new form. Subsequently migration into the Clyde basin of American engineering firms has become a very real factor in industrial development, and is now almost a tradition.

TEXTILES OVERSHADOWED

The spectacular rise of the coal and iron industries in the eighteen-forties should not be allowed to obscure the fact that, in terms of numbers employed, they still remained comparatively insignificant. The 1851 Census (Table XVIII) makes the position quite clear. Textile workers still outnumbered those in mining and iron manufacture by almost three to one. The print and bleachfields, the spinning mills, hand-loom weaving and, later, the power-loom factories still remained the main attraction for immigrants from the Highlands and from Ireland as well as from other parts of Scotland. Indeed, until almost the end of the century textiles were to remain the most important major industrial group, in terms of employment, in the Clyde basin (Table XVIII). Families dependent on these industries had swollen the population of the three counties from 216,000 in 1801 to 626,000 in 1841. Exactly half this increase was in Glasgow, which was essentially a textile town.

In the early eighteen-fifties the cotton industry was enjoying boom conditions, and there was little to suggest an imminent collapse. Since 1830, however, there had been indications of a slowing of expansion, partly because of an increasing diversion of

178

capital and enterprise into the rising heavy industries. Although the hand-loom weavers were now in a desperate plight, there was an important category of hand workers as yet unaffected by the competition of the machine—the sewed-muslin makers. Glasgow

	Textiles	Iron Industries	Mining	Shipbuilding
	per cent	*per cent*	*per cent*	*per cent*
TOWNS				
Glasgow	25	5	1	—
Paisley	29	1	—	—
Greenock	5	7	—	3
COUNTIES (excluding above towns)				
Lanark	17	2	14	—
Renfrew	53	3	3	1
Dunbarton	32	2	3	1
Thousands of persons	96·6	20·4	16·9	1·7

TABLE XVIII. Percentage of occupied population engaged in major industries, 1851.

Source: Census, 1851.

was the nucleus of a vast industry employing domestic workers, who embroidered, by hand, designs printed on various fabrics, such as book muslins, mulls or cambrics. At first the printing also was a manual process, using blocks, but after 1837 a lithographic press was applied to this work and as a result the industry expanded enormously. It reached its peak in 1857, when the four largest Glasgow firms were employing between 120,000 and 150,000 women in the city, in surrounding counties such as Ayrshire, and even in Northern Ireland. About 200,000 workers were estimated to be employed by all the Glasgow firms. In that year, however, the industry received a fatal blow with the failure of the Western Bank, which was financing most of the firms in the trade. By the end of the century the sewed-muslin makers had disappeared entirely, their hand-craft having been finally ousted by embroidery machines developed in Switzerland.

The financial crisis of 1857 had repercussions throughout the cotton industry, but by 1861 there was every sign of a recovery of prosperity, when the outbreak of the American Civil War brought the industry to a standstill. The southern states had been the chief source of supply of raw cotton, so that as a result of the neglect of its cultivation during hostilities, and the blockade of the Confederate ports, a serious cotton famine soon overwhelmed the industry in Britain. Imports of raw cotton into Scotland fell off from 172,000 cwt in 1861 to 10,000 in 1862, and 7,000 in 1864. As stocks diminished, the price of the fibre became prohibitive and widespread distress and unemployment resulted on Clydeside. The Scottish industry never recovered from the blow of the American War, partly because of its specialisation in fashionable muslins for which demand was marginal and fluctuating. Lancashire, on the other hand, produced coarser cloths for which there was a wider market at home and overseas. In any case, competition from England had become increasingly keen, and the cheapening of transport through railway development meant that Scottish manufacturers now had to meet their southern rivals on equal terms. Considerable expenditure of capital would have been required to bring the rather obsolete machinery of most mills to the requisite level of efficiency. Mechanical development seems to have been more rapid in the English factories, and Scottish mill-owners made little attempt to equal them in economy or speed of production. It was possibly not so much a question of lack of enterprise as one of lack of capital and manpower, which were tending more and more to be diverted into the prosperous heavy industries. One of the penalties of the West of Scotland's specialisation in cotton had been the loss of older branches of textiles, which might have acted as a buffer in time of adversity. Both the linen industry and silk throwing had been almost completely ousted from the Clyde basin during the hey-day of cotton's prosperity.

As for the woollen industry, the area (unlike Ayrshire and the Border counties) had never been one of its traditional centres; but in one branch—carpet manufacture—there was some notable development in the nineteenth century, particularly after 1839. It was in that year that James Templeton, a Paisley shawl manufacturer, came to Glasgow to exploit for carpet-making the invention of his fellow-townsman, William Quigley, a shawl weaver who had developed an improved method of making chenille. The success of Templeton's business led to the establishment of other carpet factories in the area, mostly by men who were at one time his employees. Besides the original concern of James Templeton & Co., only one of these firms, John Lyle & Sons (founded in 1853), still survives in Glasgow. With the application of the power-loom to the manufacture of Brussels carpets in 1856, and to chenille carpets in 1884, it became possible to employ a high percentage of female labour. This was fortunate for the industry, as the growing prosperity of heavy engineering in the area in the latter part of the nineteenth century was exerting an ever-increasing attraction on the available male labour force. Reduced manufacturing costs, the advent of mass production, and standardisation of designs, brought continued expansion in the carpet industry, which had now taken the place of cotton as the chief employer of textile labour in the district. Some of the new carpet factories, indeed, were housed in former cotton works. By 1913 almost 3,000 workers were employed in Glasgow in carpet and associated manufactures.

While the cotton industry in its main branches largely disappeared by the end of the century, some of the mills were eventually adapted to carpet-making, paper-making and other industrial processes. Textiles survived, and even expanded in specialised branches in particular localities, most notably, thread-making at Paisley and calico-printing and dyeing in the Vale of Leven. By 1860 the position in the Vale of Leven had altered considerably. The numbers employed in Turkey Red dyeing had risen and a tendency towards centralisation of control was becoming increasingly apparent. The depression caused by the American Civil War further hastened the process of amalgamation, for the smaller concerns lacked the stamina to recover from a prolonged crisis. By 1868, when the war was over, the whole Turkey Red industry of the Vale of Leven had become concentrated in the hands of three firms whose combined output of cloth and yarn was about thirty times the quantity produced in 1835, while the number of pieces printed annually had risen from 80,000 to 750,000 during the same period. The prosperity enjoyed by the Turkey Red manufacturers was due in no small measure to the new markets opened up by railway development in India, and it was shared to some extent by those calico-printing firms which had survived the crisis of the American Civil War. Ordinary calico-printing, however, had lost much of its former importance in the region by the closing decades of the nineteenth century. The printworks in the Vale of Leven together employed rather less than 1,500 workers in the 'eighties, whereas the three Turkey Red firms gave employment to fully four times that number, and the extent of their trade was correspondingly greater. There was keen rivalry between the different companies, particularly of the Turkey Red group, and before the century ended it became evident that something would have to be done to eliminate the evils of cut-throat competition. The announcement in 1897 of their amalgamation as the United Turkey Red Co. was greeted with surprise and consternation in the West of Scotland, for while it was generally admitted that the formation of such a combine would help to reduce costs and meet foreign competition, it was feared that it might prove inimical to the interests of the workers. Not long afterwards the flotation was announced in 1899 of the Calico Printers' Association, a mammoth combine with its headquarters in Manchester. Some forty-six calico-printing concerns had entered into contracts with the Association for the sale of their works, the businesses absorbed comprising about 85 per cent of the calico-printing industry of Britain. Many of the printworks taken over by the C.P.A. were subsequently closed, and the severe unemployment experienced, particularly in the Vale of Leven, during the early years of the twentieth century confirmed the popular distrust of the big combines. The fear that the larger number of English printing firms, and their preponderant influence in the Association, would ultimately cause Scottish interests to be treated as secondary seems to have been justified by after events. Within a very few years the management of the combine became centralised in Manchester, and many hitherto prosperous concerns in the West of Scotland were closed down.

The survival of the textile-finishing industry despite the collapse of the cotton trade in the West of Scotland may be attributed in part to the more enterprising spirit shown by the dyeing and printing firms in meeting the challenge of outside competition. Unlike the majority of the Scottish cotton manufacturers, they made the best possible use of natural advantages, were quick to adopt new processes and more economical methods of production, and did not allow obsolescent machinery to cripple them in their fight against their competitors. It was not until the beginning of the present century, with the growth of serious foreign rivalry from Germany, America, and Japan, that this branch of local industry really entered its decline.

Paisley's thread industry, today the most prosperous textile survival in the West of Scotland, had its origins—like the finishing of the Vale of Leven—in the early Scottish linen industry, and was similarly based on imported skills from Holland. By the end of the eighteenth century both linen and silk thread were being made in Paisley, employing about 1,500 people. In the early nineteenth century, because of competition from other districts and the introduction of cotton thread (adopted as a substitute for silk, after its export from the Continent was banned by Napoleon in 1806), the industry underwent a sudden decline but later the manufacture of cotton thread was taken up on a large scale and became one of the staple industries of the town. By the end of the nineteenth century over 5,000 workers were employed in the Paisley thread industry, which had become the monopoly of the Coats and the Clarks, who amalgamated in 1896. It was greatly stimulated by the introduction of the sewing machine in the second half of the century, especially after 1866 when the Singer Company established their first factory on Clydeside.

CHEMICAL INDUSTRIES

Intimately associated with the growth of textile manufactures in the region was the rise of the chemical industry. Its local origins might be traced back to the introduction of soap-making in 1667, but it owed its birth mainly to the requirements of the textile manufacturers in the second half of the eighteenth century; in the following century it became associated with the metallurgical and engineering industries; and in the later stages of the agricultural, as well as of the industrial, revolution the chemical industry has played an important part. Its ramifications, indeed, have become so widespread as almost to defy classification: there are few branches of industry today in which chemical processes and chemical workers, of one kind or another, are not to be found.

It is significant that two of the most prominent figures associated with the early chemical industry of Glasgow were themselves connected with the textile trade—Charles Macintosh and Charles Tennant. The former, whose father, George Macintosh was responsible for introducing the cudbear dyeing process to Glasgow, discovered a method of dissolving india-rubber and producing the 'waterproof' garments with which his name became linked. The waterproofing company founded by him in Glasgow in 1824 was subsequently removed to Manchester (his factory there is now owned by the Dunlop Rubber Co.), but the manufacture of waterproof articles remained an industry of importance in Glasgow. Charles Tennant revolutionised the art of bleaching by his introduction of 'bleaching powder' (chloride of lime), and in 1798 he founded beside the Monkland Canal in Glasgow his St Rollox works, an enterprise which later became the largest chemical factory of its kind in Europe. It was at the end of the eighteenth century also that Lord Dundas erected his works at Dalmuir for the large-scale manufacture of soda. This factory was built under the superintendence of that brilliant but unfortunate scientist, the ninth Earl of Dundonald, who had developed and patented a process for making soda from soap-makers' lyes, formerly regarded as useless waste. The Dalmuir Soda Works were subsequently purchased from Lord Dundas by Charles Todd & Co., who greatly enlarged them and extended the range of their products. Finally the concern was acquired by the Tennants of Glasgow, who removed the business to their St Rollox factory, and in 1856 the Dalmuir Works were dismantled.

Other important alkali works of later origin in the West of Scotland were those of the Eglinton Chemical Co. and the Irvine Chemical Co. in Ayrshire. About 1890 these works, together with the St Rollox factory, became part of a combination—the United

Alkali Company—formed by most of the alkali-makers in Great Britain. The 'rationalisation' which followed resulted in the suspension of alkali production in all the company's Scottish works. This was the culmination of a revolutionary change which had overtaken the chemical industry in the last quarter of the nineteenth century. After 1875 the Solvay or 'ammonia-soda' process rapidly gained favour so that by 1895 over half the quantity of salt used in alkali works was being treated by this new method. Unfortunately the Solvay process, based on the action of ammonium bicarbonate solution on strong brine, while chemically simpler and more economical and efficient than the older Leblanc method, was less suited to Scottish conditions. It could be more advantageously operated in districts like Cheshire, where supplies of brine could be pumped direct from the salt beds. Thus, mainly because of the lack of such extensive deposits of salt in Scotland, no production by the Solvay process was undertaken north of the Border. The development of electrolytic processes for the direct conversion of common salt into caustic soda and chlorine similarly contributed to the cessation of alkali manufacture in Scotland. Between 1876 and 1889 the quantity of salt used in Scottish alkali works fell from about 50,000 tons to just over 33,000 tons, and by the beginning of the present century there was not a single alkali work producing sodium carbonate, and only one manufacturing caustic soda. The cessation of soda manufacture, and other late nineteenth-century developments such as the abandonment of the preparation of alum from alum shale, were serious blows which tended to unbalance the chemical industries of the region.

Among the branches whose prosperity was declining at the turn of the century were the manufacture of ferrocyanides, the extraction of iodine from kelp, and the refining of sugar. The latter (which, like brewing and distilling, may be regarded to some extent as a chemical process) is of special interest because of its early origin in Glasgow; and because it is one of the few industries that, having once taken root in the city, did not survive there in some form. The sugar-refining industry, established in Glasgow in 1667, later moved downriver to Greenock where it was started in the second half of the eighteenth century. Until 1866 it was also carried on in Port Glasgow, but by 1875 the only refineries operating on the Clyde were those in Greenock. They then numbered thirteen, but by 1900 the number of firms was reduced to five. This decline in the last quarter of the nineteenth century was general throughout the refining industry in Britain, being attributed mainly to the bounties given to competitors by foreign countries, who were thus able to undersell home-produced sugar in the British market.

The manufacture of iodine from kelp (sea-weed ash) was another branch of local industry that was severely hit in the late nineteenth century by foreign competition. Dalmuir's association with the early chemical industry of the region was revived with the establishment of the Whitecrook Chemical Works at Clydebank about 1864. These works were originally erected for the extraction of iodine, bromine and potash salts. In the second half of the nineteenth century this factory was the cause of a widespread resuscitation of the kelp industry in the Hebrides and the West of Ireland. The first factory for processing the tangle ash was built at Bailemeadhonach on the Isle of Tiree in 1863, and the entire process was at first carried out there, but the difficulty of importing fuel led to the removal of the extracting works to the Clyde. Their establishment in the Clydebank district gave a great impetus to the trade of Bowling, which became the terminal port for the shipments of kelp from the Hebrides. Initially only iodine, bromine, muriate and sulphate of potash, and kelp salt were manufactured, but the factory was gradually extended to produce iodide and bromide of potassium for medicinal use, carbonate of potash, hydrochloric, nitric and sulphuric acids, saltcake, caustic soda, bleaching powder, and other chemicals for both the home and the over-seas markets. In the eighteen-eighties it was claimed that no other works in the United Kingdom or elsewhere combined the production of such a variety of chemicals, and that the North British Chemical Company made three-quarters of all the iodine used. In fact, the British manufacture of iodine at that period was entirely confined to two firms in Scotland, both situated on the Forth and Clyde Canal. Owing to a fall in the value of potash salts, as a result of the working of deposits abroad, among other factors, the production of iodine from kelp declined in the latter part of the century. By 1900 only four factories in Central Scotland—at Clydebank, Falkirk, Kilwinning and Bonnybridge—were engaged in the industry, as compared with twenty in 1846.

tried to improve river channel

TRADE, SHIPPING AND THE PORT

The set-back to the work of improving the river-channel, occasioned by the alarming discovery in 1854 of the Elderslie rock, was to last for many years. At first it was thought that the whole river would have to be diverted, but, eventually, a method of underwater blasting was developed. By 1869, after tremendous expense, a half-width channel, giving fourteen feet at low water had been cut. This controlled further major enlargement until 1886 when a full-width channel, giving twenty feet at low tide, was opened. This small obstruction, no more than 900 feet by 300 feet, had cost the Clyde Navigation Trust some £70,000 and had delayed the achievement of Logan's goal by many years. One may reflect, however, how fortunate it has been for Glasgow that this was the only serious obstacle ever encountered in nearly two hundred years of work. Had the natural channel been floored by solid rock, like that of the Wear, for example, improvement would have been prohibitively expensive; Greenock might have become another Liverpool and Glasgow its Manchester.

Trade did not await the removal of this obstacle. 'Scotch Pig' was making Glasgow iron merchants famous throughout the world. Coal exports, whilst small, were increasing. But even at the end of the century exports of coal and iron were still of less value than those of textiles (Table XIX) though some of the latter were Lancashire goods which had been sent to Scotland for finishing. Despite the depression of the eighteen-seventies the value of exports doubled between 1868 and 1900. The tonnage of vessels arriving in the Clyde was increasing every year, and, as steamships gradually displaced sailing ships, so a steadily greater proportion of the total passed Greenock and Port Glasgow. For a while shipments of rail-borne coal and pig-iron kept Greenock busy, but as railway facilities improved in Glasgow, this trade, at its peak in the eighteen-seventies, declined, as, for the same reason, did Port Glasgow's once large import of timber. A final, unavailing, attempt to obtain a share in the rising tide of Clyde prosperity may be discerned in the construction at Greenock of the James Watt Dock and the Great Harbour in the 'eighties and 'nineties. But this was the period of Glasgow's prosperity and, in particular, that of the Glaswegian ship-owners. The colours of such firms as Clan Line, City Line, Anchor Line and Henderson's were to be seen in every port of the world.

184

Glaswegians could even boast that Clyde-built vessels, owned in the city, were opening up the trade and navigation of regions as distant as the Irrawaddy. The tonnage registered in Glasgow had trebled between 1830 and 1850; in the following half-

	1868	1888	1900	1913
	£000	£000	£000	£000
Textiles	6,640	6,258	5,714	10,909
Coal, etc.	118	315	1,198	1,604
Iron and Steel	1,045	2,229	2,966	5,953
Machinery	331	1,132	2,227	5,138
Ships *	—	—	c. 2,100	c. 2,600
ALL EXPORTS				
Glasgow	9,719	14,461	18,109	35,917
Greenock	375	177	192	615

TABLE XIX. Value of foreign exports of Glasgow (including Bowling and Dumbarton) and Greenock (including Port Glasgow), in thousands of pounds, sterling.

* Not available before 1899; figures shown are annual rates.

Source: Annual Statements of Trade.

century it increased ten-fold, and was to reach over two million tons before 1914. It was the local demand for ships as much as the pioneering of new techniques in building that nurtured the new industry.

The first of the new shipyards in Glasgow had occupied sites just downstream of the quays at Stobcross, Kelvinhaugh and Govan, but, as the demand for trading berths continued to overtax the older quays, so new ones were built, eventually encroaching on the shipyards. The small Kingston Dock, opened in 1867, did little to ease the congestion and by 1870 the quays had been extended, almost without a break, to the Kelvin on the north bank and to Govan on the south (Pl. IV). It was at this period that several shipbuilders began to move to open country downriver. Barclay Curle and Connell moved from Stobcross to Whiteinch; Stephens, who had started at Kelvinhaugh, moved to Linthouse on the south bank (Pl. XIV) and, most famous of all, J. & G. Thomson, of Govan, gradually transferred their undertaking to a completely open site in Dunbartonshire. There they founded the town of Clydebank, where their successors were eventually bought by the Sheffield steelmasters, John Brown & Co. The Beardmore shipyard—the descendant of Robert Napier's—was established at Dalmuir in 1900.

These moves cleared the way for further harbour developments. In 1870 an Act was obtained authorising the construction of docks at Stobcross—now called Queen's

185

Ship builders moved further westwards

Dock. Like all Clyde 'docks' they are, in fact, tidal basins, the tidal range not necessitating dock gates. The same Act authorised the Trustees to subscribe £150,000 towards the construction of the Stobcross Railway, to link the docks with the coal and iron field served by the lately established railway systems. Hitherto the sharp break of slope, which had prevented a junction being made in Glasgow between the canals at Port Dundas and the Clyde, 150 feet below, had also prevented the railways from reaching the north bank of the Clyde. The Queen's Dock (Pl. XIII) was scarcely finished when ever-increasing trade necessitated construction of even more berths, and in 1883 a further Act authorised the making of Prince's Dock on the south bank at Govan; this came into use between 1892 and 1897, and was served by a branch of the Caledonian and Glasgow and South-Western Joint Railways, the Prince's Dock Railway, opened in 1903.

Meanwhile the Clyde Navigation Trust had been active in other ways as well. Increased trade brought ship-repairing as well as shipbuilding in its train and, for both purposes, three graving docks were opened at Govan (Pl. III). The first, a small one, came in 1875, the others in 1886 and 1898. Previous to 1868, the only dry docks on the Clyde had been at the mouth of the Kelvin in Tod & McGregor's shipyard, and at Greenock and Port Glasgow; none of these was big enough for the large vessels by now in use, and not infrequently Clyde ships had to resort to Liverpool for dry-docking. In 1868 a large dry dock had been opened at Greenock, and perhaps this spurred the Glaswegians into action. In 1884 the Trust inaugurated a flotilla of small passenger steamers—*Cluthas* —which, by 1900, were carrying about three million passengers annually from a number of piers between Victoria Bridge and Whiteinch—many of them no doubt the growing army of workers in the shipyards in the latter reach of the river. This service was superseded by the Underground and electric tramcars.

Changing conditions in the coal and iron industries were by now reflected in changes in the type of trade passing through the port. By 1900 coal shipments reached one-and-a-half million tons—treble the amount of only twenty years before; in addition more than a million tons were supplied for steamships' bunkers. Although the new railways enabled coal to be loaded at Queen's and Prince's Docks, where special facilities had been installed, these docks were primarily for general cargoes and could not cope with the increased mineral traffic, particularly when iron ore began to arrive in large quantities. Moreover, the growing population of the Clyde basin, coupled with the opening up of the grain lands of North America, had led to vastly increased imports of grain and flour. Consequently the Trust constructed another tidal basin at Clydebank— Rothesay Dock—opened in 1907, specifically for coal exports and ore imports. In the same year land was acquired at Meadowside, Partick, for the construction of a granary. By this time the development of the river banks was almost continuous, on the north downstream to Clydebank, and on the south to the farther boundary of Govan. Consequently, when the opportunity arose, the Trustees bought a large area of undeveloped land between Govan and Renfrew. Their foresight was not rewarded until a quarter of a century later when George V Dock was opened. This represents but a small part of the site then acquired. The changes which have since taken place in the industrial structure of Scotland, and of the Clyde basin in particular, make further dock development unlikely, but major improvements, such as the ore terminal at General Terminus Quay, continue to be made.

186

CONCLUSION

'The situation of this towne in a plentifull land, and the mercantile genius of the people, are strong signes of her increase and groweth, were she not checqued and kept under by the shallownesse, of her river, every day more and more increasing and filling up. . . .'   THOMAS TUCKER, 1656.

The industrial and commercial development of the lower Clyde basin in the eighteenth and nineteenth centuries more than justified Tucker's foresight. Indeed, the land proved even more plentiful than he anticipated, for he could have had little idea of the potentialities of coal and ironstone that lay beneath it. But, it cannot be too strongly emphasised, the 'increase and groweth' which were achieved in the two centuries owed far more to the enterprise of the people than to any combination of natural resources. This 'mercantile genius' is seen at every turn. Each opportunity was seized as it appeared, and if, as happened from time to time, one enterprise failed, then another was taken up. Thus trade with North America and the West Indies was followed by commercial expansion in Africa and the Far East; the development of textile manufacture, linen and later silk, followed and largely ousted by cotton, is seen as merely the logical extension of mercantile enterprise. After all, the hinterland of the Clyde offered little, if anything, more to the infant cotton industry than did that of the Bristol Channel. The eighteenth-century manufacture of wrought-iron ware was a similar development, the manufacturers later extending their interest to pig-iron production and so initiating the large-scale exploitation of Lanarkshire minerals. Rather different in character, but closely allied to commercial expansion, was the technical genius of such people as Henry Bell and John Robertson with their marine engine, of Neilson with the hot blast, of the Napiers, the Thomsons, the Dennys and the Elders—to name only a few of the pioneers of shipbuilding and marine engineering—and of many others. But it was the requirements of local ship-owners and not merely technical achievements, that first stimulated shipbuilding. Inventions, all too often, require an expanding demand for their proper and rapid development, as, for example, was found by James Watt: ideas are more mobile than industry. On the Clyde, in the nineteenth century, the two came together with remarkable results.

The part played by textile industries should not be forgotten (Table XX). As has been shown, these were the industries which first established a substantial industrial population in the Clyde basin. Industrially, Glasgow remained a textile town until almost the end of the century, as did most of the urban settlements of Renfrewshire and many of those in Dunbartonshire (see Table XX). It was only in the 'nineties that the coal, iron and engineering industries together overshadowed the textiles, for, true to tradition, although cotton weaving had declined, thread and the finishing trades prospered and the carpet industry expanded. Even today, the textile industries play a more important part in the economic life of the region than is commonly supposed; and even the casual visitor cannot fail to be impressed by the substantial legacy of former cotton mills now put to some other use.

A reflection of the dependence of manufacturing industries on overseas markets may be detected in their remarkable concentration on Glasgow. About half the textile factories were in the city and many of those in the surrounding countryside belonged to Glasgow firms. Outwith the city only Paisley, with its specialties—silk, shawls and thread—ranked as a large centre in its own right. It was singularly fortunate that the industrial and commercial city, so established, should also be well able to take advantage of the coal and iron field which lay mainly to the east, complementing, as it were, the textile districts to the west. Thus Glasgow became a centre of iron industries and trade

Major Industries	1851	Percentage change 1851–81	1881	Percentage change 1881–1911	1911
	000		*000*		*000*
Textiles	96·6	−18·0	78·6	−17·4	61·2
Iron and Steel	20·4	+ 7·8	28·2	+92·0	120·2
Mining	16·9	+17·0	33·9	+36·1	70·0
Shipbuilding	1·7	+12·6	14·3	+40·5	54·8

TABLE XX. The changing industrial structure, 1851–1911. Thousands of persons employed in the major industries in the counties of Lanark, Renfrew and Dunbarton, 1851, 1881, and 1911.

Source: Census Reports, 1851, 1881, 1911.

as well as of textiles; towards the end of the nineteenth century the expansion of iron, steel and engineering industries, also largely for overseas markets, accompanied the stagnation and slow decline of the textile group.

If the commercial and industrial development of Clydeside in the eighteenth and nineteenth centuries more than justified Thomas Tucker's views, then the improvement of the river must have surpassed his wildest expectation. Where, in his day, the channel could be forded at low tide there was now depth enough for the largest vessels afloat, vessels, moreover, of a size undreamed of in the sixteenth century and built on the banks of the river whose shallowness he deplored. Thus, to her functions as a manufacturing and commercial city Glasgow was able to add those of a port.

However, even before the First World War there were some ominous signs that further expansion might not be the lot of the heavy industries. More and more foreign ore was being used in the blast furnaces. The splint coals were approaching exhaustion and local coal of metallurgical coking quality was not readily obtained; in any event improved techniques were progressively reducing the amount of coal required to produce a ton of iron; steel had largely replaced cast and wrought iron, and increasing quantities of industrial scrap were available as raw material in place of the products of the blast furnaces. The introduction of motor vessels using oil fuel augured ill for the enormous trade in bunker coal on the Clyde. Finally, the tremendous dependence of the shipyards on orders from foreign owners was bound to decline as shipbuilding became established overseas. All these trends were to be re-emphasised after the First

188

World War, and this time there was no expanding world market for the Clyde merchants and manufacturers. Moreover, financial control of many firms had passed partly or wholly out of Scottish hands and, when the U.K. largely replaced the overseas market, the Clyde basin was not so well placed to serve it. The closure of chemical works was to be repeated in other fields, such as shipbuilding and textiles, in the twentieth century. Nevertheless, and despite substantial emigration, the concentration of industrial experience, labour and port facilities in the Clyde basin was to remain a powerful influence in years to come.

1. Mining is not specifically dealt with here, being the subject of another chapter.

THE GROWTH OF THE ENGINEERING INDUSTRIES

JAMES ORR

Senior Lecturer in Mechanical Engineering, University of Glasgow

AND

SARAH C. ORR

Lecturer in Political Economy, University of Glasgow

IN spite of the variety of industries represented in Glasgow, the city is essentially the centre of an area renowned for its heavy industries and its economic fortune has long been closely linked with these industries. The characteristics of the industrial structure of the area are the creation of the second phase of the Industrial Revolution—the phase based on coal and iron and the application of steam power. Of this period of development the engineering industry is itself a product. It is true that the earliest textile machines were made mainly of wood, but it is in the development of the iron industry and the successful application of the steam engine that modern engineering has its origin. Thus it is only natural that the two—Glasgow and the engineering industry—should be closely linked. Much of the industry is dependent, directly or indirectly, on the shipbuilding for which the Clyde is primarily noted, but this is by no means the whole story. Today there are few branches of engineering in which Glasgow cannot claim a share.

The history of the engineering industry is inseparable from the history of industrial development in general, to which it is indispensable. Virtually every new industrial development has its counterpart in some further specialisation of engineering, from the main branches of which may be read a fair account of Glasgow's economic history. The accumulated engineering skill, in turn, has been extended to practically all branches of the industry and has itself been a major force in the development of new industries.

The multiplicity of activities and products of the modern engineering industry makes the task of classification and the treatment of its historical development exceedingly difficult. Moreover, most firms produce a variety of products and many belong to more than one of the main sections of the industry. Historically, also, the old-established firms have often radically changed their activities and moved from one section of the industry to another. In what follows, an attempt has been made to pick out the main strands of development in the Glasgow engineering industry rather than produce a systematic and detailed account of it.

EARLY DEVELOPMENT

In the early years of the nineteenth century the Glasgow engineering industry was concerned primarily with the manufacture of steam engines. By far the largest number of these were for the textile industry, where the use of steam power spread rapidly during the first half of the century. It was only natural that the new techniques should be applied to the established industry, particularly when that was the one in which the Industrial Revolution had started. Thus the manufacture of textile machinery became a specialised branch of the Glasgow engineering industry at an early date. Some of the firms concerned started as textile firms. In the days before the introduction of steam power it was customary for such firms to manufacture their own machines and not uncommon to find the two trades carried on together. In the new steam age some of these firms chose to concentrate entirely on machinery. One such firm was that of Houldsworths, whose Anderston foundry was attached to their cotton mills. One of the Houldsworths eventually left the cotton industry and founded the Coltness Ironworks.

Another specialised branch which similarly grew out of a long-established industry was that producing sugar machinery. In the nineteenth century mechanisation was applied to the industry and the special machinery was produced on a steadily increasing scale. By the middle of the century Glasgow was exporting machinery to all the sugar-producing countries of the world. Three firms still producing sugar machinery, Blairs Ltd, Duncan Stewart & Co. Ltd, and Mirrlees Watson & Co. Ltd, were all founded in the period 1838-40.

The first major new development, however, was the establishment of locomotive engineering, a branch destined to occupy an important place in the city's economy. The manufacture of locomotives developed as steam engines gradually replaced horses over the period of railway construction. At first supplementary to the canals, by the eighteen-thirties they were established as an alternative means of transport for both goods and passengers. At first a number of general engineering firms experimented with the manufacture of the new locomotive, and some for a time combined marine and locomotive engineering. From the eighteen-fifties, however, locomotive engineering became a separate, specialised branch of the industry. The first to specialise solely in this branch of engineering was the firm of Neilson & Company, of the Hyde Park Locomotive Works. The firm was founded as a general engineering concern in 1836 by a son of James Neilson, the inventor of the hot blast, and first started the manufacture of locomotives about 1843. It is one of the three firms which amalgamated in 1903 to form the present North British Locomotive Company.

At the same time, the rapidly developing coal and iron industries of Lanarkshire were making their own special demands on the engineering industry. The improvement and expansion of the iron industry in its turn was providing the basis for a growing number of engineering products. The position by the middle of the century was one in which the textile industry still held its own, but side by side with it there existed a rapidly expanding group of metal industries. The American Civil War, however, cut off supplies of raw material and thereafter young, expanding metal industries, which had been steadily gaining on the cotton industry, reigned supreme. Among these industries shipbuilding came rapidly to the front. Its expansion in the 'sixties, based on improvements in marine engines and the replacement of wood by iron, coincided with the decline of the cotton industry. The later replacement of iron by steel completed the linking of steel, engineering and shipbuilding that was to give a peculiar unity to the heavy industries of the Glasgow area. Specialisation in marine work was undoubtedly the keynote of the half-century before the First World War and provided the major impulse to the city's growth.

Yet even in this period the dominance of shipbuilding was only relative and other engineering work was by no means insignificant. Many marine engineers themselves made products such as boilers for land use, while locomotives and other branches of engineering continued to expand. Among these were the large structural engineering firms which began to emerge with the growing use of steel in the eighteen-seventies. Not unnaturally, they specialised in the heavy types of structures, their products being used in coal-mining, the iron and steel industry, the shipyards, and factories of all types. Bridge-building became a notable accomplishment of the area, one Glasgow firm, that of Sir William Arrol & Co., being responsible for such famous examples as the Tay and Forth Bridges, and the Tower Bridge, London.

A considerable number of engineering firms specialised in the manufacture of machine tools of various types. The products classified under this heading at this time were rather different from those to which the term machine tools would be applied today. This branch of engineering catered primarily for the industry of the area, and since the area specialised in the heavy industries, the tools produced were for these industries. They included punching and shearing machines, plate-bending machines, planes, boring and screwing machines, and lathes. As well as supplying the needs of the local shipbuilding, heavy engineering and iron and steel industries, many of these firms did business in all parts of the world. Over and above the heavy tool-making, a number of firms also produced scientific instruments and appliances for a wide variety of industries. And in addition to the main branches of engineering mentioned, Glasgow's manufactures included by 1914 a multifarious collection of metal products such as brewing, milling and bakery machinery, agricultural implements, cranes, chains, wheelbarrows, gas meters, safes, springs, wringers, wire, nails, bolts, nuts and screws, stoves and grates, bedsteads, lamps, and candlesticks, and all types of non-ferrous metal products.

A younger branch which was also established in the area during this period was electrical engineering. The firm of Kelvin & White, now Kelvin Hughes Ltd, founded before the middle of the century and specialising in mathematical and optical instruments, turned its attention to electrical instruments at an early date through its association with Lord Kelvin, Professor of Natural Philosophy at the University. Its products helped to make possible the first transatlantic cable connection. Glasgow was also early in the field of electric power generation, and by 1900 there were several firms in the city engaged in the manufacture of electrical machines and appliances of various kinds for lighting, power, ventilation and other purposes.

As electrically driven machinery replaced steam in more and more industries, electrical engineering soon passed from the general to the specialised stage of development. Mavor & Coulson, the pioneering firm in this field, turned their attention to electrical coal-cutting machinery, now their main specialty. In the shipbuilding industry, much of the early application of electricity to heating and ventilation produced results capable of application in a much wider field, and for some firms this provided a healthy modification of their previous specialisation in marine work. The extensive construction of power stations and generating plant provided a new outlet for the products of the area's heavy engineering firms. Firms previously specialising in marine work turned their attention increasingly to the production of boilers and generating plant for this purpose, and for some of them, power station work is now more important than marine work. Structural engineers likewise found an additional market in the construction of power stations.

In the development of the heavy industries in the Glasgow region overseas trade played an important part from the outset, although it is almost impossible to determine its relative importance or disentangle its influence from that of domestic factors. Many branches of engineering, if not all, started originally to supply the needs of local industries. At the same time, the presence of plentiful supplies of coal and iron in the area provided the basis for an engineering industry on a scale too vast to meet only the requirements of the domestic market and thus enabled it to satisfy a growing foreign demand for metal goods. Textile machinery provides a good illustration of the inter-action of these factors. Mechanisation of the cotton industry in Glasgow was hampered at first by the lack of engineering experience and skill, but as this was gradually over-come, the manufacture of machinery became important in its own right. Some con-traction naturally followed the collapse of the cotton industry during and after the American Civil War and the virtual disappearance of the local market, but textile machinery has continued as an important export industry to the present time. Similarly, most of the main branches of the engineering industry springing up in the area soon developed on a scale beyond the capacity of the home market.

The growth of exports, more than any other factor, probably helps to explain the continued buoyancy of the area during the last part of the century. Locomotive engineering, for example, benefited from the outbursts of railway construction occurring in overseas countries and exports were made to most parts of the world. Indeed, the position was probably too comfortable, from the longer-term point of view, and keener competition at this time might have provided the spur to continued pioneering in new lines of industrial development and prevented the excessive specialisation in heavy industries, which has remained typical of the area.

THE MOTOR-CAR INDUSTRY

The end of the nineteenth century found engineers preoccupied with the internal combustion engine and the new horseless carriage, from which has been developed the present-day motor-car industry. Here, too, Glasgow can claim important pioneers. It is recorded that a Scotsman, William Murdoch, working for Watt & Boulton, used a steam vehicle on the roads in Cornwall in 1784, complete with copper boiler, firebox and flue, but was dissuaded from patenting it by James Watt, who saw no future for it. The inventor of the modern motor-car, however, was of German origin. In 1887 Daimler first put his petrol engine into a four-wheeled carriage, and for some time thereafter the Daimler engine was the most generally used in many makes of cars in different countries. The industry was handicapped in this country at first by the Red Flag Law, not repealed until 1896, according to which the maximum speed was fixed at four miles per hour and vehicles had to be preceded by a man carrying a red flag. Before its repeal, however, George Johnston of Glasgow had on the road the first all-Scottish car and was fined half-a-crown for breaking this law.

Technically Johnston's engine was claimed to be an improvement on the Daimler one, from which he had started his experiments. The car went into commercial production in 1896 when the Mo-Car Syndicate was formed, comprising Sir William Arrol, Sir Thomas Glen Coats, a Mr Millar of Paisley, and Mr George Paisley of Paisley's Warehouse, Jamaica Street. The car was of dog-cart design and the bodies were made from solid oak or mahogany by Wylie & Lochhead, cabinetmakers.

The Mo-Car Syndicate, subsequently the Arrol Johnston Company, moved to Paisley in 1901, when their Glasgow works were destroyed by fire. Some years later, probably about 1909 or 1910, they moved to Dumfries, where they continued production until the late nineteen-twenties, latterly being linked with the Aster Company. Thus the story of the Arrol Johnston cars, which gained a wide reputation throughout the country, is for the most part not Glasgow's story during this period. Mr William Beardmore, later Lord Invernairn, joined the board of the Arrol Johnston Company, and subsequently Beardmore's acquired the Paisley works where the Beardmore taxi was manufactured.

In 1906 George Johnston was associated with a new car company in Bridgeton, the A.B.C. Co. Ltd, but this venture failed financially in two or three years. The firm of Bergius for a short time also entered the car market and manufactured the Kelvin car from 1904-6. Finding production costly, they fitted their engine to a boat as an experiment, and thus the famous Kelvin marine engine was developed. A number of other Glasgow cars of this period included the Athol and Scotia, built at Bridgeton, the St Vincent which was assembled in Glasgow and the Skeoch, a cycle-car. The Halley Company, which started at Finnieston in 1902 and moved to Yoker in 1906, concentrated on industrial vehicles and continued production until the late nineteen-twenties. In 1901 they produced the first motor fire-engine to be built in Scotland, which had a Drysdale pump and used bronze castings for the crankcase and gear box. But the two most important names in the history of the Glasgow motor-car industry are Albion and Argyll.

The history of the Albion Company, which is now the sole surviving motor manufacturing concern in Scotland, is one of steady progress. The Company was founded in 1899 by T. Blackwood Murray and N. O. Fulton, both members of George Johnston's original staff. Starting with an output of one eight-horse-power dog-cart with tiller steering, produced with the aid of five works staff and two clerks, the firm expanded steadily and by 1913 it was producing over 500 vehicles annually and was employing a total works and office staff of nearly 1,000. Commercial vehicles were added to production at an early date, and with the growing demand from industry, Albion paid more and more attention to these until they finally decided in 1913 to abandon the manufacture of private cars entirely. By this time motor coaches had been added to their products, and their markets extended to a number of overseas countries. The soundness of their product earned them a number of awards in Reliability Trials.

The highest achievement of the Scottish industry in car manufacture was undoubtedly the work of the Argyll Company. The designer of the Argyll car was Alex Govan, co-founder of the Hozier Engineering Co. in Bridgeton in 1896. Although at first this firm assembled the French Darracq car, Govan's aim from the start was to produce a Scottish car of moderate price, for which he recognised the great potential demand. Govan's was a pioneering venture, before its time in its conception of large-scale production. The first Argylls used Aster engines, but later the company produced its own engines. In the 1901 Glasgow Exhibition Trials the Argyll was the only car to make a clean ascent of Whistlefield hill from the Gareloch side. With this and subsequent victories, its popularity rapidly increased. Starting with an output of six cars per week, the factory had soon to be expanded. An output of twenty to twenty-five cars per week was reached, but even this was inadequate for the demand, and a large new factory was constructed at Alexandria. A new company, Argyll Motors, Ltd, was formed with a capital of £500,000. The new factory was opened in 1906, and cost over £200,000. Govan had studied the latest factories in America and the Continent, and the Vale of Leven factory was said to surpass any in the world at that time.

Although the main scene of operations thus moved out of Glasgow in 1906, the city retained an interest in the story of the Argyll Company and the Bridgeton factory was retained. Soon after the new factory opened, Govan died of food poisoning at the early age of thirty-nine. The loss of Govan's leadership and the financial burden of the new factory soon led the company into difficulties, and by 1908, when their liabilities were over £300,000, they went into partial liquidation. The company was reorganised, however, and the factory continued. The following years witnessed outstanding technical achievements. The main development was that of the single-sleeve-valve engine, which the Argyll company adopted and pioneered. The inventor, Peter Burt, was a Glasgow engineer with his own firm, the Acme Engineering Company, later the Acme Wringer Company. Technically, the Burt engine was a remarkable achievement and a great improvement on the previous system. In developing it, however, the Argyll company had to face a series of legal battles, firstly with rival claimants and latterly with the inventors of the double-sleeve-valve engine, then adopted by the Daimler Company. A Canadian, McCollum, applied for a similar patent about the same time as Burt, and after negotiations with him, agreement was reached and the patent became the Burt-McCollum patent. McCollum was a spiritualist and negotiations were protracted while he sought advice from his dead father by means of a planchette. The case against Argyll for infringement of the Knight patent, used by Daimler, was only finally settled in Argyll's favour in 1913.

These legal disputes were both costly and damaging to the market for the new Argyll cars. In 1913, however, an Argyll car with the Burt engine was entered for the trials at Brooklands. It was only a fifteen-horse-power model and in one day of fourteen hours it broke thirteen world records and twenty-eight Brooklands class records. This car was the first to be fitted with the Perrot four-wheel braking system, now universally adopted. M. Perrot worked with the Argyll company from 1909 until 1914. In the matter of body design, the Argyll company were also well ahead. They were the first to have a hood attached to the screen, a one-man hood, a concealed hood and a domed-top saloon, and the first to stow the spare wheel in a well at the rear.

The cost of development in this period, however, again produced financial losses. Although these were small compared to those of 1908, the company went into voluntary liquidation in 1914. At this time their legal troubles were over, their car was gaining wide recognition and their market prospects good, and it now seems as if a little effort could have saved the firm. The industrial history of West Scotland in the inter-war period might have been very different if that effort had been made.

Burt's sleeve-valve engine figured in the development of another new industry in which the Glasgow engineers were showing growing interest just before the outbreak of war in 1914. In 1913 Burt designed a sleeve-valve aero-engine, which Argyll produced and entered for a competition at Farnborough in 1914. Although the crankshaft broke, due it is said to the mounting for testing, not to the design, the Argyll entry was awarded a prize. Early in the war Burt designed another aero-engine for research at Farnborough, and although the sleeve-valve engine was subsequently dropped, post-war researches proved its worth and some of the more recent developments by the Bristol Company were fundamentally similar in type to that of Burt.

Several Glasgow firms continued to manufacture cars in the nineteen-twenties, but mostly on a relatively small scale. These included the Beardmore car, the Rob Roy, produced at Carntyne, the Gilchrist, assembled in Glasgow, and the Argyll, built at the old Hozier works. The latter were acquired on the liquidation of the old company in 1914 by J. D. Brimlow and a new Argyll Motor Co. Ltd was formed with Sir John Anderson as chairman. The Argyll stocks, drawings, patterns, etc., had also been acquired, and during the war the company concentrated on spare parts for existing Argylls. In 1920 Brimlow produced a new Argyll, incorporating the Burt sleeve-valve engine. Manufacture was carried on until the late nineteen-twenties. The Halley Company continued for a time to manufacture commercial vehicles and in 1920 produced the first pneumatic-tyred passenger coach in Britain. The latter incorporated many new features, but proved costly in development and the company suffered badly in the post-war depression. They went into liquidation in 1927, and subsequently continued on a small scale until about 1930. Beardmore's produced a commercial vehicle at Parkhead until about 1930, and Carlaw produced some vans. Other commercial vehicles produced in the city included the Caledon, the Scotia, the Sentinel and the Wallace Tractor. Albion meantime were continuing to expand and establishing a growing reputation for commercial and public service vehicles of a special type and reliability. By the beginning of the nineteen-thirties, however, only Albion remained. The great depression of that period eliminated those of the others who had survived the ups and downs of the 'twenties. The motor industry had become a much more large-scale and highly competitive business and was by this time concentrating in the Midlands. Most of the components were also produced in that area and the relatively small-scale Glasgow industry could not compete. Had the Argyll works at Alexandria survived, the position might well have been very different. As it was, the Midlands, with its numerous small, light engineering workshops and its history of mobility, was ideally suited for the development of the industries essential to car assembly. In contrast, the Glasgow area, with its long tradition and skill in the heavy industries, lacked even the nucleus for their development. Typical of this is the case of castings. This area is accustomed to produce the heavy and specialised types required by the old industries, and the lighter castings necessary to the modern motor industry would have had to be imported.

AIRCRAFT

In 1895 Percy Pilcher, a lecturer in naval architecture at Glasgow University, made the first glider flight in Britain at Cardross in a glider built by himself. By 1899 he had designed a glider with a wheeled under-carriage and steel springs to absorb the shock of landing, and had begun experiments on a petrol engine to be installed in the glider. These

196

experiments were tragically terminated by his death as a result of an accident during a glider demonstration that same year, and the invention of the modern powered aeroplane was delayed until the Wright brothers' success in 1903.

At the outbreak of war, the most advanced Glasgow firm in the field of aeroengine construction was Beardmore's. They began designing and manufacturing aeroengines early in the century and by 1914 were well established in this production. During the first three years of the war more flying hours by the R.F.C. were made with Beardmore engines than with any other type. Beardmore's took up aircraft construction on an extensive scale, with factories at Dalmuir and Inchinnan, and during the war produced a total of 650 'planes, ranging from small Sopwiths to four-engined Handley-Pages. In 1915 a group of the Clyde engineering and shipbuilding firms was formed for the same purpose under the leadership of G. & J. Weir of Cathcart. The group included Stephen, Denny, Barclay Curle, Napier and Miller, and Fairfield. In all, a considerable capacity for aircraft construction and the production of its many components was created, but unfortunately practically all the firms, with the exception of Beardmore, abandoned this new development and returned to their former products when peace returned.

INTER-WAR DEPRESSION

The First World War had brought renewed emphasis and expansion to the heavy industries, but no new industrial capacity suitable for medium or light engineering in peacetime. Glasgow at the beginning of the nineteen-twenties was still an area specialising in heavy engineering. In addition, there was some motor manufacturing, and one firm engaged in aircraft construction. At first, the end of hostilities brought boom conditions to the heavy industries, but the boom was short-lived and depression quickly followed. Prosperity did not return with the end of the depression and the industry of the area remained more or less in the doldrums until rearmament began in the latter half of the nineteen-thirties. In the years of world depression around 1930, unemployment in the engineering industries was over 30 per cent, and for much of the rest of the period 20 per cent was typical. Although the belief was slow to die that pre-1914 conditions could be restored and that all would be well, world conditions had in fact changed in such a way and to such an extent as to make this impossible. The engineering industries of Glasgow suffered particularly from the contraction and depression of the shipbuilding industry, on which so many depended directly or indirectly, and from the contraction of export markets on which all branches depended to a considerable extent. Even the best years of the period were lean ones.

Although the years of general depression naturally had a particularly adverse effect on heavy engineering, all the main branches continued in the area, but mostly on a reduced scale. Some fared better than others, depending on their markets and the scope for variation in product. Locomotives continued to be built in the city both by the North British Locomotive Company and, until 1928, in the Railway Company's own works. The former, depending almost entirely on foreign markets, felt the lack of any extensive overseas construction comparable to the railway mania of an earlier period. Structural engineering, with its wider variety of products and bigger home market fared slightly better. In the production of heavy equipment and machine tools of a specialised type the contraction of the local heavy industries had an adverse effect on

197

the home market, but the area retained its superiority and in this specialised line was less affected by foreign competition.

In electrical engineering the city was not extensively involved, the main firm now concentrating on coal-cutting and loading equipment. The other main representative of the electrical engineering industry, the Macfarlane Engineering Co. Ltd, embarked on new development. Previously producing mainly A.C. and D.C. dynamos, the firm decided in the lean years following 1918 to turn their attention to more specialised electrical work, particularly in electric arc welding and in special laboratory plant. Some progress was also made in the manufacture of heating and ventilating plant, frequently started primarily for ships but with increasing application to factories, chiefly as a result of factory welfare legislation.

A few of the established heavy industries embarked on new lines in this period, but not many. Notable among them was the shipbuilding concern of Yarrow & Co., who started in 1922 to produce land boilers, the output of which is now an important part of their activity. The firm of Howden & Co. started in the eighteen-fifties as marine engineers and, adding high-speed engines and turbines for land generators early in the present century, made a special development in the inter-war years of boiler auxiliaries such as fans, air preheaters and dust collectors, for both land and marine use, and they now specialise entirely in this work. G. & J. Weir Ltd, famous for pumps and boiler auxiliaries from the eighteen-eighties, also undertook a number of new developments in this period. To their products they added compressors, petrol pumps and refuellers, evaporators and refrigerating plant. In the process they acquired a number of concerns including that of Drysdale at Yoker, the Contraflo Engineering Co., London, Zwicky Ltd, Slough, and A. G. Mumford, Colchester. In the nineteen-thirties they carried out development work on autogiros and later produced helicopters. An old-established firm of ironfounders, Robert Maclaren & Co. Ltd, founded in 1844, turned in 1922 to the manufacture of thermostats for industrial, commercial and domestic use and now specialise entirely in this work.

In aircraft construction Beardmore's continued to play a leading part until the late nineteen-twenties. Aero-engines were manufactured by them at Parkhead, flying-boats at Dalmuir, and airships at Inchinnan. They were early pioneers in transatlantic air travel, one of their airships making the double journey in 1919. The aircraft industry at this time, however, was dependent almost entirely on scanty Government orders and was tending to concentrate in the south. Beardmore's abandoned aircraft work in the late nineteen-twenties and by the nineteen-thirties the only activity in this field in Glasgow was the development work on autogiros being carried out by G. & J. Weir, who later turned their attention to helicopters, and in 1938 produced the Weir helicopter, the first to be flown in this country.

The general picture of the inter-war years, however, is one showing Glasgow at the centre of one of the main depressed or Special Areas created by the decline in the heavy industries and in the export trade. Unemployment was high and new industrial development almost negligible. This was the period of the so-called southward drift of industry and of the expansion of lighter industries concerned with the domestic rather than the foreign market. Many reasons have been suggested to explain Glasgow's failure to develop these new industries on any substantial scale. The nucleus of many of the new industries already existed in the Midlands and South of England, and the

198

domestic market, now the more important, was obviously greater there. Much has also been made of the belief that heavy industry areas and their labour force are unsuited to the lighter industries. As the period advanced, however, much of the labour force, far from being tied to the heavy skills, was in fact unskilled because of the lack of openings in the heavy trades.

In the particular case of engineering, there is evidence that Glasgow had its fair share of inventors and pioneers in the new medium and light branches. But inventors must have backing and the capital of the area was undoubtedly mainly in the heavy industries. Prior to 1914 many of the leaders in these industries had shown considerable interest in and given support to the newest developments in engineering. Typical of this was Sir William Arrol's interest in the young motor-car industry, and Sir William Beardmore's enterprises in both the car and aircraft industries. In the inter-war period, however, the depression so prevalent in the heavy industries, particularly those involved in marine work, had a damping effect on such enterprise and on the supply of capital available for new ventures. Further, in many cases, the original founder had been replaced by a less enterprising board of directors, none of whom had any personal experience of pioneering a new venture. Finally, in the lighter branches of industry, which catered primarily for the domestic market, a depressed area with heavy unemployment offered little attraction.

It was not until the late nineteen-thirties that a policy of attracting new industries to the depressed areas by the provision of industrial estates was started, and at that time the city of Glasgow was excluded from the designated Special Area. The largest estate established, however, was that at Hillington, more or less on Glasgow's door-step and now included in the Glasgow Labour Exchange area. The estate was opened in 1937 and by the end of 1938 some seventy firms were in production there. The most important single development on the estate was the construction of the Air Ministry's shadow factory occupied by Rolls Royce, Ltd for the production of aero-engines. The outbreak of war brought considerable expansion and at the peak of its production the firm employed 25,000.

From the mid-nineteen-thirties onwards there was also a steady recovery in the old heavy industries of the area, as a result of the rearmament programme. The outbreak of war again called for the mobilisation of Glasgow's traditional industries. In many cases production was at first hampered by the effects of years of stagnation and by the lack of trained labour, but the shipbuilding and engineering firms were soon geared to war production. Once more, ships, vehicles, guns and equipment of all types were produced. The effect of the war was again mainly to expand capacity in the old heavy industries, and with the notable exception of the Rolls Royce factory at Hillington, the area received little new capacity suitable for adaptation to the lighter branches of engineering. The demands on the heavy industries were made all the greater by the area's relative immunity from air attack. In spite of this, unemployment only finally disappeared in 1941 with the direction of surplus labour to the south.

PRESENT POSITION

Under the Distribution of Industry Act of 1954 Glasgow was included in the new Scottish Development Area of the post-war period. In addition to the original Hillington

Estate, now considerably expanded, there are four new estates within the Glasgow area, at Queenslie, Carntyne, Craigton and Thornliebank. In these there are now over 200 tenants, of whom nearly a half are engaged in medium and light engineering of various kinds. The largest single unit is the Rolls Royce factory at Hillington, which is now concentrated entirely on the production of jet engines. A considerable addition to light engineering has been provided by the two firms manufacturing typewriters, Remington Rand and Olivetti. The rest are on a relatively small scale, at least in comparison with the traditional heavy industries of the area, which have enjoyed almost uninterrupted boom conditions since the end of the war. In addition to the expected post-war demands for replacements and reconstruction to make good the ravages of the war years, such factors as the Korean War and extensive rearmament, full employment and the attendant expansion of productive capacity, the expansion of world trade and the export drive, have all helped to maintain the level of activity in the heavy engineering firms. Glasgow still is and must surely remain the centre of an area depending basically on the heavy industries. The object of industrial estate policy can only be to introduce a greater diversity and balance.

This essay is a shortened version of the first half of the Authors' chapter on the same subject in the Glasgow volume of The Third Statistical Account.

FUEL AND POWER

I. COAL AND GAS

R. Common

Formerly Lecturer in Geography, University of Glasgow

WITH the sanctioning of the Ayrshire nuclear power project in 1957, another new fuel will soon become available to Mid-Scotland only about 200 years after the opening of the Carron Ironworks, which, with such far-reaching consequences, introduced coal as a hitherto under-developed fuel resource.

Monastic documents reveal the existence of a mining industry in the fifteenth and sixteenth centuries, and other historic records show that coal was first shipped out of the Clyde estuary from Dumbarton in 1556, and from Irvine in 1541. Nevertheless, both the early sea and landward coal trades, in the west, lagged behind those of the Forth and Tay estuaries at that time for a number of reasons. Of necessity, the contemporary coal-mines, shallow and near the coal outcrops, were small-scale and short-lived. Coal was rarely used domestically more than two to three miles from the workings, but its use as an industrial fuel was established first in the smithy, then in salt-making and lime-burning and later in glass, soap and sugar-making. It has been estimated that in this early period the total annual output of coal in Scotland was only about 40,000 tons; but subsequently the national production was to increase to a peak of 42·5 million in 1913.

The seventeenth century was one of quickening development in Lanarkshire, especially in the Barony of Glasgow and on the Hamilton estate, where the number of sinkings grew and the volume of coal carted to nearby towns and villages increased significantly. At this time Glasgow formed an important market, and in spite of the shallowness of the Clyde it had also become a minor coal-shipment port. In Ayrshire, a smaller demand for coal from a widely dispersed rural population was only slightly offset by the Irish sea-coal trade and hence the pace of development was slower and more localised than in Lanarkshire. Some technical advances had been made in the winning of coal, as, for example, by the use of the 'Scotch gin', but extraction methods by 'stoop-and-room' workings were wasteful since as much as half the coal in a seam was often sterilised in the form of roof supports. Even so, by the end of the seventeenth century growing demands had increased the total Scottish annual production to about 475,000 tons, of which 70,000–100,000 tons came from Lanarkshire and 20,000–25,000 tons from Ayrshire.

At the beginning of the eighteenth century thriving commerce and improvements in agriculture on the one hand, and technical innovations on the other, all served to nourish the growing mining industry. The expanding trade with America required metal goods of various kinds and the demand from the forges for fuel further stimulated coal-mining. Furthermore, the subsequent deepening of the Clyde below Glasgow gave an impetus to coal exports and industrial enterprise. Later the steam engines of New-comen and Watt furnished at once a new market for coal and a source of power which allowed the coalmasters to sink shafts to 300 feet, as compared with the former depths of 120-180 feet. Whilst these engines were first employed for pumping only, they soon were adapted for winding operations, and henceforth the workings became both deeper and larger, employing up to 200 men instead of the twenty to thirty men in the older mines. About the same time, the success of the pioneer ironworks at Carron led to the founding of similar works in the West of Scotland, also based on local resources of coal, ironstone and limestone: by the close of the eighteenth century output in Lanarkshire had risen to 500,000-600,000 tons and in Ayrshire to 160,000-165,000 tons per year. Although by 1800 there were only four such ironworks in Lanarkshire and two in Ayrshire, others were added in the nineteenth century, especially after Mushet's discovery that the miners' 'wild coal' was a valuable ironstone (the blackband). Technical advances such as Neilson's hot-blast technique and the use of raw splint coal to replace coke in the production of iron completed the eclipse of charcoal as the furnace fuel.

By the very nature of the Carboniferous deposits it was often possible to draw both coal and ironstone from the same mine, so that many of the workings became dual-purpose. Later, owing to the demand for pig-iron, many mines and mining settlements were located for the ironstone alone, either switching to coal production once the ore supply was exhausted, as at Lugar, or withering when the ore reserves had gone, as at Glenbuck. As a result of the realisation of these coal and iron assets, and of growing markets, the Scottish iron industry became concentrated on the coalfield (see Fig. 42). Further important stimuli were the Napoleonic Wars, the advent of the railway and the use of iron in shipbuilding. Production of Scottish ores reached a zenith of two-and-a-half million tons by 1880, but thereafter declined to about half-a-million tons in 1914. By 1958 Scottish iron production has become concentrated in only five works—Clyde, Gartsherrie, Govan, Carron and the newly built Ravenscraig. Significantly, all these furnaces rely almost wholly upon imported foreign ores and blended fuel.

If the seeds of the mining industry were sown in the fifteenth and sixteenth centuries to germinate in the seventeenth and grow apace in the eighteenth, then they certainly flowered prolifically during the nineteenth century, when the major industries depended upon coal for fuel and power requirements as never before—and possibly never again! Changes in overland transportation during the nineteenth century also played a vital rôle in fuel and power developments, for although the position of the coalfields was favourable to the sea coal trade (and, later, the importation of foreign iron ores) the relief of the region did not favour extensive canal or river navigation. However, prior to the railways the bulk movement of coal on the Forth and Clyde Canal, as well as the Monkland Canal, had been significant but slow and restricted in nature. When the rail-way did arrive it was primarily intended for mineral traffic, and invariably its alignment, in the early days, was from mineral field to transhipment point on navigable water, e.g. 'Dixon's Railway'—the Pollok and Govan line. Once laid, the railway served to increase the availability of and demand for coal. The Garnkirk and Glasgow line, for example, was the first in Scotland to carry both goods and passenger traffic and, like the Monkland Canal before it, improved supplies and lowered the prices of coal in the city. Similarly, in the coastal areas, the hinterlands of favoured sites were extended by

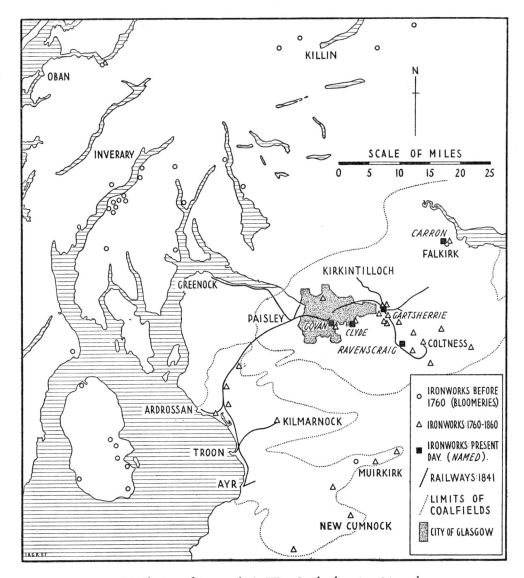

FIG. 42. Distribution of ironworks in West Scotland, 1760, 1860, and 1957.

the railway; for example, Ardrossan was linked to the Glasgow and Ayr line and Troon harbour was created to handle the coal traffic from Kilmarnock to the sea (see Fig. 43).

Meanwhile this rapid expansion was reflected in the increased numbers of miners in the area, augmented by the influx of Irish labourers into the mines after 1830. Also, a coincidence of industry and a large population developed in the coal-mining areas, particularly in Lanarkshire, where, by 1900, the output had risen to seventeen million tons annually. In Ayrshire, however, production then only exceeded four million tons for the first time, as the result of a slower and steadier development.

About this time, too, considerable attention was devoted to the assessment of coal

resources in relation to the extraction rates, for the industry was now of national importance and on a scientific basis. Since these resources are not inexhaustible and have already
been long exploited, it is necessary to make periodic reassessments of known reserves
and prudent exploration for likely additional reserves. No finer example demonstrates
how fuller information on the mineral resources can radically alter the subsequent
course of events than the New Cumnock coalfield. Here, in 1938, an area which was
considered to have a limited extraction life was re-proved and by the discovery of four
new workable seams its estimated reserves leapt from 40 to 160 million tons. The
positive results of this discovery can now be plainly seen in the rejuvenated state of this
field and its settlements. Similarly, but on a smaller scale, the recent Canonbie boring
programme has shown that an extension of that field exists, whilst nearer at hand the
proposal to develop newly proved coking coal at Milngavie has provoked a clash with
other land interests in the district.

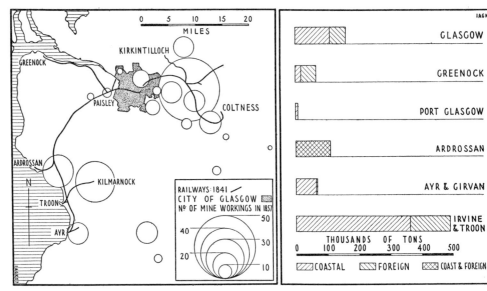

FIG. 43A. Distribution of coal-mines in Lanarkshire
and Ayrshire, 1857.

FIG. 43B. Coal exports from West
Scotland ports, 1860.

The present century has also seen a reappraisal of coal as a fuel owing to its
increasing cost, decreasing abundance and technical limitations, along with the rising
importance of gas and oil fuels as well as electric power. Thus, after the 1913 peak, the
absolute and relative decline of production in the Lanarkshire coal-mines has gained
momentum over the years, but in Ayrshire the output has remained steadier and some
of the manpower losses have been recovered (Table XXI).

The First World War inflated demands for coal fuel; it also stimulated mechanisation in production, and then left the industry to face changed conditions on home and
former overseas markets in an unbalanced state. As elsewhere, difficult and uncertain
years followed. By 1928 the active area of mining had contracted, particularly in North
Ayrshire, whilst younger and bigger mines were developing over the concealed coalfield in the Mauchline basin. Furthermore with the general spread of depressed economic
conditions there was little incentive for costly new sinkings or reconstruction work in

existing mines. Thus in spite of the 1930 Coal Act and other efforts to stabilise conditions it was only after 1935 that the upward swing of the trade pendulum favourably affected the coal industry. But by then further changes had taken place with the reduction of output and manpower in Lanark, and in spite of Ayr and Dumfries having sunk a few more mines, these counties too had lost men. The difficult years also affected mine ownership because of the increased rate at which smaller concerns were eliminated—thus enhancing the relative strength of the surviving big companies (see Table XXII). Whereas in 1928 only one mine employed over 1,000 men, since 1935 there have been four mines with at least 1,000 employees in the region. Over the years there has also been a slight change in the ratio of underground to surface workers in the industry from about 3:1 in the nineteen-thirties to 4 or 5:1 in the present decade.

With increasing demands for coal in the rearmament and war years of the late 'thirties and 'forties, the industry virtually substituted one set of problems for another.

Date	Saleable output in thousands of tons			Manpower		
	Lanark	Ayr and Dumfries	Scotland	Lanark	Ayr and Dumfries	Scotland
1910	23,713	4,462	41,335	80,101	15,196	137,873
1920	16,885	4,069	31,524	88,088	17,426	154,493
1930	15,232	3,982	31,659	50,315	11,866	98,547
1940	12,973	4,631	29,689	42,744	12,489	88,657
1950	8,532	3,539	23,294	32,568	12,985	81,492

TABLE XXI. Summary of coal output and manpower in West Scotland, 1910-50.

The chief concern was now to maintain the continuity of greater output from the ageing workings and to make the most efficient use of a more strictly limited labour pool. By the end of the Second World War, Lanarkshire alone continued to lose men, and although a significant number of closures had also affected Ayrshire, it was only in Lanarkshire that these exceeded replacements. Meanwhile the medium-sized mines had at last come into their own and were reasonably well equipped with both electricity and coal-cutting equipment. Nevertheless, although the use of coal-cutting machinery compared favourably with other mining areas, the use of mechanical conveyors had remained poor. This latter factor, however, was not entirely responsible for the continuing downward trend of output per man in the western mines, which must be attributed rather to the depleted condition of the Central Lanarkshire field.

The industry has since been nationalised and has had to use 'stop-gap' methods to maintain and augment the supply of coal for current markets as well to organise for the future. Thus by 1955, the closing of uneconomic workings had further reduced the number of mines in Central Lanarkshire and North Ayrshire and the ephemeral opencast methods had virtually ceased, although the use of surface drift-mines still persisted.

County	1928				1935				1945			
	A	B	C	D	A	B	C	D	A	B	C	D
Ayr	12	3	5	1	9	—	6	1	7	2	5	—
Dunbarton	—	2	2	—	—	1	2	—	—	1	3	—
Dumfries	—	—	—	—	—	—	—	—	—	—	—	—
Lanark	39	6	9	3	25	3	6	5	26	4	8	4
Renfrew	—	—	1	—	—	—	1	—	—	—	1	—
Part Stirling	—	—	—	—	1	—	—	—	—	—	—	—
	E	F	G	H	E	F	G	H	E	F	G	H
Ayr	47	32	7	77	38	31	5	54	49	37	7	56
Dunbarton	6	5	—	8	6	6	1	9	9	6	2	9
Dumfries	3	3	2	3	3	2	—	4	3	3	1	3
Lanark	149	127	22	201	94	78	19	156	126	91	15	148
Renfrew	—	—	—	1	—	—	—	1	1	—	—	1
Part Stirling	3	3	1	5	3	3	1	5	3	3	1	3

N.C.B. Subdivisions	1955	
	G	H
Central West Area:		
(a) Kilsyth	6	12
(b) Clyde	1	16
Part Central East Area (in Lanarkshire)	2	12
West Ayr Area	4	24
East Ayr Area	6	27

A. Mines abandoned, idle or developing;
B. Mines pumping, ventilating or with washeries only;
C. Fireclay or 'blaes' only;
D. Coal and ironstone mines;
E. Mines with electricity;
F. Mines with coal-cutting machinery;
G. Mines with 500 or more employees;
H. Total number of mines.

TABLE XXII. Summary of the state of coal-mines in West Scotland at certain dates.

The subsequent redevelopment of mines in areas of economic value and the opening of new mines have necessitated a very heavy capital investment by the industry (see Fig. 44). In Ayrshire new Coal Board projects were originally planned to include four new sinkings, twelve major reconstructions and twenty-nine surface drifts, but progress has not always been as rapid as anticipated; for instance, the new Killoch sinking encountered trouble from water in the Barren Red Measures. Over the same period of time the

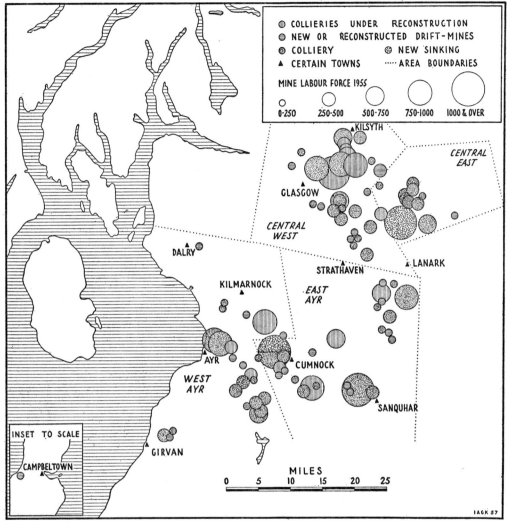

FIG. 44. Coal-mines and their labour force in West Scotland, 1955.
Source: National Coal Board and *Collieries Year Book, 1956.*

original plans for the Central Areas in Lanarkshire covered one new sinking, six reconstructions and the driving of nine new surface drifts. Here the new Kingshill 3 Colliery
has already come into production but its relatively isolated situation has necessitated a
special bus service for its workers.

Simultaneously, voluntary transfer schemes, together with preference in housing,
have been effective in moving redundant labour from Lanarkshire to developing areas,
particularly in the East of Scotland. Since 1947 over 7,000 miners have been moved,
chiefly from Lanarkshire. Whilst the current flow of miners is small it will surge again
as the new Scottish mines are worked up to full production. The general state of miners'
housing is now greatly improved compared with 1925, but the changing colliery
distribution as well as the changed location of the miners' homes has meant that travel to

207

work has become another significant factor in the industry. Miners are now prepared to live at distances up to fifteen miles from their work as a matter of course whilst a few will even travel thirty miles. Public transport caters for most of the travellers, but it has to be augmented by Coal Board transport in some instances. Cardowan, for

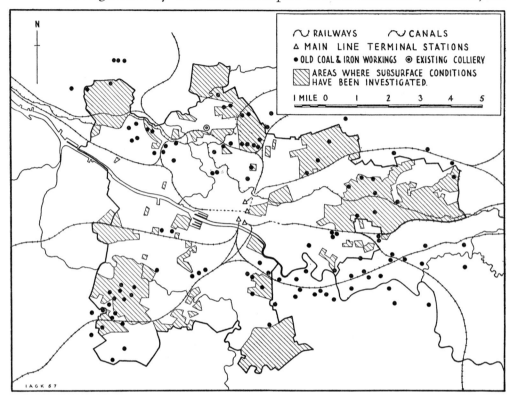

FIG. 45. City of Glasgow : known coal and iron workings and areas investigated for subsidence. Note alignment of workings along outcrop area of east-west syncline.

example, is a large mine a few miles east of Glasgow which draws most of its labour supply from the city. However, miners also travel to it from Paisley, Airdrie, Netherfield, Hamilton and Motherwell, and those from Hamilton and Motherwell have to be especially catered for by bus. Again, the Douglas colliery has a problem akin to Kingshill 3, since its labour force is dispersed and the mine is not particularly accessible. Here a subsidised bus service is essential and the railway is also used to bring men from as far afield as Hamilton, Lesmahagow and Lanark.

A serious problem still remains to be dealt with—that of the despoilation of the mining area. The landscape, for example, has suffered from varying degrees of subsidence. In Glasgow itself, the Corporation has to safeguard its interests by checking subsurface conditions on possible building sites; as can be seen, for example, in Anniesland and Govan, the risk of buildings settling on old, uncharted workings is still a real one (see Fig. 45). Further afield the semi-permanent stretches of water in parts of Ayrshire and Lanarkshire are a visible legacy of mining subsidence and these also have an underground counterpart in the wet or abandoned water-logged workings in the Shotts and

208

lower Clyde areas. To its credit the National Coal Board has tackled the problem of underground water seepage in order to reduce the risk of interference in workings set amid the old and water-logged mines, but above ground the standing water appears to be ignored (see Fig. 46). Spoil-heaps are also characteristic of the mining landscape; but

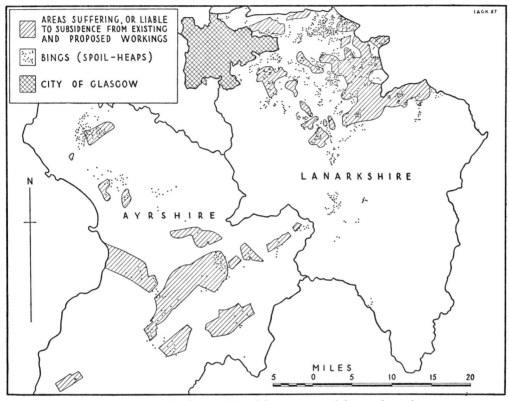

FIG. 46. Mining subsidence and spoil-heaps in Lanarkshire and Ayrshire.
Source : County Planning Reports.

they need not represent a permanent loss of amenity since they can be colonised by native tree species such as birch, sycamore and Scots pine as well as being successfully planted with exotics like Corsican and Austrian pines.

In the marketing of coal the changed trends in domestic consumption have persisted, leading to increased demands from the gas and electricity industries and reduced consumptions by the miners and household markets (see Fig. 47). Changed circumstances in railway traffic are also reflected in the amounts of coal now brought *into* Lanarkshire, especially for the gas and electricity industries; for example, Braehead power station, Glasgow, uses Fife and Lothian coal. Similarly, the coal traffic for shipment is at present on a reduced scale, but there is still some at Ayr, Ardrossan and Glasgow. The foreign coal trade from Scotland first declined after 1910 (when it exceeded ten million tons) then briefly revived between 1920-23. At this time the West ports were exporting at a scale of only about a quarter of the East Scottish tonnages, but in the following sixteen years their relative importance increased—having the Irish market, they were less affected by the recession of the overseas markets which gradually

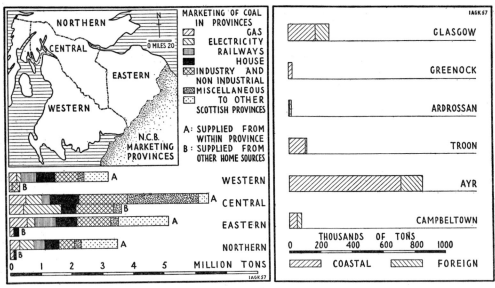

FIG. 47A. Marketing and consumption of coal in West, East, Central and Northern Provinces of Scotland, 1953-54.

FIG. 47B. Coal exports from West Scotland ports, 1953-54.

reduced total Scottish exports to four-and-a-half million tons per year. The coastwise trade has shown a steadier development, for until 1925 the shipment rates of two to two-and-a-half million tons per year were almost equally shared between west and east Scottish ports. However, the east-coast shipments soon became twice as great as those from the western ports and exceeded four million tons by 1938. During the Second World War shipments coastwise were commendably maintained, but subsequently there has been a marked shrinkage in this trade. Yet in spite of all this change in shipping fortunes one characteristic feature of the western seascape persisted—the 'puffer', delivering coal to the sea lochs and islands.

GAS

Legitimately, it may also be claimed that the coal trade proper has had, during this century, problems rising from the competition of its daughter gas industry. In its early period of development in the west, gas was first confined to lighting purposes and was produced by small concerns such as the Glasgow Gaslight Company and the City and Suburban Gas Company. As technical developments allowed, however, this primary function was augmented by heating, and this was quick to gain favour in the one- and two-roomed houses of the area. After 1900 the chemical potential of this new industry was increasingly realised, and, although the 1919 Gas Regulation Act gave a formal recognition to changing fuel supply conditions, the regional integration of the gas supply system was not to be undertaken until after Nationalisation.

Since Nationalisation, in 1949, the total number of consumers in the West of Scotland has increased to over 627,000, but their distribution remains uneven and their demands continue to range widely. Some are industrial and some domestic—obviously then the problems of production, storage and distribution vary greatly within the region and are reflected in the numbers and capacities of installations as well as gas prices over the area. To meet the present demands for gas, the industry is required to employ on an average one person per 110 consumers, but this will probably change in the future when current development work is completed (see Fig. 48).

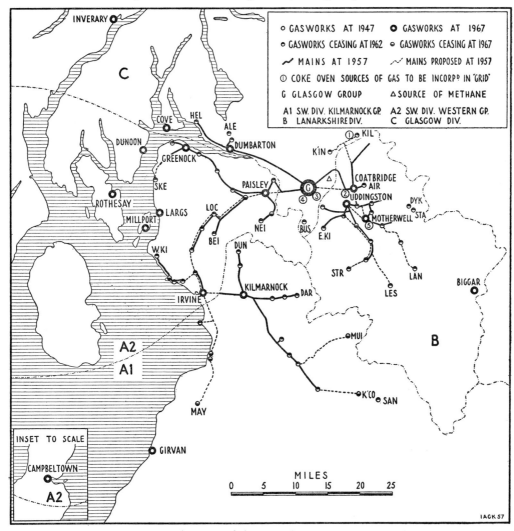

FIG. 48. Development of the gas industry in West Scotland.
Source: Scottish Gas Board.

AIR—Airdrie; ALE—Alexandria; BEI—Beith; BUS—Busby; DAR—Darvel; DUN—Dunlop; DYK—Dykehead; E.KI—East Kilbride; HEL—Helensburgh; KIL—Kilsyth; K'CO—Kirkconnel; K'IN—Kirkintilloch; LAN—Lanark; LES—Lesmahagow; LOC—Lochwinnoch; MAY—Maybole; MUI—Muirkirk; NEI—Neilston; SAN—Sanquhar; SKE—Skelmorlie; STA—Stane; STR—Strathaven; W.KI—West Kilbride.

In these developments the elimination of small and inefficient plants has already affected fifty-two works in Scotland including the Dalmarnock and Renfrew stations.

These may be joined, by 1967, by yet another eighty-three works, of which twenty-seven are in West Scotland. Dominating the whole of this current work is the project to extend and link local supply systems eventually to serve 90 per cent of the Scottish gas market in mid-Scotland. The West of Scotland gas 'grid' at present involves forty-one gasworks, chiefly in Lanarkshire, Ayrshire, Renfrewshire and Dunbartonshire, but eventually the supply of gas is to be based upon works at Dumbarton, Tradeston, Dawsholm and Provan, augmented with supplies of coke-oven gas from conveniently placed works. Holder stations will also be distributed throughout the 'grid', together with carburetted water gas plants, to accommodate variations in the demand for gas. Outwith the proposed 'grid' a scatter of twelve small gasworks is to continue production but another small 'grid' project is under consideration for the area around Dumfries.

By these various means, therefore, the gas industry hopes to maintain its place in the increasingly competitive fuel markets of West Scotland and also to provide for any increased demands made upon it. Like the coal industry it has also invested heavily in capital projects but, unlike fuel oil and electricity, the fortunes of the gas industry remain tied to that of its parent.

II. ELECTRICITY AND PETROLEUM

D. R. DIAMOND
Assistant in Geography, University of Glasgow

The industrial initiative of nineteenth-century Clydeside gave Glasgow an early start in the generation of electricity. The first practical attempts to provide an electricity supply took place in 1879 and 1880 when the St Enoch and Queen Street railway stations were lit. These efforts did not, however, develop into a general supply. The first secure public supply became available in 1893, when the Corporation station in Waterloo Street superseded the Muir and Mavor station completed in 1884 in Miller Street. Shortly after, in 1897, the Corporation purchased land at Port Dundas and Eglinton Toll for two new generating stations, and by 1900, of the ten coal-consuming electric generating stations in the West of Scotland, only those at Ayr, Greenock and Paisley were outside Glasgow.

The early pattern of development tended to parallel the early stages of the gas industry. The use of electricity was confined almost entirely to lighting, and its development on a commercial scale was speculative. For these and technical reasons the supply came from a number of small undertakings of local character, each with its independent generating station. The development of municipal organisation and enterprise, and the expansion of demand allowed the system to grow on this basis in the thickly populated areas, leaving the more sparsely populated areas entirely without supply. No attempt was made to bring about uniformity of supply and there were, in the public interest, prohibitions against the association of undertakings. Between 1900 and 1910 the number of coal-generating stations more than doubled to reach twenty-two but this marked the end of the early period of growth, for in the succeeding decade only two new coal-generating stations were commissioned, and subsequently there was no new station until

212

1951. This clearly reflects the technical development which changed the economic area of supply from under ten to several hundred square miles.

At Foyers, Inverness-shire, the British Aluminium Company opened the first hydro-electric station in Scotland in 1896, which was followed by further developments in the Highlands in 1909, 1922 and 1924. The Bonnington and Stonebyres hydro-electric generating stations, completed in 1927, were the first in Scotland to be used for public supply. These two run-of-river stations, built on the Clyde near Lanark, utilise the heads of water formed by the Falls of Clyde to supply continuously local needs. The last pre-war hydro project was the Galloway Power Company's development of the River Dee and tributaries, completed in 1936.

The small, hesitant beginning of hydro-electric power requires some explanation in the light of the enormous development since 1946. Technical difficulties together with abundant, low-cost coal were early handicaps. Later the coal-mining interests who feared competition, the Highland interests who prophesied losses of land, fishing and amenity, and legislation which was totally inadequate were further deterrents. The absence of any new power station between 1929 and 1946, despite the 'grid' scheme and the rising demand for power, must be attributed mainly to the economic effects of the depression and the Second World War.

The early, rapid expansion of the coal-using branch of the industry was based primarily upon the continual increase in electric street lighting and the success of electric traction, which had by 1902 resulted in the complete electrification of Glasgow's tramways. The initial growth of industrial and domestic demand was slow, despite the setting up, under special Acts of Parliament, of companies, such as the Clyde Valley Electric Power Company, with rights of supply over wide areas.

The power demands of the First World War exposed the weakness of the supply system and expedited the appearance of the Electricity Supply Act of 1919. This Act helped to provide a way out of the growing conflict in the organisation of the industry between the large number of small producers, municipal and private, and the technical advances in generation and transmission which required regional and even national co-ordination. A period, therefore, followed in which rising demand was satisfied from fewer stations of increased capacity and efficiency that served wider areas by high-voltage transmission. The amount of electricity supplied approximately doubled each decade while, between 1913 and 1933, sixteen generating stations in the West of Scotland closed down. Industrial and domestic demand rose rapidly, creating for the first time a continuous demand, and thus fostering increased efficiency. A major production economy is revealed by the decline in the weight of coal per unit generated, from 20 pounds in 1892 to 4·5 pounds in 1908, to only 1·4 pounds by 1938, at the same time as a change occurred from high-grade to lower quality fuels. Together with the increasing size of the efficient power station came changes in the economics of their location. The only two new stations to be built in this period, Clyde's Mill (1916) and Dalmarnock (1920), reflected the new trend in size and location, being in fact only two miles apart. Nearness to load was no longer the over-riding requirement, but only one among several location factors. Among these, the most important were: the cost of coal delivered to the station—both are close to the Lanark coalfield; availability of water for condensing—both are located on the River Clyde; possibilities of site expansion—both have been considerably enlarged and modernised; facilities with regard to the 'grid' and the efficiency of the station itself. Their present importance and capacity is a tribute to their correct location and the existence of a national grid system of main transmission lines. (See Plate XV.)

Completion of the Central Scotland 'grid' scheme in 1932 made available to any producer or distributor the aggregate reserve power of all the fifteen selected stations, ten of which were in the West of Scotland. Further efficiency, standardisation of supply and an increase in the reliability of supply as well as in the area served, resulted from this scheme. The 'grid' also made possible the first bulk-supply contract from the Highlands to the Lowlands, for 106 million units per annum (a unit is one kilowatt hour). This development was of considerable importance for the future growth of electricity supply in Scotland, for while it gave the Grampian Power Company an assured market on which it could base its development of public supplies in the Highlands, it also helped to solve the newly emerging supply problem of the Lowlands—that of peak-period demand.

The Galloway hydro-electric scheme owes its existence to the National Grid and the problem of peak load. Prior to 1930, the lack of a sufficient population, and the need for seasonal storage reservoirs, made this scheme too costly. After the construction of the grid the position changed radically, for not only was access gained to a large market, but to one already short of peak-period supply. The Galloway scheme was thus the first important example in Great Britain of plant installed primarily to deal with this daily peak which is found in the demand curve of most supply undertakings. It produces cheap, peak-period supply by storing natural run-off during hours of light demand for utilisation in peak hours. It was especially suitable for the purpose since the constructional works were relatively inexpensive and the operating charges particularly low, partly because two of the five stations are worked by remote control. The scheme has a total capacity of 102·2 megawatts (a megawatt is one million watts).

With the outbreak of war in 1939 the former objections to water-power generation in the Highlands were over-ruled by national needs, and in 1941 the Cooper Committee was appointed to 'consider the practicability and desirability of further development in the use of water power in Scotland'. With the Grampian and Galloway schemes in mind the Committee considered that if surplus Highland power were exported to the Lowlands, it could earn revenue to meet the inevitable deficit on distributing electricity in the Highlands. The Hydro-Electric Development of Scotland Act became law in 1943. The post-war developments have carried to a logical conclusion the trends emerging in the immediate pre-war period. Nationalisation in 1948 vested twenty-two undertakings and fourteen power stations into the South-West Scotland Area which employed about 6,000 persons and which, in 1955, was joined with the South-East Scotland Area to form the South of Scotland Electricity Board.

After the war it became quite clear that demand had so outstripped supply, especially peak-period supply, that load-shedding could only be overcome by increased capacity. The increased supply to cope with base load was provided by replacing obsolescent plant, as at Clyde's Mill, Dalmarnock and Yoker, and constructing new high-efficiency stations such as Braehead (completed in 1951) with a 200-megawatt capacity. That the largest of the new generating stations is under construction at Kincardine-on-Forth reflects the current and projected eastward movement in Scottish coal production and the increasing efficiency of transmission, which make minimum

214

fuel costs the object of a sound location policy. In this expansion the shortage of coal and its increasing cost hastened the search for new fuels. The first United Kingdom station designed to burn 'washery slurry', the lowest grade of residual coal and hitherto a colliery waste product, is at Barony in Ayrshire, where the first half of its modest 60-megawatt capacity was commissioned in 1957. Situated adjacent to the Number 3 shaft of Barony Colliery and the large coal preparation plant, under construction by the National Coal Board, it will utilise the large quantities of low-grade coal from nearby south Ayrshire collieries. In recent years, with the steep rise in transport costs, it has become more economic to produce electricity, when dealing with very low-grade fuels, at the fuel source, rather than close to the consumers. Chapelcross, near Annan in Dumfriesshire, will be the source of the first nuclear power to be generated in the West of Scotland. Scheduled to be in full operation in 1959, this station will have a capacity of 184 megawatts and will, in addition, serve its primary function of converting uranium into plutonium. A further nuclear station is under construction at Hunterston near Fairlie in Ayrshire.

Cheap peak power is essential in a modern industrial economy and it was to this need that the early post-war hydro-electric development in the Highlands was directed. Begun in 1946, the Loch Sloy scheme on Loch-Lomondside was the first of four stations designed to operate as a single unit supplying peak power to the Clyde industrial area. Here the high rainfall (115-120 inches per annum), together with a fivefold increase of the small natural catchment basin by artificial diversions, and the advantageous use of the high relief to give a 900-foot head of water between storage reservoir and generating station, have all been utilised to give low running costs making this an ideal station for peak-load operation.

Helped by the high price of coal, demand from the Highlands increased rapidly, and despite the programme of expansion, supply remained short. In 1955 a less than average rainfall emphasised the precarious position. The physical nature of the Highlands does not lend itself to immense storage schemes, and therefore the Hydro-Electric Board have difficulty in meeting their basic demand and are quickly affected by variations in the rainfall. Fortunately the economies derived from the use of large-scale generating plant in the Lowlands had led to the installation of capacity in excess of the base load. This surplus could be fed to the Highlands in exchange for their peak-period power.

This interdependence between Highland and Lowland Scotland, based on the use of complementary geographical conditions, will be further increased when the current proposals for development take place. The 300-megawatt capacity of the Hunterston nuclear power station will need to work continuously to attain maximum efficiency. Thus at periods of minimum demand there will be surplus power which it is proposed to use in pumped-storage schemes. The first scheme to incorporate pumped storage as a major component is planned for the outlet of Loch Awe, in Argyll. The scheme will absorb surplus energy from nuclear or high-efficiency steam stations by pumping water from Loch Awe to a high-level reservoir in a corrie, and then use it to generate peak-period power. A pilot pumped-storage plant in the Sron Mor station of the Shira scheme, near the head of Loch Fyne, with a capacity of five megawatts has been operating successfully, and several other favourable sites have been surveyed including Loch Sloy.

The present varied pattern of electricity production in the West of Scotland clearly reflects the differing potentialities of a dissected highland area with high rainfall and an industrial lowland with a diminishing coalfield. Remote districts will continue to rely on diesel stations until the hydro-generating and distribution schemes are completed. The North of Scotland Hydro-Electric Board supplies some 350 million units of peak-period power to the South of Scotland Electricity Board, in a year of average rainfall, while some 60 million units are imported to help with the increasing base load, as the area of supply grows. The South in its turn imports power from England, uses coal, nuclear energy and hydro-power for supplying base load and also has peak-power hydro-generating stations (see Fig. 49). Consumption in 1956 was 8·7 per cent higher

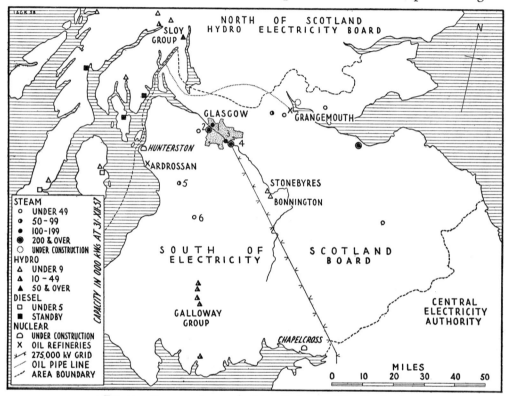

FIG. 49. Power stations and oil installations in West Scotland.

1. Yoker; 2. Braehead; 3. Dalmarnock; 4. Clyde's Mill; 5. Kilmarnock; 6. Barony;

Note:—Power stations not producing for the public supply are excluded.

than in the preceding year and as demand continues to grow in both rural and urban areas the local network of transmission lines will be extended. In the near future there are prospects of large operating economies resulting from the provision of the 275 kV 'super grid' interconnection between England and Scotland.

PETROLEUM

The petroleum industry in the West of Scotland engages in all three major branches of the industry—importation, refining and distribution. In Loch Long, at Finnart, over nine-tenths of all Scottish crude-oil imports are unloaded into the fifty-seven-mile-long pipeline, linking this deep-water ocean terminal with the major Scottish oil refinery at Grangemouth. This refinery, constructed in 1924 with an annual capacity of 400,000 tons of crude oil, is currently being enlarged from its 1954 capacity of 2·2 million tons to 3·2 million tons. As a result of the navigational difficulties of the Forth estuary it can only accommodate tankers up to 12,000 deadweight tons. It was the need for deep water close inshore, sufficient even for the projected super-tankers of 100,000 tons, that lay behind the choice of a west-coast import-terminal. This decision was further facilitated by the ease of pipeline development across the narrow 'waist' of Scotland. The pipeline, completed in 1951, has an annual pumping capacity of 3·25 million tons, thus matching the future capacity of the refinery. (See Plate V.)

The Ardrossan refinery in Ayrshire, the only other locality importing crude oil in the West of Scotland, is limited to tankers of 18,000 tons. Begun by the Admiralty as a bunkering station at the end of the First World War, the site was adopted by the Shell Oil Company in 1925. Well situated in relation to port and rail facilities, the existing area of the refinery is largely the result of two shore-reclamations, which have more than doubled the size of the original site. The major product of the refinery, whose annual capacity is 250,000 tons, is a full range of bitumens, while smaller quantities of fuel oil and lubricating oils are also produced.

Refined petroleum is brought into the West of Scotland by land and sea. The principal water-fed storage depots are at Kirkcudbright, Ardrossan, and at Bowling and Old Kilpatrick on the Clyde. The distribution of petroleum products is based on these and the more numerous rail- and road-fed storage depots, found in many of the urban areas from Stranraer in the south to Oban in the north. The recent expansion of refining and storage capacity is the outcome of increasing consumption which has in recent years been growing at a faster rate than in England. In 1956 oil consumption amounted to 2·3 million tons, which represented a 12 per cent rise over 1955 against 8 per cent for the rest of the United Kingdom. The greatest increase for any single product was for fuel oil, while aviation fuels and lubricating oils also showed marked increases. The lack of growth in demand for burning oil when compared with England must be attributed to continuing rural electrification and the availability of coal.

Increasing demand for heat and power has led to a large amount of new capital investment by each of the four industries. Modernisation and expansion of industry and transport has been closely associated with the replacement of coal by oil and electricity. 1957 saw the introduction of the first inter-city diesel service in Scotland, between Edinburgh and Glasgow, and the beginning of work on the plan to electrify seventy-one miles of railroad track mainly in the Glasgow suburban area. Although decreased reliance upon coal as the major source of fuel and power continues, its rivals have recently shown their susceptibility to adverse national and international events. The future is not clear. If the National Coal Board achieves its aim of raising the annual production to thirty million tons by 1965, from the present twenty-two million tons, and demand continues to remain stable, as it has done recently, then a resumption of exports seems likely. Further, it seems probable that coal and electricity will become less

complementary as nuclear power production expands and the electricity industry limits
its demand for the very type of coal that forms the bulk of Scottish production. These
weaknesses in local demand for coal seem to be foreshadowed without consideration of
the difficult cost position. Whatever the future, the evidence of the former importance
of coal will remain on the landscape and among the traditions of the mining communities.

The authors wish to acknowledge help from the following: The National Coal Board (Scottish
Division); the Gas Board (Scottish Division); The North of Scotland Hydro-Electricity Board; The
South of Scotland Electricity Board; British Railways (Scottish Division); Scottish Oils, Ltd; Shell
Refining Company, Ltd; Scottish Oils and Shell-Mex, Ltd; Esso Petroleum Co. Ltd; The Petroleum
Information Bureau.

THE ECONOMY OF GLASGOW

Alec Cairncross

Professor of Applied Economics, University of Glasgow

THE economy of every city is embedded in the national economy of which it forms part. What the city does, how it grows, its failures and successes, reflect the national trends and in their turn help to settle those trends. Its citizens are drawn, especially in a period of rapid expansion, from all ends of the country and from outside the country. A large part of its output is sold beyond the city limits and a large part of its everyday consumption is met from elsewhere. It competes with other centres of population as a possible site for economic activities of all kinds, drawing strength in this competition from the convenience of its location, the natural endowment of its immediate hinterland, the attractions which it can offer to those who make their life within it, and the resourcefulness, ingenuity and steadfastness of its working population. The tide of economic opportunity may sweep work and wealth towards or away from it; and since the tidal movement is rarely limited to a single city, the process of growth and decline can be understood only imperfectly in isolation from the simultaneous transformations at work in other parts of the country.

All this applies with special force to Glasgow: the Glasgow economy and the economy of Scotland are inextricably linked. The population of the city itself may be less than one-fifth of the population of Scotland, but when the rest of the conurbation, of which Glasgow is the heart, is added in, the proportion rises to over one-third. Glasgow's preponderance is still greater in terms of industrial employment: two-thirds of the insured workers in the manufacturing industries of Scotland are employed within the city or in the area that surrounds it, from Falkirk in the east to Kilmarnock in the south and Greenock in the west. The industries of the east, of Aberdeen, Dundee, Edinburgh and the Borders, may follow other rhythms; but they are scattered and subordinate. The industries of the west form a single complex, built round a single centre, and exercising a strong centripetal attraction on the rest of the economy.

The rise of Glasgow transformed nineteenth-century Scotland more powerfully than perhaps any other force. When the century began, only one Scot in twenty lived in Glasgow and one in five in the four main counties of Clydesdale—Lanark, Dunbarton, Renfrew and Ayr. When the century ended, nearly one Scot in five lived in Glasgow alone, and the population of the Clydeside area had multiplied sixfold and was not far short of half the population of Scotland. So tremendous a change in the balance of the economy, which was felt as much outside the central belt between the Clyde and the Forth as within it, meant an upheaval beyond measure in the economic and social life of the country. Large towns and modern industries were built at breakneck speed; the poverty-stricken, under-developed west, still under the influence of its Covenanting past, became at a bound one of the most prosperous areas in the world, in the forefront

219

of science and technology, a great centre of education, with a world-wide reputation for mechanical ability, philosophy and slums.

In the past half-century, Scottish life has again been dominated by Glasgow: more by the changes that did not take place than by the changes that did. Glasgow was one of the first large cities of the world to cease to grow; and the abruptness of the transition from rapid growth to stability of population was paralleled by an almost equally abrupt transition throughout the West of Scotland and, indeed, the entire country. It is probably right to treat 1914 as the turning point, although the large-scale emigration from Clydeside of the preceding decade already foreshadowed a change of trend. In the past half-century, population, instead of pouring into Clydeside, has poured out of it: a million more Scots have left the country than have returned to it, and the majority of them have gone from Glasgow and Clydeside. The city's population, already over a million in 1911, has not risen significantly since; indeed, within the limits that existed in 1921, there has been a slight but progressive fall, in spite of all the new building that has gone on. Undoubtedly there has been some overspill into the suburbs that lay outside the city in 1921 and the area that still lies beyond the city limits; but the dimensions of this have been modest and the conurbation as a whole has grown by a smaller increment in the past fifty years than was normal in succeeding decades towards the end of the nineteenth century.

What happened in Clydeside happened also in the rest of the country: the population of Scotland has grown since 1911 by little more than used to be recorded decade by decade after 1871. The country's development, slowed down by the check to the principal centre of industry, came near to realising in practice the imaginary stationary state that has so occupied theoretical economists; but what economists referred to a hypothetical future has been visible in the living reality of Scotland over the past half-century.

The absence of growth in Glasgow is apparent to the naked eye in the absence of new buildings in the square mile that contains the commercial centre of the town. Apart from an occasional bank, cinema and hotel, nearly every building in this area goes back before the First World War and there is no likelihood that many of these buildings will be pulled down in the near future. Such demolition as is planned is in the area peripheral to this, which includes the slums of Bridgeton, Gorbals and Cowcaddens, and has changed little, externally at least, in the past hundred years. It is true that, further out from the centre, new housing estates have been built and continue to be built; but these are designed to reduce overcrowding to a more tolerable degree, not to accommodate still more families within the city.

The cessation of growth had economic aspects, too. It meant an end to that cumulative process by which success breeds success and every new industry attracts another. If the city was given an opportunity of solving its housing problem, it was also deprived of the magnetic power of an expanding market and forced to reconsider the basis on which its livelihood was built.

There are normally three elements in an urban economy: the industries which make the pace by exporting to other parts of the country or abroad and generate an abundance of purchasing power that attracts first goods and then workers from outside; the industries which grow up to meet the needs of this expanding market and which take part only indirectly in the balancing of accounts with other areas; and the innumerable

220

service industries which are required because of the concentration of a large population specialised in manufacturing activities. This threefold division is not by any means hard and fast. The brewing industry, for example, might be thought to fall under the second heading; yet a firm like J. & R. Tennent, which has an existence in Glasgow stretching back over four hundred years, and has a world-wide reputation rivalling that of its famous Danish and Dutch competitors, exports over one-third of its output and contributes in this way to the settlement of accounts between Glasgow and the area from which she draws her imports. Similarly, the service trades are not by any means occupied solely in meeting the needs of Glaswegians, but fulfil a wider function, both because the surrounding area makes use of the professional and commercial services that Glasgow can offer and because Glasgow is the natural centre for training in all branches of commerce and industry.

When growth ceases in an industrial city, it is usually because of a check to the first of these three elements. When the key industries, for which the city has special advantages, lose their momentum, the others are generally incapable of maintaining it alone. So it would appear to have been in Glasgow. The heavy industries, in all of which Glasgow could equal or outdo other areas, drew along behind them other industries, which were born out of the prosperity of the area and throve on the network of facilities and skills with which it encompassed them. When the key industries faltered and steam power began to be displaced by oil and electricity, the old momentum perished and other areas, with a different range of facilities and skills, proved more attractive as locations for the newer industries. But how all this came about is a long story and cannot be told in a paragraph or two. What lay behind the rise of Glasgow, why was the rise so abruptly checked and what are the prospects that it will now be resumed?

THE RISE OF GLASGOW

Glasgow's development followed the classical pattern: first came trade, then light industry, then heavy industry. At the beginning of the eighteenth century, before the Union, it was a small rural burgh of about 12,000 inhabitants with a University, a Cathedral, a few small workshops and very little trade with abroad. The Union opened up new markets, particularly for Scottish agriculture, and the expansion of trade brought more money to the towns. Glasgow profited particularly from the tobacco trade with the American colonies; at one time, half the imports of tobacco for European consumption came via the Clyde. Whether this was because Glasgow was a more westerly port than her rivals and so offered a shorter deep-sea voyage, or because, as some alleged, it was easier to cheat the Customs' officers on the Clyde, we need not discuss; it is more probable that Glasgow merchants stood readier to make the most of a unique opportunity and pursued it with greater earnestness. By the time the tobacco trade collapsed, agriculture had improved vastly—aided to some extent by the profits earned in trade and in the colonies—and industry was beginning to stir. But there was not, as yet, a single cotton factory of any size in the West of Scotland.

It was to cotton, however, that Glasgow now turned. There was already some acquaintance in the area with the coarser textiles, particularly linen; there was water power and a temperate and humid climate, not unlike Lancashire's; there was also an increasing population, lacking employment and living on oatmeal—in other words, cheap labour. English textile manufacturers, notably Arkwright and Robert Owen, took the lead in setting up spinning mills, and local men soon followed. The first cotton factories were generally at some distance from Glasgow—for example, at Deanston, New Lanark, Lennoxtown and Paisley—but Glasgow handled the trade, importing the raw cotton and providing a market for the yarn and cloth. By the early nineteenth century, Glasgow was also actively engaged in the industry and some of the cotton factories still in existence in the town can trace their history back to just after the Napoleonic Wars.

The Paisley thread industry, which has perhaps the longest history of any local branch of the textile industries, grew up in the eighteenth century, using processes borrowed—or, to be more exact, stolen—from the Dutch and applied to the spinning of silk and linen thread. The substitution of cotton for silk was frequently attempted but succeeded only when silk became unobtainable under the Berlin Decrees and the spur of necessity was applied to technical ingenuity. By 1830 Paisley was already the principal centre of thread manufacture, the firms that dominated the trade throughout the rest of the century had come into existence and the technique of manufacture had begun to take its modern shape. Yet in some ways the decisive stage was reached later, for it was in the 'forties and 'fifties that the firm of J. & P. Coats established itself in the American market, selling in that market many times what it sold in the British market. Thus Paisley was ready to take advantage of the sewing machine when it came along.

In thread as in tobacco it was the American connection that provided the lever. But the connection was not limited to trade. By the late 'sixties Coats were busy building their first American thread mill at Pawtucket, and Clark's, their rivals in Paisley, had established a mill at Newark, New Jersey, while at almost exactly the same time the Singer Sewing Machine Company was building at Clydebank what was to become one of the largest factories in the West of Scotland. Coats became one of the first, if not the first firm in the world to operate a chain of overseas branches run by separate operating companies; and the Singer Sewing Machine Company became one of the earliest in the long stream of American companies that have come to Scotland to engage in manufacturing. Not, however, the earliest: the North British Rubber Company descends from the shipment of a complete American factory to Edinburgh in 1856.

Other industries followed textiles. Bleaching powder, for example, was produced at St Rollox from 1800 onwards in what had become by 1830 one of the largest chemical plants in Europe and was producing sulphuric acid, soda and soap as well as bleaching powder. But the chemical industries, to the development of which Glasgow contributed powerfully, have never played a major part in the Glasgow economy.

The city's development was dominated, as the century advanced, by coal and iron. The invention of the hot blast by J. B. Neilson in 1828 gave the West of Scotland a decisive advantage in pig-iron produced from the local blackband ironstone and splint coal. Costs fell dramatically and Scottish pig-iron sold readily on a rapidly mounting scale. Once again, the American market gave additional momentum as the limits of the home market were approached and at its peak in 1849 took no less than 14 per cent of the Scottish output and 61 per cent of Scottish exports.

The expansion of the iron industry was doubly significant. Scotland suddenly found herself out-distancing all other countries in the production of the commodity, which, more than any other, was the raw material of modern industry. In the middle of the nineteenth century over nine-tenths of British exports of pig-iron came from Scotland. This by itself brought prosperity and a sense of industrial destiny. But, in addition, the growth of iron production created an expanding demand for coal and forced the construction of new railways to the hitherto relatively inaccessible coalfields of Lanarkshire. Thus two major industries grew up together on Clydeside in a couple of decades after 1830.

In time, the iron industry was checked. The north-east coast soon outstripped Scotland; the local ores began to near exhaustion; what was worse, the production of steel by the new Bessemer process ran into difficulties; and the cheapness of Scottish pig-iron did not lead to the development of a flourishing malleable-iron industry on the scale that one might have expected. Nor, when the steel industry finally became established, did it win the swift ascendancy that Scottish pig-iron had enjoyed, for the Scottish steelworks could neither use local ores nor profit from a tidewater location. Nevertheless, the industry contributed to the British output of steel in at least as high a proportion as Scottish industry bore to the national aggregate.

Even before the first steel furnace had been built in 1870, what has long been the largest and best-known of Glasgow industries had shot into prominence. Until the coming of steam power, the Clyde was not a shipbuilding centre of any importance; beginning in the 'forties, however, the Clyde shipbuilders gained an increasing hold that brought them in the ensuing twenty or thirty years ahead of any other shipbuilding centre in the world. A century ago, Aberdeen was still a match for Greenock and American builders designed better vessels than either; but in an astonishingly short time, Glasgow passed all her rivals and 'Clyde-built' became synonymous with the best in shipbuilding.

The expansion in shipbuilding on the Clyde appears to have been due largely to the enterprise of the local builders in their experiments with marine engines and to their willingness to change from wooden to iron, and later steel, vessels ahead of other shipbuilders. The Clyde shipbuilders also had advantages in the proximity of their supplies of iron and steel, materials which were costly to transport, and in the existence of an experienced local industry skilled in the construction and operation of steam engines. The Clyde was obviously in a stronger position than the Thames to assemble ship plates into marine hulls. Local labour was both highly skilled and relatively cheap. Many of the shipping companies which provided the market for large vessels were either located in Glasgow or made use of the port. Finally, in shipbuilding, as in many other Glasgow industries, the American connection exercised a decisive influence, for many of the vessels built on the Clyde were for use on transatlantic routes.

Shipbuilding and marine engineering were far from the only metal-using industries that grew up in Glasgow in the course of the nineteenth century. Steam engines had been built in the city since 1800 and in 1835, before marine engineering had reached more than the most modest proportions, there were already fourteen Glasgow firms engaged in their construction. Textile and mining machinery led the way and locomotive-building followed: by 1913 the North British Locomotive Company alone employed over 7,000 workers. Sir William Arrol & Co. enjoyed an international reputation as constructional engineers. In the manufacture of boilers, pumps, tubes, heavy machine tools, cranes and so on, Glasgow was in the forefront. In machinery for sugar-refining she had almost a monopoly. A list of the engineering industries represented in the city by the outbreak of the First World War would fill an entire page.

Nor were the metal and engineering industries the only ones of any importance in the Glasgow area; far from it. These industries employed relatively few women, but there were plenty of other industries that did, notably the clothing trades: in 1921, two of every five Scotswomen in the clothing trades worked in Glasgow. The food, drink and tobacco trades were also heavily represented: for example, in grain-milling, biscuit-making, confectionery, brewing and distilling and tobacco manufacture. Several well-known printers, publishers and paper mills had their headquarters in the city. Furniture-making, paints and varnishes, glass, cardboard and wooden boxes and containers were among the host of other Glasgow industries with a long history behind them. Indeed, as one surveys the whole panorama of industrial activity, one can only echo Bramble's comment on his city in *Humphrey Clinker*: 'It is a perfect beehive in point of industry.'

THE INDUSTRIAL PATTERN

The economy that had been built up by the First World War rested heavily on a single group of industries, integrated in a complex structure in which one industry catered for the requirements of another and all were at the mercy of the pace of development overseas. If world development was rapid, the products of the heavy industries were in demand everywhere, particularly at a time when development largely took the form of the growth of a modern transport system within and between foreign countries. Steamships and locomotives, railway track, cranes and bridges, were the stock-in-trade of international development, and Glasgow could provide them all. But if depression overtook the world, as it did almost throughout the inter-war period, all these things were a drug on the market; or if the world moved on to other types of transport equipment, such as road vehicles and aircraft, Glasgow had little to offer.

Moreover, although Glasgow had a far more diversified economy than is commonly appreciated, the environment was not congenial to the newer industries: the existing complex exercised a gravitational pull on industries that could easily be integrated into it, but it repelled other industries that could not, and that flourished only if allowed to dominate and mould the economy in which they took root. The replacement of one industrial structure by another is never easy and always prolonged, most of all when deflation is slowing down the whole process of industrial change. It takes time for new growth to occur: for new firms to force their way to the front, new capacity to be created, new types of skill to be acquired. If the current has set strongly in one direction, it is hard to prepare another channel. Employment may be found at first for a few hundreds in unfamiliar pursuits; but to turn the hundreds into thousands and multiply the thousands takes years of effort and enterprise by a host of firms sustained by confidence that they can succeed, by the prospect of an expanding market and by their power to compete within it.

In the years between the wars, when Glasgow suffered unemployment and depression in almost exact proportion to her dependence on the industries most affected, it was natural to blame lack of diversification for her misfortunes. But there was, in fact, no lack of diversity in Glasgow industry, and this very diversity was urged as late as 1915 by the Town Clerk of the city as the ground of her immunity from depression in

224

the past. 'No city,' he boasted, 'has rivalled, far less surpassed, Glasgow, the commercial metropolis of Scotland. This has chiefly arisen from the city being—if the expression may be used—*cosmopolitan* in its commerce and manufactures. Glasgow unites within itself a portion of the cotton spinning and weaving manufactures of Manchester, the printed calicoes of Lancashire, the stuffs of Norwich, the shawls and mousselines of France, the silk-throwing of Macclesfield, the flax-spinning of Ireland, the carpets of Kidderminster, the iron and engineering works of Wolverhampton, Sheffield, and Birmingham, the pottery and glass-making of Staffordshire and Newcastle, the coal trade of the Tyne and Wear, and all the handicrafts connected with or dependent on the full development of these. Glasgow also has its distilleries, breweries, chemical works, tan-works, dye-works, bleachfields, and paper manufactories, besides a vast number of staple and fancy hand-loom fabrics which may be strictly said to belong to that locality. Glasgow also, in its commercial relations, trades with every quarter of the globe; and its merchants deal in the various products of every country. It hence appears that one branch of manufacture or trade may be dull while another may be prosperous; and, accordingly, Glasgow does not feel any of those universal depressions which so frequently occur in places limited to one or two branches of manufacture or commerce.'

The Town Clerk's boast was not without justification. It is arguable that Glasgow and, to a lesser extent, Clydeside had an economy more diversified than any other part of the Kingdom. There was none of the tremendous dependence on the coal-mining industry that was typical of South Wales; and the range of metal industries was much wider than on the north-east coast. No industry, not even shipbuilding, dominated Clydeside in the way that cotton textiles did Lancashire and wool textiles Yorkshire. Even Birmingham and London, although they happened to have a strong hold on the expanding industries of the present century, were in some ways more narrowly specialised than Glasgow. Comparison with Birmingham, for example, shows that in that city the metal and engineering trades accounted for 48·3 per cent of all employment in 1951 while in Glasgow the proportion was only 23·3 per cent. On the other hand, the textile, leather and clothing trades together accounted for only 2·3 per cent of employment in Birmingham compared with 7·9 per cent in Glasgow. In both groups the Glasgow figures were far nearer to the British averages than those for Birmingham.

Let us look more closely at the pattern of industry, or at least of employment, alongside the pattern for Scotland and Great Britain. The broad pattern for Glasgow, based on the figures for insured workers, whether in employment or not, is given in Table XXIII. The totals include workers at the Hillington Industrial Estate, which just lies outside the city, but they exclude all self-employed workers.

Half the men and two-fifths of the women are engaged in manufacturing; transport, distribution and the service trades occupy a further third; and the remainder are divided between the building industry, national and local government, professional services such as teaching and accountancy and—strange intrusion into an urban economy! —agriculture and mining. The fact that manufacturing industry comes to so limited a proportion of the total deserves emphasis and serves as a reminder of the commercial activities that equally sustain the economic life of the city. For the present, however, it is only with the pattern of manufacturing industry that we are concerned and other elements in the economy must be left without further discussion.

From this more limited angle, it emerges that two out of every three male em-

P

ployees in manufacturing are in one branch or other of the metal and engineering industries. For female employees, the proportion is quite different: less than one in four

Main Industry Groups	Insured Employees					
	Males		Females		Total	
	Number (ooo's)	Per Cent	Number (ooo's)	Per Cent	Number (ooo's)	Per Cent
Shipbuilding and Marine engineering	26·6	7·9	1·9	1·0	28·6	5·3
Other engineering	69·8	20·7	15·0	7·3	84·8	15·6
Metal manufacture (incl. non-ferrous smelting)	15·2	4·5	1·9	0·9	17·0	3·1
Textiles and Clothing	8·8	2·6	28·4	13·7	37·2	6·8
Other manufacturing	48·4	14·4	35·1	17·0	83·5	15·4
Total manufacturing	168·7	50·1	82·4	39·9	251·1	46·2
Agriculture and Mining	2·9	0·9	0·6	0·3	3·5	0·6
Building and Contracting	32·8	9·8	1·9	0·9	34·7	6·4
Distributive and Service Trades	52·8	15·7	73·7	35·6	126·5	23·3
Transport and Communications	42·6	12·4	9·4	4·6	51·0	9·4
Professional services	16·5	4·9	32·5	15·7	49·0	9·0
National and Local Govt. (incl. Gas, Water & Electricity)	20·8	6·2	6·4	3·1	27·2	5·0
Total non-manufacturing	167·7	49·9	124·4	60·1	292·1	53·8
Grand Total	336·4	100·0	206·8	100·0	543·2	100·0

TABLE XXIII. Estimated distribution of Insured Employees in Glasgow at mid-1955 between Main Industry Groups.

Source: Calculated from unpublished Ministry of Labour statistics.

works in this group of industries. While the men are in the heavy industries, the women are in the light: in the tailoring trades—easily the largest industrial employer of women in Glasgow—hosiery, carpets, confectionery, biscuits, tobacco, cardboard boxes, printing and so on.

Table XXIII does not give more than the most general idea of the pattern of industry in Glasgow since it divides all manufacturing into five broad groups only. For purposes of comparison with the Scottish and British pattern a rather more detailed division into fourteen categories is used in Table XXIV, which has been prepared by Dr C. E. V. Leser.

Main Industry Groups	Percentage of all Insured Employees		
	Glasgow	Scotland	Great Britain
Engineering, shipbuilding and electrical goods	12·9	9·7	9·2
Vehicles	5·6	3·4	5·3
Metal manufacture	3·1	3·0	2·7
Miscellaneous metal goods	1·6	1·4	2·4
Precision instruments, Jewellery, etc.	0·7	0·4	0·6
Total	23·9	17·9	20·2
Textiles	2·7	5·7	4·7
Clothing	4·4	1·8	3·1
Leather, leather goods and fur	0·5	0·3	0·4
Chemicals and allied trades	1·6	1·9	2·4
Building materials, etc.	0·8	1·2	1·6
Food, drink and tobacco	6·6	5·1	4·1
Wood and cork manufactures	1·8	1·4	1·4
Paper and printing	3·4	2·4	2·4
Other manufacturing industries	0·6	0·9	1·2
Grand Total*	46·2	38·5	41·4

TABLE XXIV. Distribution of Insured Employees between Main Industry Groups in Glasgow, Scotland and Great Britain, in 1953.

* Differs from total of individual items because of rounding.

Source: Statistical Account of Glasgow, Chapter 4.

Table XXIV indicates a pattern of industry that is broadly similar to the pattern for Britain as a whole. There is, of course, more industry in total in Glasgow than in a representative cross-section of the British (or Scottish) economy with a working population of the same size. It is not surprising, therefore to find many individual industries more strongly represented in Glasgow than in the national economy. But it is interesting to find only five of the fourteen groups occupying a place in the economy of Glasgow below the national average. These five are: miscellaneous metal goods (e.g.

227

wire, hollow-ware, bolts and nuts, etc.), textiles, chemicals, building materials (*e.g.* bricks and glass) and other manufacturing industries (*e.g.* rubber, linoleum, toys, etc.). The most important deficiences are in textiles and chemicals, but even these industries, or at least some branches of them, employ a large number of Glasgow workers.

A similar comparison for the hinterland of Glasgow in the Clyde Valley tells a different story. In this area, nine of the fourteen industry groups are less strongly represented than in the national economy and the degree of divergence from the national average is much greater. Of the five industries in which the area specialises, two, engineering and shipbuilding, and iron and steel melting and rolling, are in the metals group while the other three, textiles, chemicals and building materials, are all industries that play only a limited part in the economic life of Glasgow itself. Thus to some extent the industries of the Clyde Valley supplement those of Glasgow and redress the balance, and to some extent they intensify Clydeside's dependence on the heavy industries.

At a time when half the manufacturing activity of the country is carried on in the metals and engineering group of industries, it tells us very little to say that in Glasgow also the proportion is roughly half. We may agree that this rough similarity, and the general similarity between the Glasgow and national industrial patterns, bear witness to a diversity of manufactures which, superficially, is extremely striking. But a different classification of industries might yield very different results. Suppose, for example, that we could separate industries and products that did not exist half a century ago, or ten years ago, from those that existed earlier; or industries and products for which there is a strong upward secular trend in demand; or industries that are likely to be relatively immune to a contraction in world markets. Would Glasgow then compare so favourably? We cannot be certain. But it is significant that *within* the engineering group the most prominent items of manufacture are ships and locomotives, while electric machinery and appliances are relatively insignificant, providing, in total, less employment than, say, the manufacture of biscuits. The branches of the engineering group of industries, whether in Glasgow or Clydeside, that dominate the economy are, almost without exception, producer goods; on the other hand, the group of durable consumer goods which has been expanding so rapidly in the past generation is almost entirely absent.

All this is apparent from whatever angle one approaches the matter. In the steel industry the principal market is for plates which are the typical raw material for producer goods. After plates come heavy sections and structural material. On the other hand, the output of sheet and strip, which is the material *par excellence* of durable consumer goods, is negligible and there is no production of tin plate whatever. If one enters a typical engineering establishment it is at once apparent that production is directed, either to the manufacture of a single large product, or at best is organised on the batch principle. The methods of production in use, in other words, are those appropriate to producer goods for which the market is limited and individual, rather than to the manufacture of consumer goods with a mass market. Even those producer goods which admit of manufacture in quantity are relatively insignificant. The best example is perhaps that of machine tools, the bulk of the output of machine tools in and around Glasgow being 'one-off' jobs mostly for local customers. Again, the engineering trades give employment, to a degree not at all typical of, say, the Birmingham area,

228

to men rather than women because it is assumed that heavy industry is a man's job; so much so that some of the local engineering firms still view with something akin to horror the prospect of employing a woman with technical or University qualifications, except in a secretarial capacity.

This preponderance of heavy industry would be of little significance if the heavy industries were still themselves in course of expansion; and it is the fact that those industries have had long order books since the war that has accounted for the revival of industry on Clydeside much more than the arrival of a large number of new firms and industries. The fact appears to be, however, that the older heavy industries are likely to play, in the world of the future, a much less important rôle than they did in the nineteenth century; an area specialising in those industries must adapt its industrial pattern in line with this long-run trend or run the risk of participation in the general stagnation or decline.

This adaptation was delayed in the years before the war by a variety of factors. Glasgow industry had been built up almost entirely by family businesses, relatively few of which had converted themselves into public companies. This meant that the resources at their disposal were often inadequate to allow of rationalisation in conditions of depression, or to finance development work that might have allowed a new start to be made in a fresh direction. In addition, what had at one time been the strength of the area tended to become a source of weakness. As the nineteenth century progressed, Glasgow developed a labour force of unusual skill and experience, capable of taking wide responsibilities and exercising a meticulous craftsmanship that was the envy of the world. An enquiry in 1955 showed that, out of 89,000 workers employed by 395 firms in Glasgow, 29,000 were time-served journeymen and 9,000 others were graded as skilled, while a further 7,000 were apprentices. Unfortunately the very abundance of skill made it unnecessary for managements to plan their operations in advance, as they were obliged to do in the United States, so as to make the maximum use of mechanical equipment rather than human labour. The top management, particularly in the heavy industries, usually consisted of a small group of men accustomed to improvisation and skilled in jobbing work but unfamiliar with the tooling and scheduling of a production line. No systematic effort of development was thought to be necessary and no development teams were formed because the tradition was to introduce progressive modifications in design from the experience obtained in the construction of successful models. There was no market research, since sales were made on the basis of personal contact between the proprietor of the business and his customer; and it was assumed to be impossible to enforce standardisation in conditions of acute competition.

There was, therefore, little or no demand in Glasgow's industry for men whose training was primarily theoretical. Almost as a concession, some University-trained technologists did find local employment; but even in 1955, in the 395 manufacturing firms referred to above, the total number of graduates was no more than 469, of whom 83 were graduates in Arts, 124 in Science and 204 in Engineering. In the shipbuilding industry thirteen firms employing 21,000 operatives included only 18 graduates on their staff, and of these, all but two were graduates in Science and Engineering. On the other hand, the paper and printing trades, employing about a quarter as many workers, had 29 graduates, 19 of them in Arts.

Thus, although Glasgow was educating larger numbers of technologists than any other industrial city in the country, local industry failed signally to find opportunities of employing graduates in technology and refrained almost entirely from employing graduates in other disciplines. It is not surprising that the chemical and electrical industries, which have been built up through the massive employment of University graduates and which are now expanding by leaps and bounds, have almost entirely deserted the town. It cannot be said that those industries had no chance of success. The chemical industry is heavily in debt to Glasgow chemists, and some of the earliest firms in the industry established themselves in the town. Similarly, Glasgow was a pioneer in the development of electricity. Quite apart from the work of Lord Kelvin and Professors Barr and Stroud, whose efforts contributed to the early development of electrical and precision instruments in the area, electric lighting was made use of in Glasgow at an early date: Queen Street and St Enoch Railway Stations, for example, were lit by electricity as early as 1879. It is possible that it would have been an uphill fight, given the prosperity of other industries in the Glasgow area up to 1914, for the chemical and electric engineering industries to gain a sufficient foothold; but the inability of industry to make use of University-trained talent must have been an important contributing factor to this failure.

The most disquieting feature of the inter-war period was thus not the absence of diversification; nor was it the violence of the fluctuations to which the dominant industries were subject. It was, to a much greater extent, the failure of newer industries to take root and the lack of soil in which they could hope to flourish. Those who, at the end of the war, were still preoccupied with the need to diversify the economy as a means of reducing the risk of unemployment, misconceived the problem. The task confronting Glasgow was one of structural adjustment to permit new growth, not the replacement of one set of industries by a mixed bag of other industries.

Yet even before the war the pattern was changing. Dr Leser has shown that between 1923 and 1947 Scotland was by no means wholly deficient in expanding industries. His calculations, reproduced in Table **XXV**, show that nearly one worker in five was in an industry which doubled over that period while in Great Britain as a whole the proportion was one in four. In Scotland, as in the rest of the country, it was the industries with moderate rates of growth—25 to 100 per cent—that accounted for almost half the total employment.

The war and post-war years have seen a marked acceleration of the process of transformation. To this the Trading Estates, beginning with Hillington in 1937, have contributed greatly. Four industrial estates have been developed since the war in the Glasgow Employment Area and these, together with Hillington, house 214 firms, most of them small but including one, Rolls Royce, which is among the largest in Scotland. These firms employ approximately 26,000 workers in the Glasgow Employment Area, 20,000 of them in engineering establishments; a further 6,000 workers are employed by thirteen firms in factories constructed on individual sites in the Area by Scottish Industrial Estates, Ltd. These new factories (including those which were built before and during the last war) employ about one in eight of Glasgow employees in manufacturing industry.

Apart from new factories on the industrial estates, many factories have been built or extended since the war in other parts of the city. In all, some 350 new factories (excluding extensions) have been built in the Glasgow area with a total employment

230

of 50,000. About half of the total factory space created has been for firms in metals and engineering and the proportion in terms of employment is certainly higher. The new

Rate of expansion or decline in Great Britain 1923-47	Scotland		Percentage of total employment in Great Britain	Scotland as percentage of Great Britain
	Number (000's)	Percentage of total employment		
Decline:				
25% or more	173·9	11·0	10·4	11·1
Less than 25%	155·6	9·8	9·1	11·5
Expansion:				
Less than 25%	203·8	12·9	12·0	11·4
25% but less than 50%	361·2	22·8	18·6	13·0
50% but less than 100%	385·6	24·4	25·0	10·3
100% but less than 200%	178·0	11·3	13·3	9·0
200% or more	123·2	7·8	11·6	7·1
All industries and services	1581·3	100·0	100·0	10·6

TABLE **XXV**. Employment in expanding and declining industries, 1923-47.
Source: The Scottish Economy, p. 75.

factories have done nothing, therefore, to diminish Glasgow's dependence on this group of industries; but since they include aero-engines, typewriters, light metal castings and so on, they have strengthened the precision engineering and lighter sides of those industries.

The scale of new factory construction is in striking contrast to pre-war years. In 1935, which may be taken as typical of the middle 'thirties, only twenty-two new factories were built in the whole of Scotland, compared with 213 in London alone. In the years 1954-57, the average for Scotland has been nearly fifty and for the Clydeside conurbation seventeen. This compares with an estimate made in 1952 that about 100 new *enterprises* had been created annually in Scotland since the war, new enterprises being taken to mean new manufacturing businesses irrespective of the type of premises they occupied. About half of these were found to have started in existing premises and four-fifths of the remainder started in factories built with government assistance. Nearly a quarter of the new enterprises were branches of English, American and foreign firms. These figures are some indication of the part that has been played by the government and by non-Scottish enterprises since the war in bringing new industry to Scotland and, above all, to Clydeside.

American firms were prominent even in the nineteenth century—witness the North British Rubber Co., Singer's and Babcock & Wilcox, all of them still thriving concerns. Now their influence has been enormously reinforced by the arrival of at least thirty branches of American firms over the last twelve years. These branches, employing over 20,000 workers, have introduced new techniques and a new range of activities to Scotland and account for a growing proportion of Scottish exports. The Glasgow area has become the second biggest producer of earth-moving equipment in the world (Euclid Ltd at Newhouse and Caterpillar Tractor Co. at Uddingston) as well as an important producer of agricultural machinery (Massey Harris Ferguson at Kilmarnock). It is becoming one of the leading centres for business machinery (Burroughs at Vale of Leven and Cumbernauld, I.B.M. at Greenock, and Remington Rand at Hillington, as well as Olivetti, an Italian firm, also at Queenslie). In electronics, there are now several firms including two large American manufacturers (Honeywell-Brown and Ranco). Other American factories (*e.g.* Goodyear Tyre and Rubber Co.) are outside the engineering industry; those that are within the engineering group have helped to diversify engineering in the area, added a much-needed admixture of medium and light engineering, strengthened the electrical engineering component, and introduced more highly mechanised methods of assembly and manufacture.

Industry Groups	Percentage of insured employees	
	1938	1955
Metal and engineering trades	18·6	24·0
Textile, leather and clothing trades	7·8	6·8
Other manufacturing	13·9	15·4
Total manufacturing	40·3	46·2
Building, mining and gas, water and electricity	8·7	8·1
Transport and distribution	31·9	24·8
All other	19·1	20·9
Grand Total	100·0	100·0

TABLE XXVI. The Industrial Pattern of Glasgow, 1938 and 1955.

It is not possible to show in detail how the industrial pattern has changed over the past twenty years. Table XXVI shows how manufacturing has grown in relation to other activities, particularly distribution, and how, within manufacturing, the metal and engineering trades have led the way in expansion. These figures relate to numbers insured, not numbers employed. If a deduction were made for those who were unemployed at the two dates shown, the proportion under 'manufacturing' would undoubtedly shrink in 1938, when unemployment was heavy and largely concentrated in industry.

Although these figures are an impressive testimony to the magnitude of the changes in progress, they do not differ in their general drift from the changes that have taken

PL. XIII. UNIVERSITY OF GLASGOW, on drumlin centre, Park drumlin on margin right. North basin Queen's Dock fore-ground, separated by riverside railway viaduct from sidings and industrial sprawl which fronts St Vincent Terrace, originally free-standing residential. Enclosing Campsie plateau beyond with Strathblane gap left.

John Watson, Kilsyth

PL. XIV. WEST GLASGOW from the South

River flats in foreground, Southern General Hospital bottom left, Govan tenements right. On near bank of Clyde, Shieldhall sewage works left, Alexander Stephen's shipbuilding yard centre, with, left, the 24,000-ton transatlantic liner *Olympia* fitting out. Whiteinch ferry and site for tunnel entrance, right. On far bank, Barclay Curle's shipbuilding yard and Merklands Wharf right. Beyond, Scotstoun and twentieth century sprawl; Jordanhill Training College on hill in trees. Kilpatricks in background left, divided by Strathblane from Campsies right. Dumgoyne prominent (see Pl. VI), Ben Lomond in left centre distance.

Note lava plateaus encircling the Howe, which is fully built-up; industry on river flats; and obliquity of slipways to the narrow river.

W. Ralston, Ltd.

Pl. XV.
DALMARNOCK:
East Glasgow from
the south-east

River flats with
power station and
other industrial in-
stallations centre
and foreground.
Across river Shaw-
field Stadium left,
Richmond Park and
Glasgow Green
right. In distance,
Govanhill left,
Hutchesontown
centre and central
Glasgow and main
bridges right.

Aero-Pictorial Ltd.

Pl. XVI.
GEORGE
SQUARE,
Glasgow, from
the north-west.

City Chambers top
left. Square laid out
early nineteenth
c e n t u r y : only
original buildings
bottom left side.

Aero-Pictorial Ltd.

place over the same period in the national economy. Glasgow, once again, is a faithful image of the national trend and the Glasgow figures come close to the national average.

THE HEAVY INDUSTRIES

The changes at work cannot, however, be analysed in terms of aggregates. It is necessary to study some of the key industries of Clydeside to assess the prospects of the area. We shall, therefore, turn next to the coal, steel and shipbuilding industries, the rest of the engineering industries having already been dealt with in Chapter 9.

COAL

Although there is now only one coal-mine within the city limits, Glasgow is almost literally built on coal. Underneath the town lie coal workings that were abandoned many years ago; the galleries were filled with rubble and the topsoil built over without thought of subsidence—an expensive oversight, as the University found to its cost when erecting the new cyclotron at Gilmorehill shortly after the war. New borings are being made on the outskirts at Bearsden, while old sinkings in Lanarkshire are in course of abandonment. Most of the coal mined in Scotland is consumed on Clydeside and the coalfield around Glasgow is still the largest in the country.

The coal-mining industry reached its zenith before the First World War when Scotland produced nearly twice as much coal as in recent years and consumed not much more than 60 per cent of what she produced. In the West of Scotland the fall from the peak, which was also reached in 1913, was far more violent and still continues. Lanarkshire and the adjacent counties into which the Lanarkshire coalfield extends once contributed two-thirds of the Scottish output, but the proportion has fallen steadily since 1890 and is now no more than one-third. The remaining seams are thin, the better qualities of coal are increasingly scarce, and output per man is far below the rate achieved in the middle 'thirties. The cost of mining coal is rising faster in Scotland than in any other part of Britain and exceeds by a margin of 50 per cent the cost per ton in the lowest English division—the East Midlands—although only ten years ago the margin was no more than one-sixth.

This growing differential, which is equally large in west and east Scotland, strikes at one of the great locational advantages of Glasgow. Glasgow firms can no longer count on cheap coal. This affects only a limited group of industries directly; but it affects other industries indirectly. If fuel is expensive, one more adverse factor is thrown into the scale when it is already tipping against Glasgow. Major industries like steel are severely handicapped by high fuel costs and can escape them by building elsewhere; and where these fuel-oriented industries go, others, less responsive to fuel costs but obliged to be near their market, will inevitably follow. Electric-power generation, if coal-firing were not becoming obsolescent, might also move sooner or later towards the Midlands and a new grid, capable of transferring vast supplies of power to the north, would be brought into use.

A further handicap to Glasgow industry arises from the shift in the centre of gravity of the coal-mining industry. The expanding mining areas—or rather the areas where expansion is planned, for none of them has yet exceeded the level of output reached before the war—are in the east (Fife, and Clackmannan and the Lothians) or south (Ayr and Dumfries) so that coal has to be brought from a greater distance to meet Glasgow's fuel requirements, and this extra transport must ultimately be reflected in the price.

The coal problem is concentrated in special grades and sizes, and some of the coals most affected are of the greatest strategic importance to Scottish industry. This is true, for example, of gas coals and coking coals. Deposits of coking coals exist, but the cost of mining them is problematical and there is a point at which coke users would be unable to stay in the market. The steel industry already imports coking coal from England, and whatever promises have been made to it by the National Coal Board as to supplies from local sources, there can be no guarantee that those supplies will continue to be available at an attractive price. The significance of this became apparent in 1957 when strong representations were made in favour of locating Richard Baldwin's new strip mill at Grangemouth.

STEEL

The melting and rolling of iron and steel is concentrated within a few miles of Glasgow, almost entirely either within Glasgow itself or within a few miles of it. Some of the best known plants—Beardmore's Parkhead Forge, for example—are within the city, and others, such as Colville's Works at Clydebridge, are just outside. Several of the larger plants are in the Motherwell area. Of the establishments at some distance from Glasgow only the Carron Iron Works, founded nearly two hundred years ago, and Colville's plant at Glengarnock, are of any importance and both are within a thirty-mile radius. What is true of melting and rolling is equally true of re-rolling; the finishing stages are heavily concentrated in and around Glasgow.

The industry is dominated by the Colville group, which owns one alloy and six carbon steel-melting shops. These, together with Beardmore's (Parkhead), Baird's and Scottish Steel (Gartsherrie), and Stewarts and Lloyds (Mossend) produce about 90 per cent of the total output of steel ingots, the remaining 10 per cent coming from eighteen other establishments. The Colville plants are at Clydebridge, Motherwell, Hallside (near Blantyre) and Glengarnock, the Motherwell plants including the former Lanarkshire Steel Works, the old Dalzell Works of Colville's and the new Works at Ravenscraig. With the completion of the latter in 1957, the industry has now a total capacity approaching three million tons, of which the Colville group alone accounts for well over two million tons.

The Scottish steel industry has had to wrestle from the start with raw material problems. At the beginning of the nineteenth century the local ores were difficult to smelt until the introduction of the hot blast; their high phosphoric content seems to have been an obstacle in the production of wrought iron; and they were, in any event, rapidly exhausted to meet the demand for forge and foundry iron. Improvement in furnace design was delayed by the practice of using splint coal instead of coke in the blast furnaces since this called for small furnaces at a low-temperature blast. When splint coal ceased to be used, the softness of Scottish coke was alleged (with little justification) to operate in the same direction and dictate the use of small furnaces, so much so that even in 1937 the average output per furnace was no more than 33,000 tons.

234

Of these raw material problems, the one that exercised the most important influence on the industry was undoubtedly the lack of a suitable local raw material. The phosphorous content of the Lanarkshire ores practically ruled them out from use for steel-making until the introduction of the Gilchrist-Thomas process in 1878, which would have allowed them to be used for the production of basic steel. The local demand, however, was for acid steel, particularly for shipbuilding and boiler-making, and no advantage was taken of this process. The industry concentrated instead on the production of acid steel from imported ores and adopted the Open Hearth process rather than the Bessemer converter, so as to be able to make the maximum use of scrap. The use of these materials discouraged hot-metal practice; until recently there was not a single fully integrated steel plant in Scotland. As late as 1937 no hot metal was used and even in 1950, when the output of steel reached 2·4 million tons, the charge of hot metal was not more than 110,000 tons.

	Iron Ore	Pig-Iron			Steel		
		Basic	Acid	Other	Basic	Acid	Other
1870	3,500·0	—	—	1,206·0	—	—	—
1913	591·6	69·3	740·5	559·4	245·0	1,186·1	38·3
1929	26·3	91·0	286·5	229·6	919·3	652·0	10·3
1937	22·3	117·1	197·4	182·2	1,392·1	466·3	36·7
1956	—	807·3	29·3	94·8	2,207·8	154·5	156·6

TABLE XXVII. Scottish Iron and Steel Production (*thousand tons*), 1870–1956.

Since the war, the shortage of scrap has made the industry more dependent on pig-iron, and it has been necessary to erect new blast furnaces in order to add to the supply. The production of pig-iron had fallen in pre-war days to under 500,000 tons and the large exports of the mid-nineteenth century had given way to substantial imports. Moreover, although the steelworks were now chiefly in need of basic pig-iron, the output was mainly of haematite and forge and foundry iron; in 1937, only 117,000 tons of basic iron were available towards the production of 1,392,000 tons of basic steel. It was estimated that, in order to achieve self-sufficiency in pig-iron, Scotland would have required to double her output and produce about a million tons annually. This rate of output had not yet been reached in mid-1957, but has been comfortably exceeded with the new Ravenscraig furnace in full operation.

The expansion in pig-iron production raised several important issues. There was, first, the question of location. It was by no means obvious that a new integrated plant should be built at one of the old inland sites where there was no ore, insufficient coking coal, and all the added expense of assembling materials and shipping finished steel that such a site involved. The issue had been raised as far back as 1929 when a location down-river at Erskine Ferry was proposed; it was revived after the war, when a location on the Forth estuary was under consideration; it was raised again, rather obliquely, by the proposal that Richard Baldwin's should do what no Scottish steel-maker had shown himself willing to do, namely, build a plant at Grangemouth. On each occasion, the decision was against a fresh location.

Secondly, there was the question of coking coal supplies. It was—and is—not at all certain that Scotland can produce pig-iron competitively and the availability and cost of coking coal is perhaps the most important single factor involved. The output of coking coal is being expanded, but it is doubtful whether Scotland will achieve self-sufficiency; for some years, coking coal has been imported from the south, chiefly from Durham, for blending with local coals, and this practice seems likely to continue. As suggested above, the industry may be faced with fuel costs that rise in relation to costs elsewhere in Britain, and, equally important, abroad.

Thirdly, there was the problem of integration. The construction of new blast furnaces has made possible a development of hot-metal practice. Until 1957 progress was confined to the Clyde Iron Works, which send one-third of their iron hot across the river to Clydebridge; but the new Ravenscraig plant, which includes a large modern blast furnace and a melting shop with a capacity of 400,000 tons, is fully integrated. Even in 1958, however, scrap, not pig-iron, is the chief raw material of the industry and cold melting will continue to account for most of the output.

The main outlet for Scottish steel is in the shipbuilding and engineering industries and a large part of the output takes the form of plates for use in these industries. In 1956 plates and other heavy rolled products accounted for nearly 1·3 million tons out of a total of 2·1 million tons of finished steel. On the other hand, sheets came to only 73,000 tons, slightly over 3 per cent of the British output. Scotland is at once an exporter and importer of steel—she exports heavy products and imports light—but on balance, measured by weight at least, there is a considerable net export. Of the total output of the industry, 20 per cent is exported, partly in the form of plates and heavy sections and partly in the form of tubes, another important Scottish specialty.

Three major Scottish projects are included in the steel industry's Second Development Plan. Colville's intend to add a second blast furnace at Ravenscraig; Baird's and Scottish Steel plan to build two new blast furnaces at Gartsherrie; and Beardmore's are to erect new electric arc furnaces in their melting shop. In alloy and special steels, in which Scottish steel-makers have played a leading part, new developments are already in progress: Colville's are changing over their Hallside Works to the production of alloy and special steel billets exclusively and are extending their foundry at the Motherwell Works of the Clyde Alloy Steel Company.

SHIPBUILDING AND MARINE ENGINEERING

Although there are Clyde shipbuilding firms like Scott's of Greenock with a history extending back to the eighteenth century, Clyde-built ships were few and small until the coming of steam power. The tobacco trade with the colonies was built up in vessels chartered from Whitehaven or constructed in American yards. Later the shallowness of the river prevented the launching of ocean-going vessels above Port Glasgow, and the yearly tonnage built along the entire river remained less than the equivalent of a modern passenger liner until the early 'forties of last century.

236

The coming of steam propulsion, in which Glasgow took the lead, soon changed all this. Experiments beginning in 1788 culminated in the successful demonstration of the possibilities of steam by Bell's *Comet*, built by Wood of Port Glasgow and using a boiler and engine castings made in the foundry of David Napier. It was some time, however, before it proved economical to use steam in large ocean-going vessels, partly because of inefficiency in fuel consumption and partly because of the enormous bunker capacity required when trade routes still lacked coaling stations. In the meantime, iron began to replace wood in the hull, and with the replacement of the paddle by the screw propeller towards the middle of the century, wooden steamers became obsolete except in small vessels. Both of these developments were favourable to the Clyde yards, which had the advantage of a well-established engineering industry in Glasgow and an expanding local supply of iron. Clyde shipbuilders had already extensive experience in the use of steam and of iron when the founding of what was to become the Cunard Company gave a decisive impulse to their activities in 1839. The Clyde yards built many famous sailing vessels, including the *Cutty Sark*, long after that date, and the first Cunard vessels were of wood. But it was the coming of the ocean-going iron steamship in the middle of the century that turned the Clyde into the world's leading shipbuilding centre; and it was to the order of the Cunard Company that many of the first steamships were built.

Two other important developments in shipbuilding were pioneered on the Clyde. The first of these was the introduction of steel in the late 'seventies, Denny's *Rotomahana* being the first ocean-going steamer to be built of mild steel. The fall in steel prices in the 'eighties contributed to a rapid transition to the new material and within ten years iron had been almost completely superseded on the Clyde. The second development was in marine engineering. Until about 1878 when improvements in the quality of steel made it suitable for marine boiler construction, steam pressure was the limiting factor in engine development. The common working pressure had climbed from about 10 pounds per square inch in the 'forties to 60 pounds in the 'sixties; with the introduction of steel it climbed to over 100 pounds per square inch. These higher pressures demanded a cylindrical form of boiler in place of the box-like boilers in use up to the 'sixties. In 1862 James Howden, whose firm still flourishes on the Clyde, designed a cylindrical tank boiler which, although not the first cylindrical boiler to be fitted to a ship, was the first of the so-called Scotch boilers which were to be almost universal in the British mercantile marine for the next two generations. The water-tube boiler which was to supersede it goes back to one installed in 1857 by John Scott of Greenock. This installation, and a later one by John Elder in 1870, was not a success, but Yarrow was more successful with a torpedo-boat installation in 1879. By the close of the century John Brown & Co. and Fairfield's were manufacturing water-tube boilers for installation in their warships and Babcock & Wilcox in 1879 had established at Renfrew the largest factory in Britain for the construction of water-tube boilers, both for marine and land purposes.

A third development, in which the Clyde also took a leading part, was the introduction of the steam turbine at the beginning of the century. The first application of the turbine for the propulsion of a merchant ship was in the *King Edward*, a small passenger vessel built in 1901 by Denny's for use on the Clyde. It was also a Glasgow Professor, Sir John Biles, who suggested to Parsons the use of speed-reduction gearing between the turbine shaft and the propeller shaft as a means of making the turbine an economic proposition for use in ships of moderate speeds. The first ships designed and built with geared-turbine machinery were completed by Fairfield's at Govan in 1912.

The volume of construction grew rapidly from not much more than 100,000 tons in the early 'sixties to 750,000 tons in 1913. In that year about 60,000 men were employed in the Clyde shipyards and marine engineering shops, apart from those engaged in making ancillary equipment and components or producing materials for incorporation in ships. Since shipbuilding had become largely an assembly industry, the number of workers directly dependent on the industry was probably in the neighbourhood of 100,000. The range of output was as remarkable as its volume. True, no sailing vessels had been built since 1907 and comparatively little repair work was done. But almost every type of vessel, from barges, ferries and dredgers to Atlantic liners and battleships, was represented in the year's production.

The prosperity of those years stands out in contrast to the prolonged depression that overtook the industry between the two world wars. The naval work that had occupied many of the Clyde yards during the race with Germany before and during the war disappeared almost entirely; mercantile construction recovered in the 'twenties but never regained the pre-war proportions. The great slump after 1929 brought one yard after another to a standstill and the berths stood empty year by year. The climax was reached in 1931 when work was suspended on the *Queen Mary*. In the next two years output fell to a mere 60,000 tons—a level never experienced since the rise of shipbuilding in the eighteen-fifties. At least two-thirds of the men normally engaged in the industry were unemployed—not, unfortunately, for a month or two, but for a succession of years.

It was natural, therefore, that when recovery took place and the industry found itself again with more orders than it could cope with, some uneasiness for the future should persist. In spite of twenty years of almost unexampled pressure on the industry, the future is still eyed with a distrust as deep-seated as the hopefulness with which it was formerly approached in the days before 1914 when prolonged depression seemed equally unthinkable.

The most notable achievement of the Clyde between the wars was undoubtedly the construction of the *Queen Mary* and the *Queen Elizabeth*. Of these the first is now well over, and the second approaching, twenty years of age, but both continue to provide that regular weekly service across the Atlantic for which they were so carefully planned. During the war, the Clyde's contribution included 700,000 displacement tons for the Royal Navy, 1,700,000 tons of merchant shipping, and a major part of the Mulberry Harbour. Since the war, naval work has again dwindled to negligible proportions but, in contrast to experience after the First World War, mercantile construction has remained ample to keep the industry fully occupied. In the early post-war years, the yards were busy reconverting tonnage to civil use. As this petered out, the new tonnage launched climbed slowly and had reached 480,000 tons in 1954, when the total value of output, including repair work, was estimated to be about £55m.

At the end of the war the Clyde yards were faced with the need for extensive modernisation in order to keep abreast of the changes that were taking place in construction methods. The most important change arises from the introduction of welding and prefabrication in place of riveting and piece-meal erection on open berths. This has a

238

double advantage since welding not only saves weight but allows work to proceed under cover without the loss of time in stormy weather that is necessarily involved in riveting. In the early days, the hull was built up of innumerable pieces, lifted separately by small wooden derricks and connected on the berth. With the adoption of welding it becomes economic to connect large pieces on the ground, within a shed, and to transport them to the building berth for connection to other large parts, fabricated in the same way. To lift these large pieces it is necessary to make use of steel lattice-work cranes with a capacity of at least twenty to forty tons. Not only does this change the appearance of the berth; it also involves much heavier capital expenditure and much more careful planning of the use of the cranes. Yards which previously used relatively little capital and offered little scope for modern techniques of management now find themselves in need of both.

The adoption of prefabrication techniques has led to a change in the pattern of the shipyard trades and most obviously to a decline in the number of riveters, holders-on and angle-iron smiths. The change that has taken place since 1930 is summarised in Table XXVIII.

	April 1930		April 1939		May 1955	
	Journey-men	Appren-tices	Journey-men	Appren-tices	Journey-men	Appren-tices
Riveters and holders-on	2612	207	1440	150	685	30
Angle-iron smiths	—	—	67	8	5	—
Electric welders	73	—	452	381	1806	480

TABLE XXVIII. Tradesmen and Apprentices employed in the Clyde Shipbuilding and Ship-repairing Industry, 1930-55.

The pattern of the trades has also been affected by the much greater elaboration of the internal arrangements and fittings of the modern ship. An indication of the trend can be gleaned from the figures of employment in two particular trades—plumbers and electricians. In 1895 there were 123 plumbers and 20 electricians employed in Clyde shipyards (the figures include apprentices). In 1905 the figures had risen to 251 and 89 respectively. For 1955 they were 1,044 and 1,292.

A second change has been in the size and type of vessel on order. The small tramp has almost disappeared, the number of passenger liners has remained relatively low and the dry tonnage built has consisted increasingly of cargo liners of the larger sizes. The most striking change, however, has been the rise of the tanker. Half the output of the Clyde yards now consists of vessels of a type which, even in the 'thirties, represented only a small proportion of the total. Since tankers are much simpler vessels to build and a large proportion are of a similar size, they offer far less scope for the peculiar craft of the higher-class yards and, for the same reason, can more easily be built by other shipbuilders, particularly those making the fullest use of prefabrication techniques. Although the Clyde has been able to keep pace with the rapid increase in the size of the average tanker on order and could build tankers up to 100,000 deadweight tons, the increased dependence of the industry on the tanker market is likely, in the long run, to reduce the share of the Clyde in the shipbuilding of the world.

Other changes affect the marine engineering side of the industry. The diesel was already making its appearance before the First World War and gradually displaced the steam reciprocating engine, but the Clyde was slower than Continental yards in making the change, chiefly because British ship-owners preferred to instal a well-tried engine capable of repair in distant ports, rather than trust themselves to a new type of engine that might save fuel but might also waste time. Many of the Clyde engine-shops hold a licence to build diesels designed abroad; but none of them has successfully evolved a diesel engine of its own design and it is doubtful whether any of them has the staff necessary for this purpose. The integration of marine engineering with shipbuilding, while understandable enough, has prevented the emergence of large engine-building firms specialising in marine work and able to concentrate systematically on improvements in design and able also to profit from the substantial economies that orders for several engines of the same type would afford.

The gas turbine and the nuclear reactor are still at the development stage and the main work is being undertaken by the research association rather than by individual firms, although it was on the Clyde that the *Lucy Ashton* carried out the first trials of a marine gas-turbine installation and many Clyde firms are in close touch with the development work in nuclear engines. At present, as has so often happened in the past, the new types of engine are of greater interest to the Admiralty than to commercial owners because, while they may increase speed or range, they do not offer any substantial immediate economy in operation. But it is obvious enough that the Clyde cannot afford to repeat with these new engines its failures with the diesel if it is to hold its own with the increasing number of efficient competitors in shipbuilding in other countries.

CONCLUSION

Anyone looking back on Glasgow's history is bound to feel a sense of diminution from former glories. The textile industry, which first brought factories to Glasgow and from which much of the manufacturing of the area descends, has almost disappeared. The coal-mines of Lanarkshire, long the source of the cheapest and best coal in Scotland and comparable with the best in Britain, have declined steadily for half a century and are increasingly uneconomic to work. The iron industry which once supplied the bulk of the world's imports of pig-iron became in time the prime example of the backwardness of the heavy industries and, although now in course of rejuvenation, has still to struggle with competitive handicaps such as high fuel costs. The steel industry, after its efforts in the last two decades of the nineteenth century to keep pace with the growing requirements of the local shipbuilding industry, has remained tied to the fortunes of that industry and supplies a much diminished proportion of the British output. In

240

shipbuilding itself, although the industry has never enjoyed such consistent pressure of demand, output has expanded little and the Clyde's share of world output has fallen in the past ten years from 15 per cent to 5 per cent.

Against all this can be set the growing importance of the newer industries which have come from outside, and the new developments that have taken place within the local industries. If there has been little net expansion in the volume of manufacturing activity over the past generation, there has nevertheless been a determined effort to tackle the difficult task of industrial renewal: of grafting on to an industrial stem, which, if old, is also sturdy, the shoots that will continue in the next generation to 'Let Glasgow Flourish'.

This essay is based on material by Professor A. M. Robb, Dr. C. E. V. Leser and Dr. R. H. Campbell, published in the Glasgow volume of The Third Statistical Account.

POPULATION DISTRIBUTION AND CHANGE

Joy Tivy

Lecturer in Geography, University of Glasgow

THE City of Glasgow, with a population of over a million in 1951 (1,089,767) and ranking third, numerically, among the cities of Britain, forms the dense nucleus of Scotland's major and indeed only large concentration of urban and industrial population. Set in the heart of Highland Britain within sight of the Scottish Highlands and of the Southern Uplands, in an elongated basin hemmed in by an encircling rim of uplands, the great urban agglomeration clustering round Glasgow occupies a site in marked contrast to those of comparably large urban areas in England which have, physically, less restricted access to adjacent lowlands. The present pattern of both urban and rural settlement in West Central Scotland in fact, follows closely, and its development has been conditioned by the configuration of a land surface, a large proportion of whose area is occupied by extensive upland masses of 1,000 feet and over in height and whose lowlands are underlain by coal deposits. In addition, the rapid growth and concentration of urban population, consequent upon the commercial and industrial development of the Clyde estuary and the Lanarkshire coal and iron resources in the nineteenth century, within an area of restricted low ground, is reflected not only in a concentration of urban centres but a density of population unparalleled in Britain today.

The encircling rim of bleak, sparsely populated upland moors—sweeping eastwards from the Kilpatrick Hills behind Dumbarton to the Campsies and continued southwards and westwards in a wide arc by the plateaus of eastern and southern Lanarkshire to the Renfrewshire Heights behind Greenock—all but separates the lower Clyde basin, the heart of the Lanarkshire coalfield, from the adjacent lowlands and coal basins in Stirlingshire, the Lothians and Ayrshire. While this separation has tended to confine and to accentuate the pronounced concentration of population around the lower Clyde, well-developed valleys and gaps breaching the surrounding rim provide long, though narrow, tentacles of low ground which link this area with the adjacent lowlands. The consequent channelling of settlement along these lines serves to emphasise the centrality and the centripetal attraction of Central Clydeside (Fig. 50).

Three major furrows—the Clyde estuary to the west, the Lochwinnoch gap to the south-west and that pronounced trough which, continuing the line of the upper Kelvin valley, carries the Forth-Clyde Canal to the north-east—cut through the encircling upland rim, and each is followed by a belt of important settlements. Along the Clyde estuary the shipbuilding and marine-engineering centres of Dumbarton (23,702) on the north and of Port Glasgow (21,618) and Greenock (76,292) on the south bank, as well as the smaller residential and holiday centres of Cardross, Helensburgh and Gourock, are hemmed in by steeply rising ground along the narrow marine

242

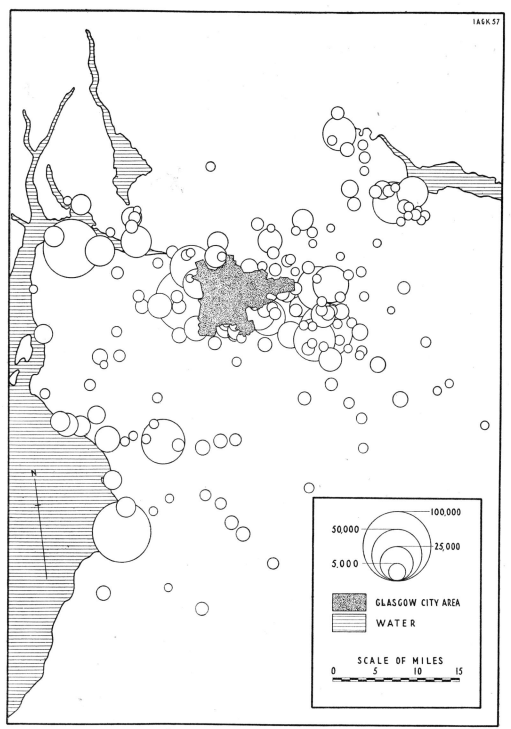

FIG. 50. Urban population of West Central Scotland, 1951.
Based on data from the *Census of Scotland*; urban populations are taken as those in settlements of over 1,000 and are represented by circles proportional to number of people. The City of Glasgow with 1,089,767, cannot be shown by a circle on the same scale.

terraces fringing the Clyde. Only north of Dumbarton is there any significant penetration of urban settlement inland. In the glaciated trough of the Leven Valley—the main gateway to Loch Lomond—the small textile 'conurbation' of Alexandria (9,715), Bonhill (3,984), Jamestown (1,240) and Renton (5,170) repeats again the pattern of congestion consequent upon urban and industrial development within a restricted site. Southwards along the Ayrshire coast a continuation of the fringe of marine terraces links the Clyde and Glasgow with the Ayrshire lowlands. It is followed by a line of coastal towns and villages whose high amenity value and ease of access to Glasgow make even the larger and more remote centres between Saltcoats and Ayr attractive residential areas for the wealthier of Glasgow's workers, as well as popular summer holiday resorts. (See Plates VII, IX, X, XI.)

A further and more direct line of access to the Ayrshire basin is provided by the Lochwinnoch gap, which links Paisley and Johnstone with the Ardrossan-Kilwinning-Irvine triangle. This route, which linked Glasgow with its former outport at Irvine, is followed by a line of small mining and manufacturing towns—Lochwinnoch (1,950), Kilbirnie (6,535), Beith (4,347), Glengarnock (1,068) and Dalry (4,024)—whose activities are related on the one hand to the North Ayrshire coalfield, on the other to the metallurgical and textile industries of Clydeside.

Eastward of the lower Clyde basin the continuation of the Lanarkshire coalfield with that of Stirling and Clackmannan is, geologically, uninterrupted and the topographical barrier is less formidable. Easy and direct access across the narrow 'neck' of Scotland from the Clyde basin to the Forth Valley and the east coast is provided by that straight narrow gutter which parallels the foot of the Campsies. Aligned along its course the small burghs of Milngavie (7,885), Kirkintilloch (14,826) and Kilsyth (9,922), together with a number of small mining villages, all but link the Clydeside urban area with the now fast-growing industrial agglomeration centred on Falkirk and Grangemouth.

South-eastwards the constriction of the Clyde Valley in its narrow steep-sided gorge up-stream of Motherwell and Hamilton marks the limit of the giant urban agglomeration of Central Clydeside. Two lines of towns—Law, Carluke and Lanark on the east and Larkhall, Stonehouse and Kirkmuirhill on the west—lie parallel to the plateau edge above the Clyde gorge. The former are largely agricultural centres serving the stock-farming areas to the south and east, the latter, mining settlements along the southern limits of the Lanarkshire coalfield. To the east of the Clyde, between the Kirkintilloch gap and Lanark, and particularly east of Airdrie and Wishaw, a scatter of small mining settlements on the eastern part of the coalfield have spread on to and over the lower part of the moorland plateau between the Clyde and Lothian basins. To the west, however, the upland rim is higher and presents a more continuous barrier. The settlement pattern is, as a result, more rigidly controlled by the line of the Avon-Irvine valleys linking the ancient textile centre of Strathaven with those of Galston, Newmilns, Darvel and Kilmarnock and that of the Douglas-Ayr valleys linking Lesmahagow, Cumnock and Ayr—both providing access between the middle Clyde Valley and the southern part of the Ayrshire coalfield.

Within the West Central Region of Scotland, given the initial impetus and momentum for urban growth, possibilities for expansion were limited. The limitations are reflected in a well-defined radial pattern of urban settlements converging on Glasgow and its satellite towns. Also, a high degree of industrialisation and urbanisation within economically favoured, though restricted, lowland areas, together with a high proportion of ground above the limit of cultivation (600-800 feet), has resulted in a small population (less than 10 per cent of the total) which, living in scattered farmsteads or in settlements of less than 1,000, is arbitrarily classed as non-urban. And to a considerable degree the distribution of this section of the population is a faint reflection of that formed by urban settlements. The densest rural populations are those in the Ayrshire lowlands, the Bishopton area, the middle Clyde Valley and the Forth carse-lands in the east, where rich agricultural lowland has for one reason or another escaped as yet sterilisation by either mining, subsidence or urban development.

THE CENTRAL CLYDESIDE CONURBATION

The River Clyde between its estuary and its lower gorge-like tract forms the natural artery and focus of that massive agglomeration of urban communities designated the Central Clydeside Conurbation.[1] In comparison with the English conurbations, it contains a strikingly disproportionate amount not only of Central Scotland's but of the whole country's population. With 34 per cent of the total and 36 per cent of the gainfully occupied population of Scotland, Clydeside overshadows the urban and industrial life of the country and its sphere of influence is out of all proportion to the area it occupies: in comparison, London, the greatest of the English conurbations, contains only 11 per cent of the total and 8 per cent of the working population of England and Wales. Clustering around and hemming in the city of Glasgow are seven large burghs with populations ranging from twenty-four to ninety thousand and five small burghs of between seven and twenty thousand each, as well as a great number of non-burghal communities, several with populations of over ten thousand. In all, nearly two million people live within an area some ten by fifteen miles in extent.

The concentration and consequent fusion of many of these tightly packed and industrially integrated communities, has resulted in a great urban sprawl of continuously or practically continuously built-up areas centred on the main block of Glasgow and from which fingers of urban growth project towards and, in some instances, almost reach the surrounding upland rim: the principal salients of urban development are (Fig. 60): Clydebank→Old Kilpatrick following the north bank of the Clyde estuary; Bearsden→Milngavie to the north-west; Baillieston→Coatbridge and Airdrie following the line of the Monkland Canal to the east; Rutherglen→Cambuslang to the south-east; Giffnock→Newton Mearns to the south; and Paisley→Elderslie→Johnstone to the south-west.

Defined simply and solely in terms of a *continuously* built-up area, what is normally accepted as the Central Clydeside Conurbation falls naturally into two clearly defined sections. *First*, a compact and continuously built-up area focussed on the city of Glasgow and including all those radial projections—Clydebank, Milngavie, Airdrie and Coatbridge, Cambuslang, Newton Mearns, Paisley and Johnstone—which are completely joined to Glasgow (Fig. 60). The general pattern is that of an asymmetrical star with its longer projections as at Johnstone, Newton Mearns, Airdrie and Milngavie, extending practically to the moorland edge or, as in the case of the Clydebank and Coatbridge-Airdrie projections, carrying the conurbation beyond the limits of the lower Clyde basin. South-west and north-east of this compact block, along or just within the moorland edge, is a fringe of small urban outliers which have as yet escaped engulfment by the projecting tentacles of the main conurbation; these include the older and now residential settlements of Kilmacolm, Bishopton, Bridge of Weir, Eaglesham and the new town of East Kilbride to the south and south-west: and the mining communities of Torrance, Kirkintilloch, Lenzie, Stepps, Muirhead, Gartcosh and Glenboig in the north-east corner of the Lanarkshire coalfield. Indeed, in that triangle contained between Coatbridge-Airdrie, Glasgow and Kirkintilloch, considerable housing developments have taken place recently—particularly since the end of the last war. The gaps within this part of the conurbation and between it and the rapidly growing Bonnybridge-Falkirk-Grangemouth industrial area are fast diminishing.

Second, a complex, less compact, less coherent and much less continuous urban agglomeration to the south-east of the main Glasgow conurbation. Here the large burghs of Hamilton and Motherwell-Wishaw dominate the scene. The rapid unplanned growth of a host of non-burghal mining and residential settlements during that period when the Central Lanarkshire coal and iron resources were being most vigorously exploited, and indeed of uncontrolled housing development more recently, has led to the fusion of extensive built-up areas. But here physical features have acted as an effective brake to complete fusion and have influenced strikingly the location of the main urban centres. Liability to flooding and subsidence within the flood plain, the steep valley-side slopes of the middle Clyde, and the deeply incised lower courses of its tributaries—the North and South Calder, the Rotten Calder and the Avon—have combined to cause and maintain a degree of separation not only between this area and the main Glasgow conurbation but between various sections within the former. To the west of the River Clyde, the gorges of the Rotten Calder and the Avon have contributed to the clean-cut separation of the Blantyre-Hamilton sprawl from the main Glasgow conurbation to the north and from Larkhall in the south. Similarly, constrictions along the North and South Calder break the continuity of built-up areas between the Uddingston-Bothwell-Bellshill group and Coatbridge and Airdrie to the north and Motherwell-Wishaw to the south. Landforms have, as in the broader pattern, tended to determine the main centres of population; without these natural barriers a much more continuous spread of built-up areas, from both Coatbridge and Cambuslang southwards, might well have developed in spite of the fairly extensive sterilisation of land by past and present coal workings and by actual and possible subsidence.

If the extent of the Central Clydeside Conurbation in terms of the built-up areas be compared with the limits as defined by the 1951 Census, it will be seen that the latter encloses a very much wider region (Fig. 51). Based on administrative divisions, it embraces an area which extends, particularly in the south and east, far beyond the margins of the built-up areas and which contains within it considerable stretches of the sparsely populated moorland rim. It serves, however, to define the main functional zones of a conurbation which, though lacking complete morphological cohesion, is nevertheless a closely integrated industrial and economic unit.

In both area and size, the city of Glasgow dominates the region. It is, however, worthy of note that in the west the burgh boundaries of Barrhead and Renfrew, of Milngavie in the north, of Coatbridge in the east and of Rutherglen in the south coincide with those of the city. Also the two main groups of large satellite towns to the east and west respectively provide a virtually unbroken extension of the main industrial

246

zone of the city which, with the commercial core, is elongated along the line of the river. The two major industrial zones contain the main urban salients extending from Glasgow—associated, in the west, primarily with shipbuilding, marine engineering and ancillary industries in the riverside wards of Govan, Fairfield, Whiteinch and Yoker and the large burgh of Clydebank and the engineering and textile industries of Renfrew, Paisley, Barrhead and Johnstone: in the east and south-east with the coal-mining, iron and steel and metallurgical industries of the Central Lanarkshire coalfield. To the north-east, however, between Glasgow, Coatbridge-Airdrie and Kirkintilloch, urban expansion

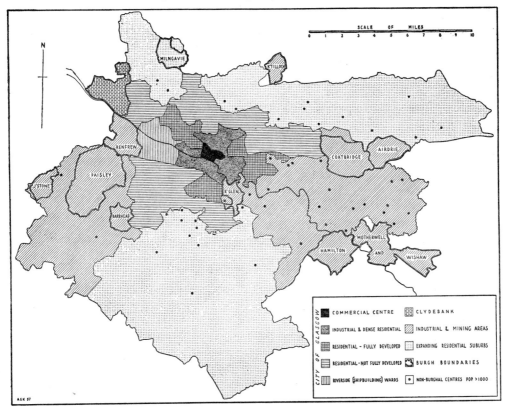

FIG. 51. The Central Clydeside Conurbation: functional zones.
According to the *Census of Scotland*, which gives greater detail for Glasgow than for adjacent burghs.

is associated not only with dormitory residential areas for Glasgow but with a recent marked increase of mining activities in this less depleted part of the Lanarkshire coalfield.

Industrial and residential developments, combined with physical separation and constriction, have resulted in the crowding together in Clydeside of people and houses to a degree unknown elsewhere in Britain. Figures for the over-all density of population within the Central Clydeside Conurbation and a comparison of these with other large urban areas in Britain is, however, invalidated by the exceptionally extensive areas of virtually unoccupied land contained within the administrative limits of this region. The excessive crowding of people within restricted areas, however, as reflected in the condition and density of occupation of houses in Central Clydeside, compared with the

247

A Conurbation	Percentage of all households *without* exclusive use of the following household arrangements (excluding those sharing houses).				
	Cooking Stove	Piped Water	Kitchen Sink	Water Closet	Fixed Bath
Central Clydeside	2·1	0·6	0·6	29·2	43·0
Greater London	0·6	3·2	1·5	2·6	14·4
West Midlands	1·8	5·8	3·6	8·9	32·2
West Yorkshire	1·8	2·7	0·6	24·1	39·4
S.E. Lancashire	2·1	1·7	0·4	5·1	37·3
Merseyside	1·6	2·0	1·4	1·1	23·9
Tyneside	0·9	3·2	6·7	9·0	34·4

B Conurbation	Percentage of total occupied dwellings with the following number of rooms							
	1–2	3	4	5	6	7	8–9	over 9
Central Clydeside	42·7	29·9	17·3	6·1	1·9	1·0	0·8	0·3
Greater London	5·6	11·8	19·4	32·3	17·4	5·9	5·5	2·1
West Midlands	2·3	10·3	27·0	41·9	14·1	2·6	1·4	0·4
West Yorkshire	11·4	24·3	30·6	25·4	5·5	1·4	1·2	0·2
S.E. Lancashire	2·6	10·0	44·4	30·1	8·9	2·4	1·3	0·3
Merseyside	2·5	6·8	26·3	38·7	15·9	5·7	3·0	1·1
Tyneside	12·6	26·9	31·7	19·8	4·4	2·6	1·6	0·4

C Conurbation	Percentage of population in all households living at the following densities (persons per room)				
	Over 3	3 and over 2	2 and over 1½	1½ and over 1	1 or less
Central Clydeside	7·0	16·3	20·1	22·9	33·7
Greater London	0·2	1·5	7·1	17·9	73·3
West Midlands	0·5	2·8	8·3	17·4	71·0
West Yorkshire	0·4	2·5	7·6	16·8	72·7
S.E. Lancashire	0·1	1·0	5·0	16·0	77·9
Merseyside	0·7	4·7	9·1	19·3	66·2
Tyneside	1·3	4·5	14·0	21·4	58·8

TABLE XXIX. Conurbations of Britain: *A*—physical condition of houses; *B*—size of dwellings; *C*—density of population per room.

Tables reproduced from Grieve, R., *The Clyde Valley—A Review*.[2]

English conurbations, gives some idea of the degree and nature of the congestion and its startling individuality (see Table XXIX). Over 40 per cent of the houses in Clydeside are dwellings of two rooms or less, the majority in those grim blocks of four- to six-storeyed tenements with common stairways and shared lavatories (nearly one-third of *all* houses)—blocks which are such a distinctive architectural feature of the older and more crowded areas, particularly of nineteenth-century housing; 39 per cent of the population in all households in the conurbation occupy this size of house. Further, nearly a quarter of the population is living at an occupancy rate of over two per room. As Mr Grieve so aptly points out, 'there are over *700,000* households living at a density of over two per room, nearly three times as many as in Greater London which has four times as many households'.[2] The nearest English figures in Tyneside (12 per cent of its dwellings with two or less rooms; 5·8 per cent of its population living more than two per room) appear insignificant in comparison.

The density of houses and people, however, varies considerably from one part of the conurbation to another, from the higher densities of the older and industrial to the much

	Population 1951 (000's)	Pop. per acre	House size % total houses			% pop. living more than 2 per room	% houses with shared w.c.
			2 rooms or less	3–4 rooms	Over 4 rooms		
Clydeside Conurbation	1,758·5	—	43	47	10	23	29
Glasgow	1,089·8	28	48	45	7	25	27
Paisley	93·4	15	48	45	7	19	48
Motherwell-Wishaw	68·2	15	43	49	8	19	34
Coatbridge	47·5	13	45	49	6	25	28
Clydebank	44·6	16	36	59	5	11	15
Hamilton	40·2	14	32	56	11	17	24
Airdrie	30·3	15	26	63	10	14	18
Rutherglen	24·2	23	43	44	13	15	30

TABLE XXX. Population and housing conditions in large burghs in the Central Clydeside Conurbation, 1951. *Source: Census of Scotland.*

lower figures in the newer residential areas. Table XXX provides, for large burghs only, some measure of the variation, though in all cases, gross densities mask considerably higher net residential densities. Again, Glasgow dominates the scene. Figures for residential densities produced by the City Engineer at the time of the Planning Report (1944-45) revealed that in and around Central Glasgow, on an area of some 1,800 acres, people were living at an average gross density of 400 persons per acre and in some parts of the same area at net residential densities of as high as 700 per acre; 700,000 people—practically one-seventh of Scotland's population—were compressed into three square miles in the heart of the city.[2]

THE CITY OF GLASGOW

Glasgow contains two-thirds of the population of the Central Clydeside Conurbation and a fifth of the total population of Scotland. It far outstrips the three other cities of Scotland, being twice the size of its nearest rival, Edinburgh (466,761). In 1951, only London and Birmingham had larger populations in Britain. Glasgow, however, had an average gross residential density of population in 1944 nearly two-and-a-half times that of its larger rival—Birmingham (Table XXXI). This reflects not only

Land Use	Glasgow		Birmingham		Manchester	
	Acres	%	Acres	%	Acres	%
Open Space	4,343	11·3	6,970	13·7	2,466	11·5
Undeveloped (including Agriculture)	16,016	41·5	15,190	29·7	4,462	20·8
Industry	3,388	8·8	3,450	6·7	1,770	8·2
Commerce, Public Buildings and Transport	5,844	15·1	3,640	7·1	3,710	17·3
Housing	9,007	23·3	21,900	42·8	9,073	42·2
Total	38,598	100·0	51,150	100·0	21,481	100·0
Total Population	1,089,767		1,112,340		702,384	
Density of Housing Areas in persons per acre	121·0		48·1		77·4	

TABLE XXXI. Comparison of areas of different land uses. The Glasgow figures are for 1944, those for Birmingham are taken from the Survey of the Black Country by the West Midland Group in 1948 and those for Manchester from the City of Manchester Plan; the latter excludes Wythenshawe.

Table reproduced from Grieve, R., *The Clyde Valley—A Review*.[2]

Glasgow's smaller acreage but particularly the very much smaller percentage of land within the city limits occupied by housing: only half that in Birmingham. On the one hand this is related to a higher proportion of land occupied by dock facilities and an even higher percentage which is undeveloped, much of the latter being unusable owing to the danger from subsidence consequent upon extensive mining operations in the past. On the other hand, it is also related to the original congestion of people consequent on the rapid growth of population and the original housing conditions within the former and more restricted boundaries of the city.

Unfortunately, a complete and up-to-date survey of residential densities is not available. However, average densities on the basis of the city's thirty-seven wards (Fig. 52) reveal a pattern of three practically concentric zones:

1. The less densely occupied core (30-49 per acre) on the north bank of the river: centred on Exchange Ward, this is the heart of the shopping and commercial centre of the city with a relatively small residential population (Pls. XIX and XX). Although

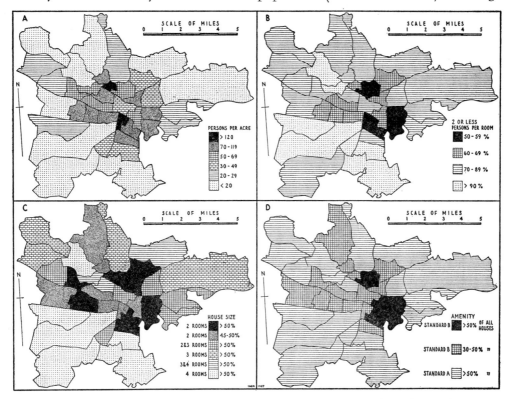

FIG. 52. City of Glasgow showing certain population and housing conditions by wards, 1951.

    A. Population density; number of persons per acre.

    B. Percentage population living at occupancy rates of up to two per room.

    C House size: percentage houses of given sizes.

    D. Housing 'standards': percentage of all houses.

        Standard A = all amenities.

        Standard B = exclusive use of cooker and sink, but no bath; water closet is shared

        Based on data from the *Census of Scotland*.

this functional zone extends beyond the limits of Exchange particularly into the neighbouring wards of Park and Anderston, to the west, it is masked by the much higher residential densities of these latter wards which are part of—

2. The inner zone of high densities which, on both sides of the river, completely encircles the central core. Within this zone, nearly 60 per cent of the city's population is living at average gross densities of 50-120 per acre, and maxima of 145·4, in the Gorbals and 158·8 in Woodside. There is, in addition, a pronounced concentration of high

densities in those wards immediately south of the river and to the east of the commercial centre on the north bank.

Within this zone is concentrated the bulk of the older and poorer blocks of tenements together with a high proportion of the city's varied industrial concerns and very considerable extensions of the main shopping centre along the principal routes. With the exception of Park and Partick West, over 45 per cent, and in several of the east-end wards, over 60 per cent of the dwellings are of two rooms or less. The former, despite a decline in the condition of property and an extension of shopping centres within them, still retain, particularly in their average house size, something of their former high-class residential respectability. Not only are occupancy rates high in this zone—in many wards over 40 per cent of the population is living more than two persons per room—but poor, inadequate and cramped housing conditions have tended to perpetuate the slum conditions created in the nineteenth century; in most wards, a third, and in the east-end up to 70 per cent (Hutchesontown), have no bath and no separate or internal lavatory, and high blocks of tenements built around hollow squares effectively help to cut down Glasgow's already naturally meagre amount of sunlight. In addition, in many of the most cramped and congested areas of this zone, the percentage of children under five is higher than elsewhere in the city. Such are some of the conditions which have undoubtedly contributed to Glasgow's record incidence of tuberculosis, to her bitterly resented 'Gorbals' reputation, and to an 'overspill' problem of outstanding magnitude which has necessitated the initiation of major redevelopment schemes in such areas as Hutchesontown, the Gorbals and Anderston. (See Pate XVIII.)

3. In contrast, the outer residential zone—suburban Glasgow—is one not only of much lower residential densities (usually less than 30 per acre) and a greater proportion of open spaces but of newer and better middle and high class dwellings. Some 40 per cent of the city's population is spread over a wide peripheral area, to the north and south of the centre of the city particularly. With the exception of the former burgh of Maryhill in the north, dwellings are larger, occupancy rates are lower and housing conditions and amenities are considerably better. In this zone are included the newer, more substantial and spacious tenements to the north-west and south of the city, together with inliers of large eighteenth- and nineteenth-century mansion houses, once respectably situated without, now well within, the city boundary, and the extensive and fast-expanding modern housing estates on the northern and southern peripheries. (Pl. XX.)

POPULATION GROWTH AND CHANGE

The rapid growth and massive agglomeration of urban population in the Clyde basin was restricted in time as well as in space; it was a characteristic product of the economic and industrial developments of nineteenth-century Britain. The rate of agglomeration was, however, more marked in this region than elsewhere in Britain; while Glasgow contained 5 per cent in 1801 and 12 per cent in 1851 of Scotland's population and London accounted for 10 per cent and 13 per cent of that of England and Wales in the same years, by 1931 Glasgow accounted for 22·4 per cent and London only 11 per cent of their respective countries' totals. It was certainly more accentuated in the Clyde basin and caused a greater transformation there than in any other part of Scotland. During the period of greatest growth, from the beginning of the nineteenth

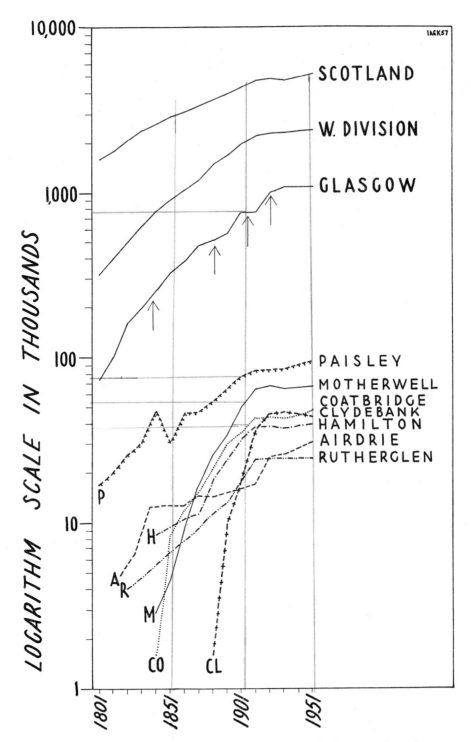

FIG. 53. Population growth, 1801-1951, in Scotland, the West Central Division of Scotland, Glasgow and large burghs of Central Clydeside. Arrows indicate date of major extensions to the boundary of the City of Glasgow.

Based on data from the *Census of Scotland*.

century to the end of the first decade of the twentieth, the population of West Central Scotland (including the counties of Ayr, Lanark, Renfrew and Dunbarton) increased at a very much greater rate than that of Scotland as a whole (Fig. 53); up to 1841 the decennial rate of increase was twice, between 1841 and 1891 nearly three times as great. Although by 1951 Scotland's population was three times its total in 1801, that of Lanarkshire had increased ten, Dunbartonshire eight and Renfrewshire four times within the same period. Similarly, the tendency to excessive urbanisation within this region was more marked than elsewhere in the country; in 1861, 57·7 per cent of the population of Scotland, 79·8 per cent of that of the West Central Division, were classed as urban; by 1951 these proportions had increased to 82·9 per cent and 93·9 per cent respectively.

The foundations and lines along which the urban and industrial expansion of West Central Scotland eventually developed were laid during the course of the eighteenth century. The opening up of the North American markets to Scotland after the Union in 1707 brought increased trade and commercial activity which, together with the influx of capital that ensued, stimulated the development of an indigenous textile industry. The emergence of Glasgow as the commercial and trading centre of the region was related on the one hand to the enterprise of her merchants in face of competition from the rival burghs of Dumbarton and Rutherglen and of the natural obstacles to navigation downstream of the city, on the other, to the advantages of a position commanding the lowest crossing place on the Clyde. Paisley, bridging the White Cart, astride the main route to the Ayrshire lowlands, and already the headquarters of the *entrepreneurs* of the domestic linen industry, became the natural focus for modern textile-manufacturing. And with the rapid development of maritime activities in Greenock, some of the main points for future population growth had, by 1801, been fixed. By the end of the century the manufacture of cotton had replaced that of linen and the introduction of machinery early in the nineteenth century resulted in the concentration of a formerly dispersed textile industry in urban centres whose growth was stimulated by the consequent influx of labour. These expanding textile centres—some newly established by the introduction of mills as at New Lanark, others older agricultural villages and small towns—became concentrated particularly in those areas on the moorland edge to the south, south-west and north-west of the Clyde basin and around the Ayrshire amphitheatre, as well as in the constricted valleys of the middle Clyde and its tributaries and the Leven trough, where an abundance of water was available. By 1841 (Fig. 54) the influence of the cotton industry on the growth and distribution of population in the region was complete. Glasgow, to which the early use of steam power attracted a large number of cotton mills, and whose population had trebled in the first four decades of the century, had established its supremacy and centrality. Paisley (48,426), dominating the main concentration of urban population outside Glasgow, and Greenock (36,135), by now the largest burgh in the estuary and the principal shipbuilding centre, had far outstripped both Dumbarton (3,782) and Rutherglen (5,623) in size.

From 1830 onwards, however, the impetus to population growth and urban concentration provided by the rise of the cotton industry was superseded by the increasing exploitation of local coal and iron resources. Facilitated by the technical developments of this era and a rapidly extending network of canal and rail communica-

254

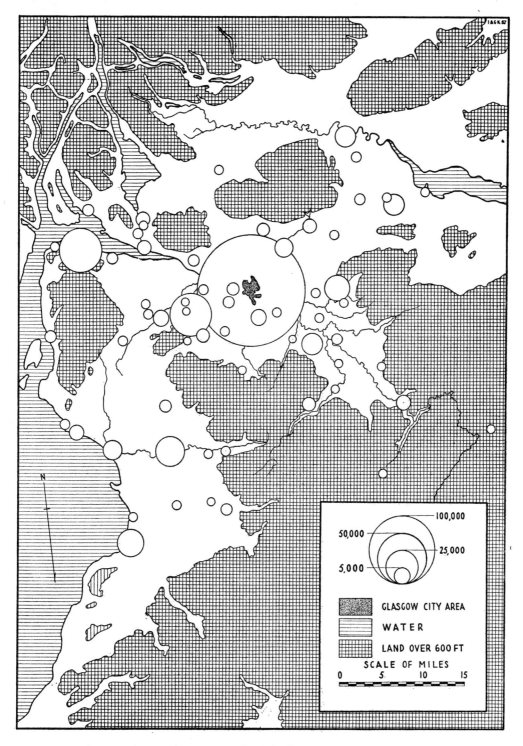

FIG. 54. Urban population of West Central Scotland, 1841; Glasgow (Parliamentary Burgh) 255,650. Circles proportional to numbers of people. Based on data from the *Census of Scotland*.

255

tions, the latter was associated with a phenomenal growth of urban population, particularly in the middle Clyde Valley, which continued unabated until the end of the century. The concentration of ironworks and blast furnaces in the eastern outskirts of Glasgow and along the line of the Monkland Canal, particularly round Coatbridge, and where, as at Motherwell and Wishaw, the railway could most easily be carried up on to the plateau, was reflected in the extremely rapid growth of these formerly modest settlements (Fig. 53); between 1841 and 1871, the population of Coatbridge leapt from 1·6 to 16 thousand (+888 per cent), Motherwell and Wishaw from 3 to 16 thousand (+414 per cent). Concurrent with the expansion of these larger towns was not only the urban growth of a great number of formerly small settlements but also the creation of as many more new industrial and mining towns and villages, in the eastern part of the Clyde basin: metallurgical centres, particularly between Glasgow and Coatbridge; a swarm of pit-head villages which extended eastwards up on to the moorland edge between Coatbridge and Motherwell; as well as considerable intermixture of residential areas, particularly in the sector between Rutherglen, Hamilton, Coatbridge. In contrast the rate of growth of the older textile area to the south-west of Glasgow was very much slower. Although Glasgow continued to expand at a steady rate, practically doubling its 1841 population and all but attaining the half-million mark by 1871, probably more spectacular was the rapid development of residential suburbs immediately to the west and south-west of the city, which had attained a gross population of somewhere in the region of seventy thousand. This era saw also a similar though less spectacular growth of urban areas associated with the development of the Ayrshire coalfield, particularly along the Lochwinnoch gap and around the inner edge of the coal basin. The extension of rail and steamer communication allowed the popularisation of the Clyde-Ayrshire coastal sites as fashionable residential and watering places, the use of the more adequate port facilities constructed at Ardrossan and Troon, and the growth of the planned town of Helensburgh as a select place of residence to which the wealthy citizens of Glasgow could escape from the city they were helping to create.

By 1871 (Fig. 55), the pattern of the modern Clydeside Conurbation and its principal extensions was all but complete and the last decades of the century witnessed its 'filling-in'. The spectacular growth of population in the middle Clyde Valley, south-east of Glasgow, continued at an undiminished rate right up to the beginning of the twentieth century. Between each of the periods 1871-91 and 1891-1911, Motherwell and Wishaw doubled their population: in a matter of sixty years, they jointly increased from less than 5 to over 65 thousand. Similarly, Coatbridge, Rutherglen and Hamilton expanded at comparable rates. This, together with the continued growth of numerous smaller urban areas and the extension of mining activities towards the east and north-eastern margins of the coalfield and of residential and industrial areas to the east and south-east of Glasgow, resulted in the gradual massing and merging of old with new settlements, pit-heads and mining villages with residential centres and industrial sites, into the ungainly sprawl of today.

Towards the end of the century, however, came the last great upward surge of population that was to complete the extension westwards towards Dumbarton of the third major salient of the Clydeside Conurbation (Fig. 56). The new developments in steel ships and marine engineering in the nineteen-seventies and -eighties and the estab-

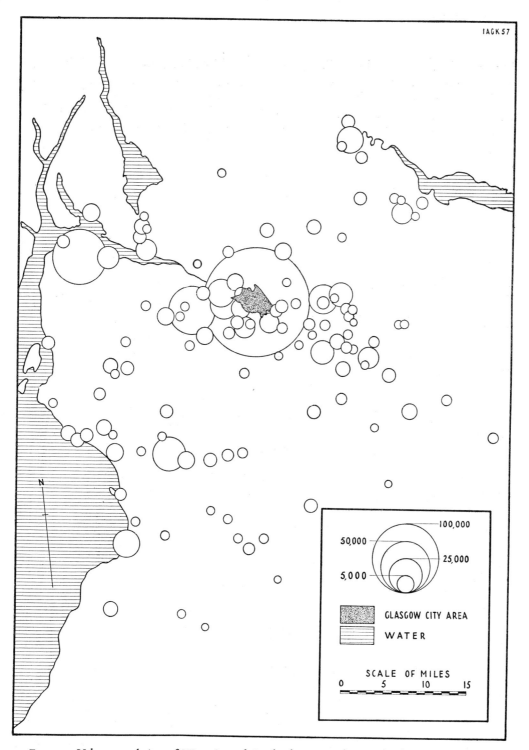

FIG. 55. Urban population of West Central Scotland, 1871: Glasgow (Parliamentary Burgh) 477,732. Circles proportional to numbers of people. Based on data from the *Census of Scotland*.

R

lishment of the Clyde as the leading centre of the shipbuilding industry in Britain was reflected in the considerable growth of those riverside burghs west of Glasgow—Govan, Partick, Renfrew—each of which doubled its population between 1881 and 1891, and the appearance, virtually overnight, of the burgh of Clydebank whose growth from 1·6 thousand to 46·5 thousand within the short space of forty years was even more spectacular than that of the earlier 'boom town'—Motherwell—in the east (see Fig. 53). Indeed, while the rate of growth of all other burghs in Clydeside had, by 1901, passed their maximum, that of Clydebank and associated centres continued to expand during the next decade and the latter's increase of 79·9 per cent in the period 1901-11 exceeded that of any other town in Britain.

This rapid increase and agglomeration of urban population during the course of the nineteenth century was brought about not only by a natural increase of population but also, to a marked extent, by the movement of people, particularly during the first half of the century, into the growing industrial centres of Clydeside and Lanarkshire. And the resulting influx of predominantly young people of working age served to maintain and perpetuate a high rate of natural increase in later decades even after the main flow of immigration had subsided. The degree to which immigration contributed to the increase of population in the Clyde Valley is reflected in the proportion of incomers recorded in the decennial Census reports from 1851 onwards in the counties of Lanark, Dunbarton and Renfrew and in all the large burghs within the region: between 1851 and 1891, the proportion of incomers in these counties was never less than 30 per cent and frequently over 50 per cent of the total population; indeed, in 1861, 61 per cent of the population of Dunbartonshire had been born outside the county. And during the period 1861-71, over half of the total increase of population within Glasgow and its immediate suburbs (119·6 thousand) was due to inward migration.[4]

A high proportion of those immigrants who helped to swell the urban population of Clydeside were drawn from the surrounding rural areas in Central and particularly West Central Scotland (Fig. 57). The supply of labour from lowland Scotland was, however, insufficient alone to keep pace with the demands of expanding industries and other constructional developments. From the end of the eighteenth century, Clydeside was also the centre of attraction and focus for important and distinctive streams of immigrants from the Highlands, and from Ireland. Stimulated by the breakdown of the clan system and by the Clearances at the end of the eighteenth century in the former and by the aftermath of the 1798 Rebellion in the latter, such movements were further encouraged and facilitated by the deliberate efforts of Clydeside manufacturers to attract more labour to the new mills, factories and pits. The Highlands, in fact, made a relatively small, though nevertheless constant, contribution to the population which has been maintained without great variation in proportion to the present day. Except in Glasgow and Greenock, the Highlanders seldom exceeded 10 per cent of the incoming population of the towns of this region in any decade. In the former they accounted for between 15-20 per cent of all incomers from 1851-1951; in the latter, although they only accounted for 14 per cent in 1951, in 1851 and 1861 they represented 27 per cent of the immigrant population and over 10 per cent of the total population of the burgh.

The Irish contribution to Clydeside's urban population was much more important

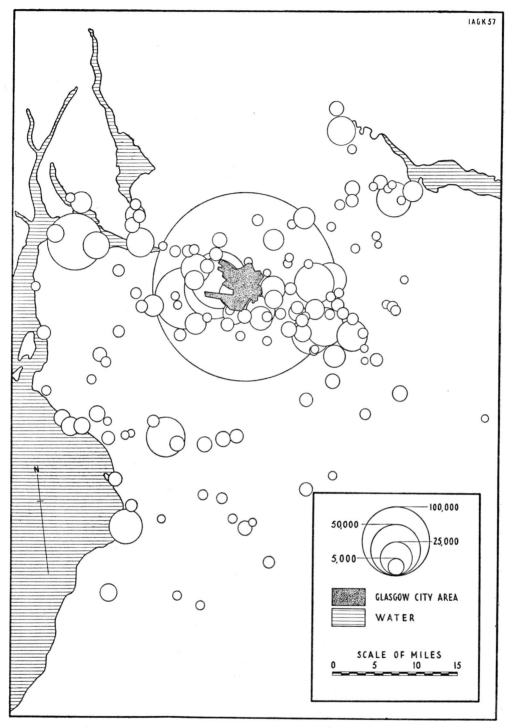

FIG. 56. Urban population of West Central Scotland, 1901. Glasgow (Municipal Burgh)
761,712. Circles proportional to numbers of people.
Based on data from the *Census of Scotland*.

and extensive. Although the seasonal migration of Irish labour into the agricultural regions of lowland Scotland, particularly Ayrshire and Wigtownshire, had become very common during the eighteenth century, permanent migration into urban areas only assumed importance after the establishment and concentration of the modern cotton industry in the third decade of the nineteenth century. By mid-century, it was virtually dependent, particularly in Ayrshire and Renfrewshire, on Irish labour, and it was said that at this time the cotton spinners of Scotland were exclusively Irish.[3] Though the peak of Irish immigration was reached by 1851, they still continued to form an important element in the population of urban Clydeside up to 1891. Between 1851 and 1891, over 30 per cent of the incomers in all the major towns of the region had been born in

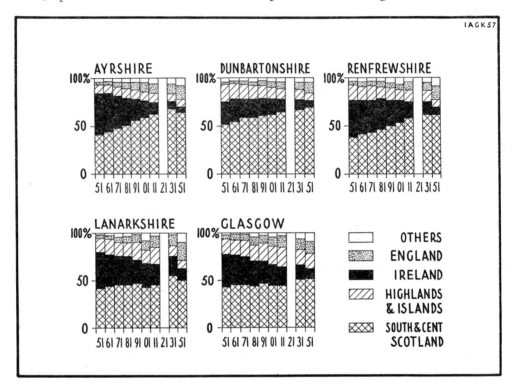

FIG. 57. Origins of incomers in counties of West Central Scotland, and Glasgow, 1851-1951: 1921 is omitted because Census in this year was taken in June, when normal conditions were complicated by both absence and presence of holiday-makers.

Based on data from the *Census of Scotland*.

Ireland: and in Airdrie (54 per cent in 1851), Hamilton (42 per cent in 1851), Rutherglen (50 per cent in 1881), Coatbridge (42 per cent in 1891) and Port Glasgow (60 per cent in 1851) the Irish formed the largest single group of immigrants in certain decades. In fact, during the greater part of the period 1851-1901, at least one in ten of the total population in each of the principal towns was Irish born; and they represented 27 per cent of the total population of Port Glasgow and 18 per cent in Glasgow and Dumbarton in 1881 and in Airdrie in 1861. Indeed, during the period 1851-91, 70-80 per cent of the total Irish-born population in Scotland were concentrated in the West Central Division with over half in Lanarkshire alone (see Table XXXII).

Their influx was facilitated by easy access to the Clyde from Irish ports and the incredibly cheap passages (fourpence to sixpence per head for the Belfast-Glasgow passage) resulting from the excessive competition between the multiplicity of steamship companies which had come into being on the Clyde in the early part of the century. Also during the later part of the century, they provided one of the principal reservoirs of unskilled labour without which the canal, rail, mining and other constructional work could not have developed and expanded so rapidly. And although the tide of Irish immigration ebbed perceptibly towards the end of the nineteenth, and had

	Total Irish-born living in Scotland (thousands)	Percentage of Total Irish-born in:				
		Lanark-shire	Dunbarton-shire	Renfrew-shire	Ayr-shire	West Central Scotland
1851	207·4	43·1	2·6	12·4	10·1	68·2
1871	204·1	51·3	3·1	13·8	7·7	75·9
1881	218·7	52·6	3·9	13·9	6·4	76·8
1891	194·8	55·4	5·0	12·7	5·7	78·8
1901	205·1	59·1	4·8	12·4	5·2	81·5
1911	174·7	57·4	5·8	12·3	4·8	80·3
1931	124·3	15·4	6·0	10·7	4·8	36·9
1951	89·0	12·1	6·1	10·4	5·2	33·8

TABLE XXXII. Percentage of total Irish-born population in Scotland living in West Central Scotland, 1851-1951. *Source: Census of Scotland.*

been reduced to almost a third of its original strength at the beginning of the present century, it has left an important legacy in the very high proportion of those of Irish descent in Clydeside, who, through the maintenance of religious and political allegiances, and other distinctive racial characteristics, contribute a conspicuous element to the population of this area.

Although the concentration of immigrants in Glasgow was an important factor contributing to the growth of the city during the nineteenth century, Cairncross has shown that the balance of migration was not, in fact, constantly inwards [4] (see Table XXXIII). Pronounced movements out of the city between 1870 and 1890 reflected not only the attraction of overseas colonies, but also extensive reconstruction within the older built-up areas; during the period 1870-78, when the demolition and conversion of buildings reached its peak, about a sixth of the houses in the centre of the city were rebuilt. There was, however, a constant migration into that contiguous suburban area which was eventually to be incorporated into the city. Twice as great as the more localised emigration, this inward migration into the larger area of Glasgow and its suburbs continued, though at an ever-decreasing rate until 1901. Whereas 56 per cent of the population of Glasgow had been born elsewhere in 1851, this figure had fallen in 1891 to 47 per cent and to 31 per cent in 1931.

Year	Net increase in population (000's)	Excess of births over deaths (000's)	Balance of migration (000's)	Migration to Glasgow (000's)	Migration to suburbs (000's)
1861–1871	119·6	55·0	+64·6	+41·0	+23·6
1871–1881	102·9	79·1	+23·8	−38·0	+61·8
1881–1891	103·8	93·1	+10·7	−11·0	+21·7
1891–1901	140·1	102·6	+37·6	+28·3	+ 9·3
1901–1911	27·8	118·8	−91·0	−82·6	− 7·4

TABLE XXXIII. Balance of migration into and out of Glasgow and its suburbs, 1861-1911; reproduced from Cairncross, A. K., *Home and Foreign Investment, 1870-1913*, Cambridge, 1953: p. 23.

Not only did Glasgow's population increase tenfold, at a rate far exceeding that of the country as a whole during the course of the nineteenth century, but up to 1871 it outpaced considerably that of West Central Scotland; it increased six (from 77·4 to 477·7 thousand), the latter less than four times in this period. Thereafter, however, although the city maintained a high rate of increase until the end of the century, its pull on the immediately surrounding region was not so great. This outstanding increase in Glasgow's population was, however, artificially inflated by successive extensions to the city's boundaries (Fig. 58) which obscure and certainly greatly exaggerate the actual rate of increase within the *present* area of the County of the City of Glasgow.

Until 1800 the area occupied by the city was that of the ancient burgh which, on the north bank of the Clyde, had as its axis the line between the Cathedral and the river ford. Between 1830 and 1938 there were four major as well as a considerable number of smaller extensions to the city boundaries. These not only increased the total acreage of the city but brought about the absorption of large well-established urban populations. The first, in 1846, incorporated the burghs of Anderston and Calton to the west and east respectively of the old town as well as the already fashionable suburb of the Barony of Gorbals to the south of the river. The next, in 1891, was significant in adding some 6,000 acres to the city, engulfing an already existing population of over 90,000. This represented not merely the gathering into the fold of suburban offshoots from the original town but the wholesale absorption of six adjacent, independent burghs. The rapid growth of these burghs during the preceding period had hemmed in the city on the north, west, and south and their obstinately held burgh status—acquired under the Police Acts of 1850—effectively obstructed the growth of Glasgow in these directions. The remainder resisted incorporation longer until the third major boundary extension in 1912 when another 6,000 acres and a population of some 226·3 thousand, including the not inconsiderable towns of Govan (89·6 thousand), Partick (66·8 thousand) and Pollokshaws (12·9 thousand) were added to Glasgow. Only the ancient

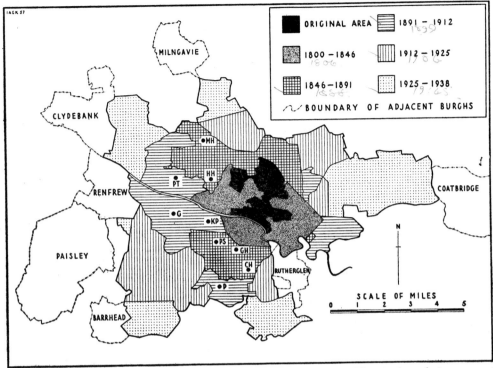

FIG. 58. City of Glasgow showing main stages in the extension of the city boundaries :—

Police Burghs			1861	1871	1881	1891	1901	1911
Annexed 1891:								
Crosshill .	.	CH	—	2,265	2,960	3,798	—	—
Govanhill .	.	GH	349	—	9,636	14,340	—	—
Maryhill .	.	MH	3,717	5,835	12,884	18,134	—	—
Hillhead .	.	HH	—	3,718	6,648	7,738	—	—
Pollokshields .	.	PS	580	3,314	6,464	9,709	—	—
Annexed 1905:								
Kinning Park .	.	KP	651	7,217	11,552	13,679	13,852	—
Annexed 1912:								
Govan .	.	G	—	19,200	49,560	61,589	76,532	89,605
Partick .	.	PT	—	17,707	27,410	36,538	54,298	66,849
Pollokshaws .	.	P	—	8,921	9,363	10,228	11,183	12,932

Based on the *Census of Scotland;* since going to press Bearsden (south of Milngavie) has acquired burgh status.

royal burgh of Rutherglen successfully resisted absorption and still retains its administrative individuality to-day. The final period of major boundary extensions, between 1926 and 1938, differed from those preceding in that, although the acreage of the city

263

was again doubled and considerable modern suburban developments were brought within the city, no large burghal areas were involved. Also these more recent additions included a much higher proportion of undeveloped land than ever before, which contributed to the drop in the over-all density of population in the city from its high gross figure of over 90 per acre at the end of the nineteenth century to its comparatively low figure of 27 per acre at the present. Also, these later extensions finally brought Glasgow's municipal boundaries into contact with those of the major burghs to the east and the west, as well as extending them almost to the limit of the upland edge to the north and south of the Clyde basin.

Although these extensions of its municipal boundaries continued to supplement Glasgow's rise of population up to 1938, the rate of growth within that area now occupied by the city slackened markedly after 1901—from a net increase of 15 per cent between 1891 and 1901 to one of 1·1 per cent during the period 1901-11. This abrupt transition from a period of rapid to one of slow growth, followed by virtual stagnation and even a net decline of population in some urban areas, during the first two decades of this century was a feature which Clydeside shared in common with Scotland as a whole (Fig. 53). It was a trend, however, more pronounced and indeed more persistent in Glasgow than in either Scotland or even the West Central region. Between 1901 and 1951, the latter increased by 25 per cent, Glasgow by only 14 per cent. While the country's population and that of the region have both risen by about 5 per cent during the period 1931-51, the increase of 0·8 per cent in Glasgow owes much to that final boundary extension in 1938 which added 9,681 acres and a population of 4,876 to the city. Indeed, after due allowance is made for those temporarily in residence or away from Glasgow at the time of the Census, a decrease in the population of some 4,340 within the present area of the city between 1931 and 1951 is, in fact, revealed. However, war deaths amounting to 9,202 and the absence in the Armed Forces of a greater number than in 1931 of those normally resident in the city contributed to this decrease; otherwise a small net increase would probably have ensued.

This marked retardation of growth in the major urban areas of Clydeside at the beginning of the century is associated with the replacement of a dominant inward by an outward movement of people. Emigration, long a feature of Scotland, began for the first time since the beginning of the nineteenth century to affect seriously the population of Clydeside and, with the falling birth rate characteristic of Britain, to account for the generally slow rate of increase since 1901. From 1901-51 the outward movement of people from West Central Scotland as a whole and from practically all the large burghs of Clydeside has been dominant (see Tables XXXIV and XXXV). The severest losses by emigration from all the major urban areas coincided with the economic and industrial depression during the nineteen-twenties and -thirties and the resultant chronic unemployment particularly in the heavy shipbuilding, engineering and metallurgical industries. The average rate of unemployment for 1932, 1936 and 1939 was between 30 and 40 per cent in Alexandria, Port Glasgow and in all the large burghs of Lanark, and between 20 and 30 per cent in Glasgow, Clydebank, Dumbarton and Greenock. During the period 1921-31, West Central Scotland lost 9 per cent of its population as against 8 per cent from the whole country. In Coatbridge, Motherwell, Hamilton, Dumbarton and Greenock emigration exceeded natural increase and there was a net decrease in the total population of these towns;

those with a greater diversity of industry, as in Paisley, Renfrew and Glasgow itself, were not quite so severely hit. Although emigration has continued, losses in the longer period 1931-51 have been much smaller and many centres show a slight but perceptible recovery of population. Since 1931 there has been a net inward movement into Ayrshire, Dunbartonshire and Renfrewshire, but Lanarkshire and all its large burghs except Motherwell-Wishaw have continued, consequent upon the exhaustion of the Central Lanarkshire coalfield and the recession in the heavy metallurigcal industries, to lose population by emigration. Also Port Glasgow, Clydebank, Greenock, Rutherglen and Glasgow continued to sustain, between 1931 and 1951, losses as heavy

	Scotland			Lanarkshire (including Glasgow)		
	N	T	M	N	T	M
1861–71	+416·3	+297·7	−118·6	+ 94·4	+133·7	+ 39·3
1871–81	+468·8	+375·6	− 93·2	+128·0	+139·0	+ 11·0
1881–91	+507·9	+290·1	−217·8	+149·8	+141·6	− 8·2
1891–1901	+499·8	+446·5	− 53·3	+172·5	+293·3	+120·8
1901–11	+542·9	+288·8	−254·1	+206·4	+107·7	− 98·7
1911–21*	+360·2	+121·6	−238·6	+175·1	+ 92·4	− 55·4
1921–31	+352·4	− 39·5	−391·9	+156·8	+ 46·4	−110·4
1931–51*	+502·3	+253·4	−220·0	+226·6	+ 28·3	−172·6

	Dunbartonshire			Renfrewshire		
	N	T	M	N	T	M
1861–71	+ 8·3	+ 6·8	− 1·5	+22·7	+39·4	+16·7
1871–81	+ 9·3	+16·5	+ 7·2	+26·5	+46·4	+19·9
1881–91	+13·2	+19·2	+ 6·0	+31·4	+27·4	− 4·0
1891–1901	+14·8	+19·4	+ 4·6	+30·7	−21·8	−52·5
1901–11	+18·2	+25·9	+ 7·7	+35·3	+45·6	+10·3
1911–21*	+18·1	+11·0	− 4·4	+31·8	−15·6	−42·0
1921–31	+13·5	− 3·1	−16·6	+25·9	−10·3	−36·2
1931–51*	+18·6	+16·5	+ 0·9	+39·4	+36·0	+ 2·2

TABLE **XXXIV**. Intercensal changes of population in Scotland and counties of the West Central Division, 1861-1951. Population in thousands.

N=Natural change: T=Total change: M=Migration.

* Allowance has been made for war deaths in periods 1914-18 and 1939-45 in calculation of migration figures. *Source: Census of Scotland.*

as those in the preceding decade, and at a rate far exceeding that of other centres; while Scotland lost 4·5 per cent of the 1931 population by migration during this period and the West Central region 7 per cent, Glasgow lost 11 per cent and Clydebank 17 per cent.

Three types of movement have contributed to Glasgow's heavy losses of population and have affected Central Clydeside to a lesser or greater degree. First there has been, since the First World War, the increasing tendency—in Glasgow and many of the other large burghs of the region—for people to move out from the centres to the margins

	1901–11			1911–21		
	N	T	M	N	T	M
Glasgow	+91·5	+8·9	−82·6	+93·0	+26·0	−67·0
Paisley	+ 9·2	+5·1	− 4·1	—	—	—
Greenock	+ 8·4	+6·2	− 2·2	—	—	—
Motherwell and Wishaw	+ 8·2	+9·2	+ 1·0	—	—	—
Coatbridge	+ 7·4	+6·3	− 1·1	—	—	—
Clydebank	—	—	—	—	—	—
Hamilton	+ 7·8	+5·9	− 1·9	—	—	—
Airdrie	—	—	—	—	—	—
Rutherglen	—	—	—	—	—	—
Dumbarton	—	—	—	—	—	—
Port Glasgow	—	—	—	—	—	—

	1921–31			1931–51		
	N	T	M*	N	T	M†
Glasgow	+87·8	+36·9	−72·5	+134·4	− 3·5	−122·0
Paisley	+ 6·7	+ 1·6	− 6·2	+ 11·4	+5·3	− 5·8
Greenock	+ 7·6	− 2·1	−11·8	+ 11·8	−2·7	− 13·1
Motherwell and Wishaw	+ 7·8	− 4·2	− 12·4	+ 11·4	+2·5	+ 8·1
Coatbridge	+ 5·1	− 0·9	− 6·2	+ 9·2	+4·0	− 4·6
Clydebank	+ 5·5	+ 0·4	− 5·5	+ 6·6	−2·4	− 8·1
Hamilton	+ 5·1	− 1·6	− 7·0	+ 8·0	+2·1	− 4·9
Airdrie	+ 3·4	+ 0·5	− 3·0	+ 5·7	+3·6	− 1·7
Rutherglen	+ 0·4	+ 1·3	− 0·9	+ 1·2	+0·96	− 1·8
Dumbarton	+19·8	− 1·4	− 3·6	+ 3·0	+1·9	− 0·8
Port Glasgow	+ 2·7	− 1·4	− 4·5	+ 5·0	+1·8	− 2·9

TABLE **XXXV.** Intercensal changes of population, 1901-51, in Glasgow and other large burghs of West Central Scotland. (*cf.* Table XXXIV.)

* Approximate allowance made for temporary residence in 1931 and abnormal movements of population in 1921 and † for war deaths in 1939-45. Population given in thousands. *Source: Census of Scotland.*

of the older urban centres, to suburban residential areas and to newer dormitory towns on the periphery and even to resorts along the Clyde estuary and the Ayrshire coast. In Glasgow this movement is clearly revealed in the decrease of total population in the centre and the inner, older and very congested residential zone of the city between 1921

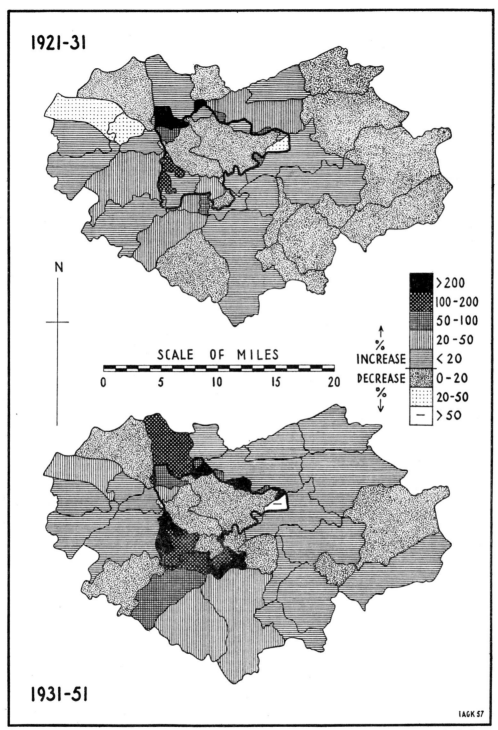

FIG. 59. Population change between 1921 and 1931 and between 1931 and 1951 in Central Clyde-side, by parishes. Thick black line indicates the boundary of the County of the City of Glasgow.

and 1951 and a contrasting and very considerable increase of population in the peripheral and newer suburbs (Fig. 59): of the former the Gorbals, Hutchesontown and Cowcaddens had in 1951 lost up to 23 per cent of their 1931 totals; of the latter, the most striking increases occurred in the southern and most outlying suburban wards of Camphill and Pollokshaws (+52·7 per cent) and of Craigton and Pollokshields (+178·8 per cent). The gradual movement of people away from the city centre has, however, not stopped at the city boundaries but, extending beyond them, has contributed to the very great increases, particularly since 1931, of suburban populations immediately to the south, south-east and north-west of the present city. In contrast to the older and more static industrial centres of Clydeside these newer and fast-expanding residential areas, such as Bearsden and Milngavie to the north-west and Clarkston, Giffnock and Cambuslang to the south and south-east, have experienced a high absolute and percentage rate of increase between 1901 and 1951. The growth of the suburban areas by about 67,000 in this period can, however, account for only a very small percentage of the total loss by migration of some 361,000 people from Glasgow.

Although some undoubtedly helped to swell the growing populations of the 'dormitory' towns on the outskirts of the Clyde basin and of the Ayrshire coastal settlements, a large proportion must have participated in the second type of movement—the general drift out of the Clyde Valley, particularly from the exhausted Central Lanarkshire coalfield, to the expanding mining and industrial regions of Stirlingshire, Clackmannan and Fife. The change in status of Lanarkshire, from the county with the largest gain by migration to that with the greatest loss, reflects the inability of the industry of the region to absorb the natural increase. Lastly, Glasgow and Clydeside must have made at least a proportionate contribution to the particularly heavy emigration out of Scotland from 1921 onwards. It is estimated that of the 220,000 people who left Scotland between 1931 and 1951, Glasgow alone probably accounted for about 45,000. Some idea of the direction of this movement is given by the estimate for the period July 1st, 1946, to June 30th, 1950, that the city lost 5 per cent of its population (Scotland lost 2·3 per cent in the same period) of which 1·6 per cent was to other parts of Scotland, 1·5 per cent to England and 1·6 per cent overseas. As would be expected, the greatest number of emigrants were, and continue to be, from the younger working and particularly the male section of the population. This is reflected in a reversal, by 1931, of the once higher proportion of males to female in all areas except Clydebank and Coatbridge, a slight decrease in the 15-65 age group and an increase in the proportion of those over 65 particularly in the older parts of the region. Although it resulted, therefore, in a slight loss of vitality, Glasgow and the main industrial areas of Clydeside still have higher birth, as well as higher death rates, than in Scotland as a whole, and in the city gross and net reproduction rates are sufficient to replace the existing population.

Emigration is the principal factor which has and still continues to maintain that relatively slow rate of population increase characteristic of West Central Scotland and the majority of its older urban areas since 1901. But although that inward flow which was the mainspring of population growth in the nineteenth century has been reversed, its effects have not been eliminated. It has left a legacy of congestion in the older urban centres which emigration either out of the area or into peripheral suburbs has only slightly relieved. The latter decentralisation has served to all but fill up most of the

268

remaining available space within the narrow confines of the Clyde basin. It was calculated in 1952 that the redevelopment of the worst congested areas in the centre of Glasgow alone would involve the rehousing of some 400,000-500,000 people—nearly half its total population and equivalent to the estimated overspill of Central London, which has a population three times as large. But the encircling upland rim and the ever-prevalent danger of subsidence within the extensively undermined and restricted lowland imposes a strict limit on land still available either within or without the city boundaries for future urban expansion.

1 *One Per Cent Sample Tables*, Part II, *Census of Great Britain, 1951*. London, 1952 (see Conurbation Supplement).

2 Grieve, Robert. *The Clyde Valley—A Review*. Paper delivered at the Town and Country Planning Summer School held at the University of St. Andrews, 1954, under the auspices of the Town Planning Institute

3 MacDonald, D. F. *Scotland's Shifting Population, 1770-1850*, Glasgow, 1937.

4 Cairncross, A. K. *Home and Foreign Investment 1870-1913*, Cambridge, 1953. Chap. II 'Fluctuations in the Glasgow Building Industry': pp. 12-36.

Other sources used included the *Annual and Decennial Census Reports* for Scotland; *The Clyde Valley Regional Plan*; *The Third Statistical Account of Scotland, Glasgow*—in particular the chapter on 'Population' by D. J. Robertson.

Grateful acknowledgement is due to Miss Catherine Smith, M.A., for her invaluable assistance in the abstraction of statistics used in this chapter.

THE GLASGOW OVERSPILL PROBLEM

Berenice D. Baker

Research Officer, Department of Health for Scotland

THE Glasgow overspill problem is perhaps the over-riding problem of the region in our time. Concentration of population and industry has reached the point of acute congestion in many places in the Central Clydeside Conurbation, but in Glasgow itself, hemmed in by these towns and by a vast sprawl of development outside town or city boundaries, the problem of congestion is so exaggerated that it dominates the region and is the most intractable problem of its kind in Britain. The scale of the Glasgow overspill problem is much greater, in relation to the existing population, than even the problem of Greater London: it is estimated that some 300,000 people now living in Glasgow will have to be housed outside the city and that a corresponding proportion of industry must also move away.

The main reason why the Glasgow problem is so different in scale from the overspill problems of the English conurbations lies in the exceptional densities in the central area of the city: within three square miles in and around the city centre some 700,000 people are crowded together at an average density of 400 persons to the acre and at net densities which rise as high as 700 to the acre, and in the four-storey tenement blocks which are typical of this area there are fewer rooms to the house and more people to the room than in any other British city. The overcrowding in these houses, their physical condition, the density of the houses on the ground and the extent to which they are inextricably mixed with industrial concerns of every tackle and trade—all these things combine to make social conditions which are plainly appalling, and if these conditions are to be improved, whole tracts of the city must be cleared and completely redeveloped. What this means in terms of overspill can perhaps best be illustrated by the hard facts of the Hutchesontown-Gorbals district, which is the first of the redevelopment areas to be tackled by Glasgow and on which work has now begun. When the Corporation surveyed the area for redevelopment they found that there were 7,600 houses of which as many as 87 per cent consisted of only one or two rooms. The standard of these houses can be gauged by the fact that only 3 per cent of them had a bath and only 22 per cent had an internal water closet, the remainder sharing with two or three other houses a closet off the common staircase. The net residential density of this area of 111 acres was nearly 460 persons to an acre and there were over 100 industrial or commercial concerns, most of them small and many of them occupying cramped and insanitary premises. It is not surprising that the Corporation's proposals for redeveloping this area involve a reduction of population from 26,000 to 10,000 people, which means a displacement of nearly two-thirds of the population and the majority of its industry. And this is only one of twenty-nine such areas which, when they are tackled, will together mean a displace-

270

ment of 550,000 people, or half the present total population of Glasgow. It is the enormous task of redevelopment, added to the ordinary housing needs of a large city, that has made the Glasgow problem so formidable, and although Glasgow has built over 40,000 houses since the war in new housing areas, and has so far been able to concentrate on the building programme in her own territory, she has now come virtually to the end of her housing land and can build further new houses in the city only by clearing away existing buildings. Thus, the overspill of both houses and industry is a vital condition of any further building progress in Glasgow, and there is an edge of urgency to the task of providing houses and work for the 300,000 people who must move away from the city altogether as the central areas are developed.

The scale of the problem in Glasgow is, however, only part of the overspill problem, and perhaps the greater part is the complexity of the operation itself. The Clyde basin is no broad plain on which an orderly plan of new communities can be made, with a calculated depth of green belt between them and the city; hemmed in by hill and moorland, it is a restricted battle-ground of competing land uses in which there is little enough room even for manœuvre. Except along the valleys of the Clyde and the Kelvin, upland areas lie within ten to twelve miles of the city in all directions, and along these valleys much of the land is likely to flood, or cannot be drained because the water table lies too near the surface. Along the valley of the Clyde there is the additional complication of mining subsidence which also cuts out large areas which could otherwise be used for building in the north of Lanarkshire and the detached portion of Dunbartonshire. The buildable area is further limited by the working of sand and gravel and fireclay and by water catchment areas, and the remaining areas of good building land are also the remaining areas of good agricultural land, containing some of the most productive dairy farms in Scotland.

It is against this complex physical background that the huge demands for land, not only of Glasgow but of the whole conurbation, have had to be assessed, and indeed the pressure of post-war housing needs was so great that there was a strong argument for making use of every buildable plot of ground in the Clyde basin and for planning the redevelopment of the conurbation as one homogeneous urban mass with reasonable standards of density and open space and with a natural green belt and barrier in its surrounding upland and moorland areas. In fact, however, the decision was made to prevent the further coalescence of the built-up areas and to plan the conurbation on the green belt principle. This was done by limiting the further expansion of Glasgow and by directing the expansion of the surrounding urban areas away from the city; the many jigsaw pieces of land which were unbuildable or of high agricultural or scenic value were then connected up into a green belt system separating the urban units. The result was no classic green belt; it was rather a green background within which the built-up areas of the conurbation were set in a close but discontiguous pattern, and in these conditions there was very little choice of sites for new towns to take overspill population from Glasgow. They could not be set on the other side of the green belt, for its outer line was the moorland edge of the surrounding uplands, and in fact there were only three areas which were of sufficient size to take a new town without coalescence with other urban areas, south-east of Glasgow at East Kilbride, north-east of Glasgow at Cumbernauld and west of Glasgow in the Houston-Bishopton area. The site furthest away from Glasgow at Cumbernauld was no more than six-and-a-half miles from the built-up edge of the city, and the nearest, East Kilbride, was only three miles away.

The scale of the Glasgow overspill problem was first revealed by the Clyde Valley Regional Plan, and more recent estimates have confirmed its comprehensive assessment. The recommendations of the Plan for dealing with the problem have also stood the test of events; in brief these recommendations were that new towns, together with the expansion of some of the existing towns in the Clyde Valley and the Ayrshire Plain, should accommodate some 200,000 people from Glasgow, leaving 100,000 people to be housed outside the region altogether in an inter-regional redistribution of population. Two of the new-town sites suggested by the Plan are now being developed under the provisions of the New Towns Act and are being planned for a population of 50,000 each. East Kilbride, which was begun in 1949, had reached a population of about 20,000 by the end of 1957. There was, however, no definite arrangement whereby houses in East Kilbride were specifically reserved for people on the Glasgow waiting list, and although the primary purpose of the new town was to relieve congestion in Glasgow it has done so by a process of natural attraction; 50 per cent of the new-town population comes from Glasgow and currently about two out of every three houses and the bulk of the employment is going to people from Glasgow. Cumbernauld, on the other hand, was set under way in 1957 with special arrangements by which Glasgow undertakes a proportion of the financial liability for the new town and in return nominates tenants for the houses there. Cumbernauld is therefore designed to deal almost exclusively with the Glasgow overspill problem and it is expected that over 40,000 of the planned population of 50,000 will come from Glasgow. The two new towns are also being built on quite different principles, for whereas East Kilbride is planned as a low-density town which is more like a garden city than a Scottish industrial town, Cumbernauld is being planned at a much higher density. Although this is due in part to the more restricted and exposed nature of the Cumbernauld site, the higher densities are also a reflection of a different philosophy, and at Cumbernauld the aim is to combine the advantages of urban 'couthiness' with those of suburban elbow room by designing a compact urban unit with the majority of its playing fields and other open spaces on the periphery of the town. These two new towns will therefore each have their own advantages, and the difference between them will provide a valuable element of choice for Glasgow families who are intending to move to a new town.

Although the possibility of a third new town to deal with the Glasgow problem is not ruled out, the complementary method of re-settling overspill population by the expansion of existing towns is first being pursued; the Housing and Town Development Act, which received the Royal assent in July 1957, now makes it possible for Glasgow to enter into 'Overspill Agreements' with other housing authorities who agree to provide housing accommodation for Glasgow people, and these 'Receiving Authorities' may also make arrangements for the provision of new community facilities such as water supply, schools, shops and factories in a scheme for town development. Overspill housing attracts a preferential housing subsidy from the Exchequer and expenditure by the local Receiving Authority acquiring land and services attracts a 75 per cent Exchequer grant. The operation of this method has yet to be tested out in Scotland, but by the end of 1957 several towns had expressed interest in the possibility of housing overspill population. Some of these towns, such as Kirkintilloch, Hamilton and

Johnstone, are in the Clyde basin, and expansion of such communities will have to be fitted into the tight regional pattern already described. Others, however, are outside the region altogether in the Lothians and as far afield as Arbroath and Inverness. These towns are no doubt taking the view that by attracting new population and industry they will be making an investment which will in the long run enable them to provide a wider range of facilities and services than they can at present offer their own citizens. The next decade or so may therefore see some planned inter-regional dispersal of population from Glasgow and provide an answer to the enigma of the 100,000 people for which the Clyde Valley Plan could make no provision.

Whether overspill is dealt with by building new towns or by expanding existing communities, the key to success is that the dispersal of population should be accompanied by the dispersal of industry. Since the war there has already been some movement of Industry away from Glasgow, the result partly of the hampering industrial congestion in the city itself and partly of the attraction of other places: the Scottish Industrial Estates, which were located with the over-all plan of dispersal in mind, have attracted some Glasgow firms, three have moved to East Kilbride and others have moved to places outside the region altogether, in Ayrshire, Fife and the Borders. For the same reasons, new industries which might in an earlier day have insisted on a site in Glasgow have been attracted to the Industrial Estates and to East Kilbride and Cumbernauld. The trend towards dispersal is, therefore, already significant, and in the next few decades it will be in the interests both of Glasgow and of the new towns and other overspill-receiving towns to increase this trend so that dispersal of industry is on a scale proportionate with that of dispersal of population. For as Glasgow embarks upon the redevelopment of the city a great number of industries must inevitably be displaced, and although the redevelopment programme will be a long process, even the firms who will not be affected for some years will have to plan for a limited future in Glasgow. Redevelopment in Glasgow is, therefore, conditional upon the movement of industry away from the city. Similarly, the receiving areas will need to be assured that there will be employment before they agree to provide houses for Glasgow families.

The solution of the Glasgow overspill problem cannot be an easy or a speedy one: the laconic and impersonal term 'overspill' sums up the most complex and human of planning problems to be tackled in Scotland and it will mean some thirty or forty years of effort and co-operation on the part of Glasgow, the new towns and the other towns which take part in this operation before the final results can be mapped as a reality. But it is reassuring that the problem is fully recognised and accepted as an urgent and major task in Scotland, and there is every prospect that within the next two or three decades we shall see a redistribution of population for the better in this part of Scotland.

Abercrombie, Sir Patrick, and Matthew, Robert H. *The Clyde Valley Regional Plan, 1946*, Edinburgh, 1949.
Grieve, Robert. *The Clyde Valley—A Review*, 1954.

TRANSPORT IN GLASGOW

JOHN F. SLEEMAN

Lecturer in Political Economy, University of Glasgow

GLASGOW's transport problems are in many ways those of any large city. Not only does it contain over a million inhabitants within the city boundaries and several hundred thousand more in the immediately contiguous built-up area, but it is also the business and commercial centre of a large industrial area and the regional capital for a much wider region still. Like all large cities, it suffers from traffic congestion, and has to face the difficulties of the growing dispersion of industry and population from the central districts to new estates on the outskirts. Like all large cities, it faces the problem of the growing competition between public transport services and the privately owned car or lorry. Common also to the big city in general is the problem of how to adapt or modify the existing transport systems so as best to serve the changing needs of the community.

The form which these problems take in Glasgow, however, is affected by certain local characteristics. The site of the city is hemmed in by high land to the north and south, while to the west the hills close in on either side of the lower reaches of the Clyde. Only to the east, towards the Lanarkshire coalfield, is the country reasonably open. These geographical factors have influenced the main directions of population spread and hence the main lines of traffic. The pattern is also affected by the fact that this, one of Britain's large urban and industrial areas, is a long distance from other such areas and is surrounded by open and high country. Moreover, in spite of the presence of large towns like Paisley, Greenock, Motherwell and Hamilton, the central city dominates the whole area, as regards concentration of population and industry, to a much greater extent than in conurbations such as those of Lancashire, the West Riding or the West Midlands.

In addition, Glasgow, at the lowest crossing place on the Clyde, is an important port, and this causes further complications. The densely populated areas north and south of the river are separated by navigable water used by ocean-going ships right up to the bridges in the city centre. At present there is no way of crossing the river below the King George V Bridge, except by inadequate ferries, or, for passengers, the Corporation Underground Railway. Not until the Whiteinch tunnel is opened will this problem be eased.

THE PORT OF GLASGOW

Glasgow, as the main centre of trade and industry, has far outstripped the other ports of the Clyde, such as Greenock, Dumbarton, Ardrossan and Troon, which are nowadays of comparatively minor importance. The Port of Glasgow is entirely man-made; it now contains some twelve miles of quays and deep-water berths covering about 370 acres of water, with a low-water depth ranging from thirteen to twenty-eight feet. All are open to the river without any need of locks. The quays stretch down the river on both sides from the city bridges, interrupted in the region of Govan, Partick and Whiteinch by a series of shipbuilding yards. The main docks are, on the north side, the Queen's, at Finnieston, and Rothesay, between Yoker and Clydebank, and on the south side, the Prince's, east of Govan, and the King George V, between Shieldhall and Renfrew. The port is administered by the Clyde Navigation Trust, a body representing the local authorities and port users of the area and whose jurisdiction extends from Albert Bridge, Glasgow, to Newark Castle, Port Glasgow, a distance of eighteen miles. Most of the trade and port facilities are, however, in the upper reaches and mainly within the city boundaries. (See Plates III, IV, XIII, and XIV.)

Glasgow ranks fifth among British ports in value of foreign trade, coming after London, Liverpool, Hull and Manchester and handling some 4 per cent of the total. As an exporting port it ranks third, after London and Liverpool, because of its valuable exports of machinery, ships and other local manufactures, but as an importing port it takes only seventh place, behind Bristol and Southampton, which are more favourably placed for the import of foodstuffs for the national market.

The pattern of trade has shown a number of changes in recent years. On the export side there has been a drastic decline in coal shipments. In 1906-10, these, including both foreign and coastwise trade, averaged over three million tons annually, and even in 1931-35 they still averaged some two-and-a-quarter million tons, whereas in recent years they have fallen as low as 100,000 tons.[1] This has caused problems through the disuse of the specialised coal-handling equipment provided at General Terminus Quay and in Rothesay Dock, and also through the absence of return cargoes for ships bringing in bulk imports. On the other hand, recent years have seen a rapid growth of imports of iron ore, which have now once again reached the volume of about one-and-a-quarter million tons a year, which they averaged before 1914. With the development of new blast furnace capacity in Scotland in the last few years, these have largely displaced the former larger imports of pig-iron. Iron ore is handled at Rothesay Dock, and new facilities for handling it have now been built at General Terminus Quay, in the Plantation area (Pl. IV), whence it can easily be transported by rail to Colville's Clyde Iron Works at Tollcross and to their new works at Ravenscraig.

Imports are predominantly bulky goods of low value. Of a total tonnage—foreign and coastwise—in 1954-55 of 4,700,000, iron ore accounted for 26 per cent, oil for 17·5 per cent and grain for 12 per cent. Exports, on the other hand, are predominantly valuable manufactured goods; and out of a total tonnage of two million, the only bulk goods of importance were iron and steel (22·5 per cent) and coal (12 per cent).[1] By value in foreign trade, the most important imports were crude petroleum, grain, fruit and vegetables, with the bulky but cheap iron ore considerably further down the list. Among foreign exports the most valuable classes were machinery, whisky, iron and steel goods, vehicles, ships, cotton goods (mainly sewing thread from Paisley), metal manufactures and floor coverings.

The changes in the pattern of imports and exports have led to changes in the direction of trade also. The trade with South America, based on coal exports, has largely fallen off, and so has the export trade to many European countries, which consisted largely of coal. Iron ore imports, which used to come mainly from Spain, have grown

275

enormously and now come from Sweden, Norway, Eastern Canada, North and West Africa and Venezuela. Imports from India, on the other hand, have fallen, because pig-iron is no longer imported from there. Hardwood timber, which before the war came mainly from the United States, now comes from West Africa, and imports of fruit and canned goods from the U.S.A. and West Canada are also less than they used to be.

In shipping, the emphasis has shifted from the tramp steamer to the more or less regular cargo liner. Ships are now larger and faster, so that the same tonnage of goods can be carried by means of a smaller number of sailings. Having regard to the changes in the pattern of trade, however, the facilities available to merchants and manufacturers on the Clyde, in the form of regular sailings to different parts of the world, do not compare unfavourably with the past. Many services make Glasgow their terminal port, the ships going on from there to fill up at Liverpool or London or other ports, with the reverse procedure on the inward voyage. It is very much otherwise as regards passenger sailings. Before the war the Anchor Line and the United States Lines operated regular services to the United States, and the Donaldson Line ran a similar service to Canada during the season when the St Lawrence was open. Up to 1931 the Canadian Pacific also operated regularly to the St Lawrence. Nowadays there are no all-passenger services, and all that is available is a few berths in the cargo-passenger services of the United States and Donaldson Lines. With the growth in the size of ocean liners and the increasing importance of quick turn-round, Glasgow, twenty miles up a narrow river, cannot compete with the much better facilities of Southampton, Liverpool and Tilbury, which are also much better situated to serve the biggest centres of population in Britain. Short-distance passenger sailings such as the regular services of the Burns-Laird Line to Belfast and Dublin are still important, though the 'all-the-way' sailings by pleasure steamers to the Firth of Clyde are only a shadow of their former selves, owing to competition from the car and the motor coach.

As a regional port, serving an important industrial area and indeed the whole of Scotland and parts of Northern England, Glasgow holds its own. The Clyde Navigation Trust has carried out much in the way of extensions to quays and improvements of cranes and other equipment in recent years and has plans for further developments, if required, for which there is ample room on the west side of King George V Dock. The development of the port must, however, be limited to some extent by its position far up a navigable river. This has been illustrated by such features as the lack of a graving dock big enough to handle the large tankers now coming into use which, though often built on the Clyde, must go elsewhere for repair. Among Scottish ports, Glasgow is still pre-eminent, but one feature of recent years has been the comparative rise of Grangemouth, the centre of a rapidly developing industrial area.

RAILWAY FACILITIES

Its size and importance have made Glasgow a major railway centre. Main rail routes radiate from it in all directions: south-east to Carlisle via Clydesdale and Annandale, connecting with the west-coast line to England; southwards the alternative route to Carlisle via Kilmarnock and Dumfries, which links with the Midland route to the south; south-west to Ayr and Stranraer, for Northern Ireland; and westwards to

Greenock and the Clyde coast; north-westwards, via Helensburgh, to Fort William and Mallaig by the West Highland Line; north-east to Stirling, Perth, Dundee, Aberdeen and Inverness; and eastwards to Edinburgh, linking with the east-coast route to England, with an offshoot into Fife via the Forth Bridge.

In addition there is a dense network of local lines, serving the city and district and the neighbouring industrial areas. These lines were built in the days of rapidly growing population, when the railways had a monopoly of traffic. Competition between the three companies, the Caledonian, the North British and the Glasgow and South-Western often led to duplication, resulting in, for instance, two lines between Glasgow and such places as Dumbarton, Coatbridge and Airdrie, Hamilton, Ardrossan and Greenock. With the rise in road transport much of this rail network is now very lightly used. Some lines have been abandoned and passenger services have been withdrawn from many others. Where it is possible to provide reasonably fast and frequent passenger services, as between Glasgow and such towns as Helensburgh, Greenock and Gourock, the Ayrshire coast towns, Paisley, or Motherwell, traffic remains heavy. Otherwise, it has been very largely lost to the more frequent and convenient buses, or else to private cars.

In particular, the suburban railway system, developed before the rise of the electric tramway, nowadays has a great deal of unused capacity. This includes the two underground steam lines which run through Queen Street and Central Low Level Stations respectively, and their connections to Dumbarton, Clydebank, Milngavie, Maryhill, Rutherglen, Coatbridge and Airdrie, and also, on the south side of the river, the Cathcart Circle and its offshoots. The electrification of these lines may lead to a growth of traffic which would relieve the congestion on the roads, provided a frequent enough service can be offered at sufficiently low fares to attract passengers from the more convenient trams and buses. Indeed, there is some evidence that local rail travel has begun to increase in recent years. A survey of bookings from the suburban stations of the former Caledonian Railway showed that, whereas the yearly total of these had fallen by 57 per cent as between 1913 and 1949, between 1949 and 1952 it rose by 25 per cent. The biggest increases were recorded by stations serving new housing estates.[2]

The fact that Glasgow is essentially a terminal point rather than a junction is emphasised by its possession of four main line stations, a number equalled among provincial cities only by Manchester. All are termini and all are situated in the centre of the city within less than half-a-mile of each other. Central and St Enoch Stations are both capable of handling a good deal more traffic than they now normally do and Buchanan Street Station, though somewhat ramshackle and out-of-the-way, is reasonably adequate from the traffic point of view. Queen Street Station, on the other hand, is very cramped: at the bottom of a gradient of 1 in 42, one-and-a-half miles long and with only two tracks emerging from a tunnel which begins only a few yards from the platform-ends, it must be one of the most difficult and costly stations in the country to operate. As a long-term policy it is proposed to close Queen Street High Level station and divert the traffic to a new station on the site of Buchanan Street. Meanwhile the position is being eased by converting the Glasgow-Edinburgh services to diesel operation and diverting the Fife trains from Queen Street to Buchanan Street (Pl. XIX). These four Glasgow termini are used by an average of some 1,300 short-distance and 130 long-distance trains daily, and handle a daily average of about 112,000 passengers.[3]

The three main goods depots, Buchanan Street, College and High Street, are also situated near the city centre, lying close together on its north-east side. They handle the bulk—some 1,000 tons daily—of the general goods traffic to and from the city, especially the heavy traffic, in small consignments to and from the shops and warehouses of the central area. The total weight of all goods, excluding coal, forwarded from twenty goods stations in the Glasgow area was estimated in 1952 to be about a million-and-a-half tons a year. About 40 per cent of the total consisted of the materials and products of the iron and steel industry.[4] Other substantial traffics were those arising from distilling, brewing, textiles, chemicals, engineering, tobacco, confectionery and preserves, together with imported goods such as grain, timber, fruit and dairy produce.

ROADS AND ROAD TRAFFIC

The distinctive features of the road system have already been mentioned. The streets in the older areas of the city are fairly wide and regular, those in the centre laid out on a gridiron pattern with intersections at right angles roughly every fifty yards; but they serve a dense population, tightly packed into four-storey tenements. The main roads leading out of the city are mostly inadequate for modern traffic, being closely built-up and often congested, especially by tram lines. The worst examples are perhaps London Road, Paisley Road and Dumbarton Road, but most of the others are little better. There are only two arterial roads which could be called adequate. Great Western Road provides a broad highway from St George's Cross right out to the city boundary at Drumchapel and is continued by the Boulevard to Dumbarton and, from Alexandra Park outwards, the Edinburgh Road forms part of the modern Glasgow-Edinburgh trunk road. Even these, however, can only be reached from the city centre by means of congested streets. There is, however, an absence of adequate ring roads, by which the city centre can be avoided. This disadvantage is exaggerated by the lack of river crossings below the George V Bridge, so that cross-river traffic must either make its way through the centre of the town or else rely on the inadequate and overcrowded ferries at Finnieston, Govan, Whiteinch, Renfrew and Erskine (Pl. IV).

Congestion in the city centre is becoming increasingly serious, as is the case in most other large towns. The number of vehicles using the streets grows steadily. The total number of vehicles licensed in Glasgow and the surrounding counties and burghs of Lanarkshire, Renfrewshire and Dunbartonshire, which in 1938 was about 70,000, excluding agricultural tractors, had risen by 1956 to 139,000.[5] In other words, the number of vehicles which might be expected from time to time to use the Glasgow streets has about doubled since before the war. Private cars are up by 80 per cent, goods-vehicles by 130 per cent, and motor cycles (including scooters) by no less than 160 per cent.[5] More and more people are using their own cars and more and more traders' goods-vehicles are coming into use.

The gridiron pattern of the central streets eases the situation to some extent, by providing alternative routes. It also lends itself to a system of one-way traffic, which has been extensively developed in recent years. On the other hand the frequent intersections, often controlled by traffic lights, result in constant interruptions of the stream of traffic. The situation is made worse in many cases by the presence of tramcars occupying the centre of the road and of stationary vehicles along the kerb, in streets which are not

278

unduly wide. It is not uncommon in Renfield Street, for instance at the rush hour, for several blocks to be jammed solid with tramcars, so that when the lights change, traffic cannot move forward, because the next block is full. Among the worst places for congestion are Clyde Street and the Broomielaw, at the approach to the bridges; Argyle Street, between Hope Street and Glassford Street; the stretch of Hope Street beside the Central Station, where there are three sets of traffic lights in less than a hundred yards; Renfield Street; the lower part of Buchanan Street; and Sauchiehall Street, between Renfield Street and Cambridge Street. A survey by the Road Research Laboratory indicated that the average speed of traffic through Central Glasgow was appreciably slower than through Central London, with its wider streets and less frequent junctions. A recent report would suggest that the position is getting worse, for whereas the Road Research Laboratory gave the average speed attainable in early 1952 as about nine miles per hour, a Corporation spokesman stated in September, 1957, that this had fallen to seven miles per hour.[6] (See Plates XIX and XX.)

The Corporation is attempting to deal with the problem by extending the system of one-way traffic in the central area, and by drastic restrictions on parking and waiting in central streets, together with efforts to provide more parking space in areas just outside the centre. The provision of more parking space, however, is difficult because of the lack of suitable streets and open spaces. In September, 1957, during an enquiry into proposals for further restrictions, it was reported that official parking space could be provided in the centre of the city for 2,142 vehicles. This includes unilateral parking space and private garages. Within a half-mile radius of the centre there would be places for another 2,880 cars.[7] Meanwhile, the average number of cars found parked in the central streets outside official parking places had risen from 1,750 in 1950 to between 4,600 and 4,800 in 1956. A recent census revealed that 40 per cent of these were parked for periods of over an hour, though the proportion of all-day parkers was small, less than 2 per cent.[8,9] Since it is not possible, without drastic and costly reconstruction, to adapt the streets to the growing traffic, the aim is to ease circulation by trying to adapt the traffic to the streets, and in particular to discourage the flood of private cars from entering the city centre, thus freeing the streets for the passage of public transport.

Within the city and a number of immediately surrounding areas, public road-passenger services are provided by the Corporation Transport Department, which operates trams, motor buses, trolleybuses and the municipal Underground Railway. Glasgow is still the great stronghold of the tramcar, and in fact it now has about half the trams still operating in Britain, though even here they are beginning to be displaced. The compactly built nature of the city made it well suited for tramway operation, which needs a dense traffic to make use of the higher carrying capacity of the trams, and thus spread their higher maintenance and capital costs over more passengers. Even in 1955-56, when a number of tram routes had already been abandoned, out of a total of 661 million passengers carried on the system, the trams still accounted for 367 million, as against 215 million on the motor buses, 44 million on the trolleybuses and 34 million on the Underground.[9]

Nevertheless, it has been becoming increasingly clear in recent years that a change will have to be made. Although Glasgow has about 300 modern bogie cars, nearly all built since 1938 and many of them almost brand new, it also has about 600 old four-wheeled cars, some of which are up to fifty years old.[10] The decision to scrap these has already been taken, and once they are replaced the modern Coronation cars will then be due for replacement. According to the Transport Manager's figures, the capital cost of replacement of the old trams by modern trams would be £11,230,000, as against £5,539,000 for motor buses and £7,412,000 for trolleybuses.[11] Certainly, the average life of a tram is much greater, but against this must be set the need to reconstruct the track.

At the time of writing the controversy is still raging in the local press, for the Glaswegian has a strong attachment to his 'caurs', with memories going back to the model service they gave in the days of the late Mr Dalrymple before 1914. It is true that a tram holds more people and that you can read in it. It is true that modern trams on good track can be comfortable, and if it were possible to run coupled, single-deck cars at high speeds on their own tracks, as in some Continental cities, there might be much to be said for them. But this cannot be done in the Glasgow streets, and meanwhile the trams cause congestion and their rails and cobbles make the streets bumpy and dangerous for other traffic. Moreover, though trams last longer than buses, they are route-bound and their services cannot easily be adapted to changing traffic needs. Already Edinburgh and Dundee have replaced their trams and Aberdeen has also recently done so, while in most of the English cities they have either disappeared or are on the point of doing so. Whatever the final decision in Glasgow, however, they are likely to remain for another twenty years or so.

Like most urban road-passenger undertakings, the Corporation has faced difficulties in the last few years. With the growing use of private cars and motor cycles, and the tendency to stay at home in the evenings watching television, the number of passengers has tended to decline, especially at off-peak periods. Meanwhile the continued dispersal of population into outlying housing estates accentuates the peak-hour problem. More mileage has to be run on services which are almost empty in one direction, and more and more passengers tend to become concentrated into short periods, morning and evening. Between 1950 and 1956, in spite of some curtailment of services outside the city boundary, total vehicle-mileage operated fell by only 6 per cent, whereas the number of passengers carried fell by 18 per cent. At the same time inflation has led to a constant rise in wage rates and the price of materials and fuel, with little scope for counteracting this by increases in productivity, such as are possible in manufacturing industry. As a result a system which used to boast of its maximum fare of twopence (for which one could travel twenty miles on a tram) and which had half-penny fares up to the Second World War, has, like most other municipal undertakings, been constantly faced with a deficit.

The Corporation Underground Railway, or 'Subway' as it is popularly called, is a unique institution. It is a circular system of shallow tubes, running from St Enoch, via Kinning Park, Govan, Partick, Hillhead, and St George's Cross, back to St Enoch, and vice versa. Opened by a private company in 1897, it was cable-operated for many years before being taken over by the Corporation in 1923 and converted to electric traction in the 'thirties. Its fuller development is hampered by its narrow gauge of four feet and by the very cramped dimensions of its tunnels and stations, which will only allow two-car trains of special stock to be used. To anyone used to the scale of the London Underground, it looks almost like a toy, but it is very efficient nevertheless, with its three-minute service and its fares ranging from twopence to fourpence. It is

280

much faster than surface vehicles and it is particularly useful as a means of crossing the river below the bridges. Its heaviest regular traffic therefore is between Govan Cross and Merkland Street or Partick Cross, but it really comes into its own when Rangers are playing at home, for Copland Road station is very convenient for Ibrox Park. The fact that it carries thirty-four million passengers a year is evidence of its general usefulness.

Road-passenger services between Glasgow and places outside the city boundary are provided by the nationalised companies of the Scottish Group, namely Scottish Omnibuses, Alexanders, with its subsidiary, Lawsons, the Western S.M.T. and the Central S.M.T. In addition, Macbrayne's provide regular services between Glasgow and the West Highlands. A dense network of bus routes connects the city with the neighbouring towns and, in fact, it is possible to travel conveniently by bus to most places of any size in central and western Scotland. The three bus stations at Killermont Street, Dundas Street and Waterloo Street are reasonably commodious, but conditions are less satisfactory at the three open-stances at Clyde Street, Carlton Place and St Enoch Square, from which many routes depart, especially for places to the south of the city. Plans for the building of a new bus station, in Clyde Street or Carlton Place, have so far come to nothing, partly because of the continued use of Custom House Quay by river steamers unloading sand and gravel. It was estimated for the Inglis Report in 1949 that a total of about 7,625 buses ran into and out of the city every day and that they carried some 239,000 passengers daily.[11]

It is less easy to give a picture of goods transport. A total of about 20,000 goods-vehicles were licensed within the city in 1956, and a further 15,000 (excluding agricultural tractors) were licensed in the neighbouring counties and burghs of Lanarkshire, Renfrewshire and Dunbartonshire.[12] About public carriers some information is available. British Road Services, for instance, in 1956 had about 450 vehicles engaged in the Glasgow area and they carried about 1,200,000 tons of long-distance traffic and about 130,000 tons of local traffic. Among independent hauliers, the Road Haulage Association had, in 1956, 450 members with headquarters in Glasgow, with a total licensed vehicle-tonnage of 6,457 tons.[13] This gives no account, however, of the large and growing numbers of 'C' Licence vehicles operated by traders to carry their own goods.

AIR SERVICES

Air transport is now beginning to play an appreciable part in the transport facilities available to Glasgow's citizens. Over longer distances, the advantage of speed is beginning to outweigh the disadvantages of higher cost, less frequent services and the long distances between city centres and airports. A businessman can get to London and back in a day, for instance, without having to spend two nights in the train and at a cost little more than that of first-class rail with sleeper. Even where journeys are shorter, air travel has an advantage in speed and comfort if sea crossings are involved. Thus the air services between Renfrew and Campbeltown and Islay, the Outer Hebrides, Orkney and Shetland are well patronised even though the short flights and frequent landings and take-offs and the limited capacity of the planes make their operation highly uneconomic. The Belfast and Dublin services also are well used.

281

Glasgow's airport at Renfrew, just outside the city boundary, is operated by the Ministry of Transport and Civil Aviation, who have recently completed new buildings. It is reasonably conveniently situated, but lies near the river and hence is rather liable to fog. The number of passengers has doubled since 1950 and freight tonnages, though still small, have quadrupled. In 1956 the airport handled 374,000 passengers, 1,692 tons of freight and 497 tons of mail.[14] Traffic is still largely concentrated on the summer months, but the proportion of winter traffic is increasing, over a quarter of the passengers now being carried in the five months November to March. Glasgow also benefits from the international services which use Prestwick airport, thirty miles away, though the problem of providing faster communications between the airport and the city has still to be solved.

THE FUTURE

The future of Glasgow's transport has two interrelated aspects. First, there is the problem of the future development of the physical facilities, the roads and the railways. Secondly, there is the problem of how public transport can best be organised to meet the changing needs of population and industry. Both are bound up with future policy about the location of housing and factories, which will largely determine the volume and the direction of the traffic to be handled.

Improvement of the road system is difficult because of the closely built-up nature of most of the city. Work has at last begun on the most urgently needed improvement, namely the Whiteinch Tunnel which, when completed, will provide a road connection under the river between the north-western and south-western areas of the city. The proposal for a high-level bridge in the Finnieston area, to provide a link in the inner ring road similar to that which the tunnel will provide in an outer ring, has recently been revived, though there are obvious problems in the avoidance of interference with navigation. The City Development Plan, published in 1951,[15] provided for the eventual building of a system of two ring roads and nine arterial roads, intended to have dual carriageways and ultimately to be restricted to certain types of traffic and to have their connections with the ordinary roads reduced to a minimum. The line of existing roads was to be followed as far as possible, but nevertheless it would be extremely difficult and costly to carry out these plans.

The chances of any drastic improvement of the present road system are remote. Attention has, therefore, naturally been turned to the possibility of making more use of the well-developed local rail network. This was one of the central recommendations of the Inglis Committee, whose Report was published in 1951.[16] This proposed the electrification of the suburban lines and of the lines leading to such towns as Gourock, Wemyss Bay, Helensburgh, Balloch, Airdrie, Hamilton, East Kilbride and (eventually) Kilmarnock and Ayr. A beginning has, in fact, been made on the electrification of the Queen Street Low Level line and its connections to Helensburgh, Balloch, Milngavie, and Airdrie, and of the Cathcart Circle and the line to Kirkhill; it is estimated that this will be completed by 1960. The hope is that faster and more frequent electric-train services will attract much traffic that would otherwise go by road, either in private cars or in buses. Hence the Report envisaged the development of feeder bus services based on convenient stations and the curtailment of certain through bus services between the outer areas and the centre of the city. It is probable that electrification will encourage increased traffic, as it has done in London, though it must be remembered that the distances normally travelled are much shorter than they are round London, so that the railways' advantage of speed is not so likely to counterbalance their less frequent services.

On the question of organisation, the Inglis Committee emphasised the need for closer co-operation between Glasgow Corporation, the railways and the Scottish Group bus companies. It was recommended that as far as possible the Corporation services should be concentrated within the city boundary. In pursuance of this policy, the Corporation has recently withdrawn a number of tram and bus services which operated outside the city, in areas such as Paisley, Renfrew, Milngavie, Coatbridge, Airdrie and Uddingston and these have been replaced by bus services operated by the Scottish Group. The dispersal of population and industry from Central Glasgow will also cause problems. Already the Corporation has had difficulty in providing adequate bus services at peak periods to meet the needs of the people rehoused in large outer estates such as Drumchapel, Castlemilk and Easterhouse. In fact, the co-operation of the Scottish Group has been enlisted in serving some of these areas. The development of the new town of Cumbernauld will raise the problem even more acutely, unless provision of more balanced local employment is made for those who are rehoused there.

Meanwhile, it is likely that the trend from public to private transport will continue, with private cars and 'C' Licence vehicles growing at the expense of the public carriers by road and rail. This will make the work of public transport operators more difficult, unless indeed it is checked by the growing difficulty of finding parking space in the more crowded areas. In London, it is hoped, by introducing parking meters, to encourage people to leave their cars in the outskirts and travel in by train or bus. This has not so far been suggested in Glasgow, though the drastic restrictions on parking now being introduced may have the same effect.

How successfully is Glasgow adapting its transport system to changing needs? It is hampered by several disadvantages, such as closely built-up streets, lack of space for new roads, a navigable river in the city centre and the pre-war trade depression which delayed investment in improvements. There is not much hope of any drastic alteration of the physical pattern of roads and streets, but the effort is now being made, by railway electrification and the gradual replacement of the trams, to make the best of the available facilities. Glasgow in twenty years' time *should* have a more efficient and better organised passenger transport system. As for goods transport, the pattern here depends more on national policy, which is now developing on the lines of free competition between railways, public and private road hauliers, and traders using their own vehicles. The railways' modernisation plan includes improvements in freight handling in the Glasgow area, such as the provision of new marshalling yards, and resignalling, which has already been carried out at Cowlairs. There are also improvements in port facilities being undertaken to meet trade and industrial developments—notably the new iron ore handling equipment at General Terminus Quay, and also modernisation and extension schemes at Queen's Dock and Meadowside Granaries and new terminal buildings for the Irish steamers at the Broomielaw.

Glasgow's transport system, like its architecture, may at first sight appear to be still largely Victorian, or at best Edwardian. Behind the scenes, however, it is undergoing a process of transformation.

1 Clyde Navigation Trust—Annual Returns.

2 Figures supplied by courtesy of British Railways.

3 British Transport Commission—*Report on Passenger Transport in Glasgow and District, 1951* (Inglis Report), and material provided by courtesy of British Railways.

4 Figures supplied by British Railways.

5 Ministry of Transport and Civil Aviation—*Annual Census of Mechanically Propelled Road Vehicles.*

6 *Glasgow Herald*, 11 September 1957.   7 *Glasgow Herald*, 7 September 1957.

8 Figures supplied by Glasgow City Engineer's Department.

9 Glasgow Corporation Transport—*General Manager's Report 1955-6.*

10 *Ibid.*   11 *Glasgow Herald*, 25 June 1957.

11 British Transport Commission—*Report on Passenger Transport in Glasgow and District, 1951.*

12 Ministry of Transport and Civil Aviation—*Annual Census of Mechanically Propelled Road Vehicles.*

13 Figures supplied by British Road Services, and by the Road Haulage Association, Scottish Area.

14 Scottish Civil Aviation Division, Ministry of Transport and Civil Aviation.

15 Corporation of the City of Glasgow—Development Plan 1951.

16 British Transport Commission—*Report on Passenger Transport in Glasgow and District, 1951.*

GLASGOW'S SPHERES OF INFLUENCE

H. A. MOISLEY

Lecturer in Geography, University of Glasgow

THE City of Glasgow performs as varied a set of functions as any town in Britain, save only London. As has been shown, it was established as an ecclesiastical centre, grew to prominence as a commercial and university town and gained world-wide fame and prosperity as a port and industrial city. All these functions continue, and there are many more besides. But the administrative boundary of the County of the City, carved relatively recently from the adjacent counties of Lanark, Renfrew and Dunbarton, is merely a line of convenience, delimiting Glasgow for one purpose only—local government. For many other purposes the effective civic unit is different and usually far wider. Then, in addition, many of the services provided in Glasgow are utilised, to a greater or lesser extent, by the population of far wider areas. Such 'service areas', 'urban fields' or 'spheres of influence' differ in extent according to the nature of the particular service. Thus, for example, whilst the cattle market attracts stock mainly from farms within a few miles of the city boundary, the abattoir and meat market receive fatstock from all parts of Scotland and beyond, a contrast which will be further discussed below. Similarly, whilst only one government department—the Board of Trade—has its Scottish headquarters in Glasgow (and very few have more than a local office), the Scottish Milk Marketing Board controls by far the greater part of Scottish milk supplies from a Glasgow office, and Glasgow markets and wholesalers distribute foodstuffs to all parts of the country. Again, whilst the University and the Royal College of Science and Technology draw the majority of their Scottish students from a clearly definable local area (as, in their own regions, do the other Scottish Universities), the circulation of Glasgow newspapers is widespread throughout Scotland. Thus, for every function or service there is a region. Sometimes it is readily defined, sometimes it defies definition. In a brief essay we can but select a few examples at random and comment on them in the hope, thereby, of displaying not only the variety of Glasgow's activities but also the extent of its influence and interest in other parts of the country.

THE 'URBAN FIELD'

The 'journey to work' is a phenomenon common to all modern cities. In so far as certain towns, villages and amorphous urban areas send the majority of their productive population to work in the city, they are part of the civic unit, even though they lie outwith its administrative boundary. There are many such districts fringing the boundary (see Fig. 60), and, beyond them, lie still others which, whilst having some local *raison d'être* other than as dormitories nevertheless contribute a substantial proportion of their working populations. Thus, according to the 1951 Census, Rutherglen, with a working population of some 11,000 sends 5,500 to work in Glasgow. Paisley, with a working population of 44,000, of whom some 40,000 are employed locally, also sends 3,600 into the city. In this connection it should be remembered that Glasgow is merely the central, and largest, of the urban units which make up the continuous built-up area of Clydeside; the city itself contributes no less than 59,000 workers to places beyond its boundary. It must be added, immediately, that about 11,000 of these were travelling daily to the burgh of Clydebank alone in 1951 and that this is in part the aftermath of the Clydebank 'blitz', when almost every house in the burgh was damaged and a very large number totally destroyed. The daily outflow to Paisley (2,600) and to the industrial towns of Lanarkshire is by no means so significant. There is, however, a daily outflow of several thousand workers from Glasgow to the small burgh of Renfrew and thereabouts, where the Hillington Industrial Estate (which lies astride the city boundary), Babcock and Wilcox, the India Tyre Co. and other firms are large employers. Effectively this district is merely an extension of the Glasgow industrial complex—a suburb in the strictest sense—and has little separate identity. Finally, there is a wide area (Fig. 61) from which some daily workers are drawn to the city. A full understanding of the commuting pattern on Clydeside would require detailed analyses of transport services and of the changing pattern of employment in the various parts of the region. It could only be based on data more detailed and more reliable than those at present available. Nevertheless, it is clear that Glasgow does exert some influence, as a place of work, as far as Stirling and West Lothian in the east, and south to Lanark, Ayr and beyond. To the west the flow is restricted by defective communications—places which formerly had rapid and frequent steamer-rail connections across the Firth are now, effectively, further away. To the north, beyond the Vale of Leven and the upper Forth Valley, lie the relatively unpopulated Highlands.

Even though some of the urban settlements of the conurbation, and many of those beyond it, are industrially more or less completely independent of the city, they may still look to Glasgow for a variety of services. With its enormous population the city can offer far greater variety of shops, of all classes, than any other town in Scotland, not excluding (let it be whispered) Edinburgh itself. Indeed, there can be little doubt that Glasgow yields pride of place to no British city outside London in the number, and standard, of its high-class stores. Thus it is not surprising that the service areas of Glasgow stores—high-class and popular alike—extend far beyond the Clydeside conurbation. The answers to the Geographical Association questionnaire (Fig. 62) define a smaller area than that within which many stores find a weekly delivery service worth while (Figs. 63 and 64), reflecting perhaps, the use of Glasgow for 'occasional' shopping. The deficiency of surrounding towns, particularly as to high-class furniture and clothing shops, is noteworthy, though difficult to define with precision. By contrast, the regular delivery area of Edinburgh stores is far less extensive, and less frequent. In addition, as will be mentioned later, many Glasgow stores carry on a remarkable postal trade with the Highlands and Islands, but this is a regional rather than a local function.

Other local urban functions include professional services and cultural activities, entertainment and sport. Many professional services are provided locally, even in purely dormitory districts, since, unlike rural areas, such districts usually have sufficient population to support at least a doctor and a dentist. In the field of entertainment, however, Glasgow plays a big part. Although each industrial district has its football team,

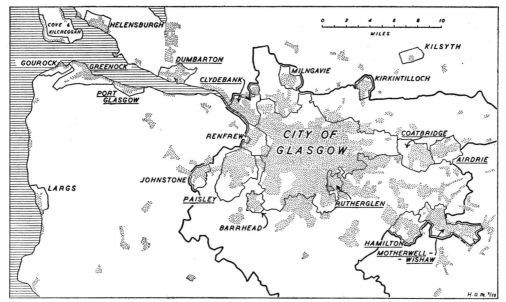

FIG. 60. The city, the adjacent burghs and the conurbation. Burgh boundaries are shown and each is named; large burghs are underlined. The closely built-up area is stippled and the conurbation, as defined by the Registrar-General for Scotland, is outlined by the thick line. The absence of large burghs from the northern and southern flanks of the city leads to the city providing many urban functions for these districts. These are the districts also which are largely dependent on the city for productive employment (see Fig. 61).

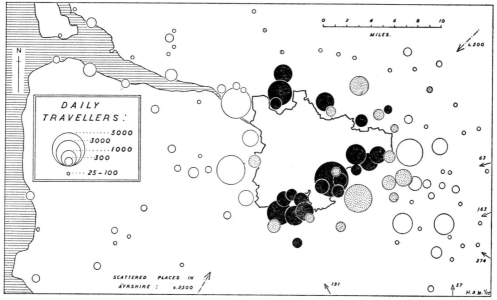

FIG. 61. Daily travellers into Glasgow. The circles are proportionate to the number travelling from each place. Places sending more than 20 per cent of their total population (i.e. half or more of their employed population) are shown in black—places sending more than 10 per cent are stippled. Arrows indicate smaller numbers from scattered places beyond the area of the map. Note that this diagram takes no account of daily travellers *out* of Glasgow, e.g. to Clydebank and Renfrew.

the Glasgow teams attract many 'fans' from beyond the city, as well as the supporters of the visiting teams. With five 'live' theatres (six until one was recently lost to television), and several top-grade cinemas, Glasgow also attracts substantial custom from surrounding districts. The theatres, in particular, draw their audiences from a large part of Scotland. Again, the 'service area' has proved elusive to define, but it is known that organised coach parties come from the Borders and from the north-eastern counties, particularly in the pantomime season (December-March). As in the case of retail stores, the huge local population allows Glasgow to offer variety unattainable elsewhere. In a rather similar category are the various societies and institutions which offer popular, scientific or philosophical lectures, or concerts. Their membership is by no means restricted to city-dwellers and is probably mainly limited by the availability of late transport to outlying districts. (See Figs. 62B and 62C.)

That the effective local urban unit is more extensive than the city boundary is underlined by the fact that many public bodies, official and unofficial, define a 'Glasgow district' more extensive than the city alone. The postal and telephone districts are cases in point, as are the local areas of the Ministry of Labour (for labour exchanges) and National Assistance Board (Fig. 67). It should be noted that these 'working' areas, are designed for the convenience of the public and the efficiency of the particular service; they are not merely arbitrary administrative units. Examination of a large number of such areas suggests that, for many purposes, the urban field of Glasgow extends westwards and north-westwards into Dunbartonshire, where it meets competition in a few respects only, from such places as Clydebank and Dumbarton, and in rather more respects (e.g. shopping) from Helensburgh. Northwards, the lack of any well-developed alternative urban centre—Milngavie and Bearsden offer the barest minimum of urban facilities—extends the field of Glasgow through Strathblane and Killearn well into Stirlingshire. Competition with Stirling is met with in the neighbourhood of Balfron and Aberfoyle. North-eastwards the picture is rather similar in spite of a number of small urban settlements such as Lenzie and Kirkintilloch. On the other hand, to the east the built-up area is virtually continuous with a number of substantial industrial towns— Coatbridge, Airdrie, Hamilton, Motherwell and Wishaw, which take over from Glasgow the provision of many—though by no means all—of the urban facilities required in north and central Lanarkshire. There are local head post offices, local labour exchanges, markets for farm stock, and weekly newspapers are published. The circulation areas of the latter are as good a guide as any to the zone around Glasgow, which still preserves a feeling of local independence.

MARKET FUNCTIONS

Since the twelfth century, when the King granted to the Bishop the privilege of holding weekly markets and an annual fair, buying and selling have played an important part in the life of Glasgow. The early Charters and a series of Acts since 1800 authorise the operation of markets for livestock, meat, fruit, vegetables, cheese and fish, but the commercial functions of the annual fair have long since been displaced by those of the wholesale and retail merchants. Glasgow still retains to some extent its function as an agricultural market. Store sales, *i.e.* of stock bought by farmers for breeding and fattening, are limited to the sales of imported cattle (mainly Irish) at Merklands Wharf,

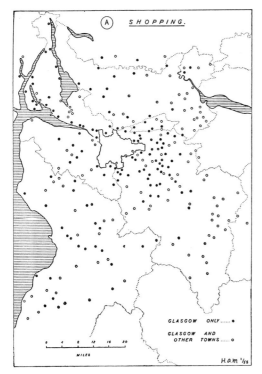

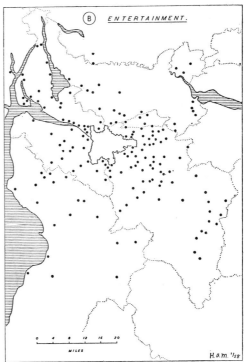

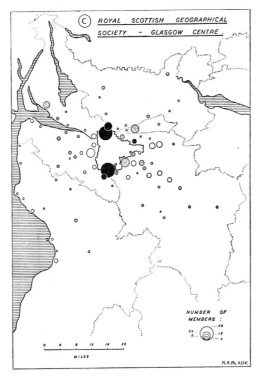

FIG. 62.   Glasgow as a local urban centre.

A. Shopping: places from which Glasgow is visited frequently for 'occasional' shopping (i.e. other than regular weekly shopping).

B. Entertainment: places from which Glasgow is visited for weekly entertainment, including sport.

C. Cultural activities: the city provides these for a wide region. Membership of the Glasgow Centre of the Royal Scottish Geographical Society is plotted as an example; almost half the members live beyond the city boundary. The symbols for places having more than one member *per thousand population* are stippled; for places having more than two members per thousand the symbol is in black.

Note: A and B are based on Geographical Association 'Urban Spheres' questionnaires.

T

and of store pigs, sheep and lambs in the Cattle Market. Although the latter come in from twenty or thirty miles around, as a store market Glasgow ranks well below Lanark, Stirling and Edinburgh, its nearest rivals, and maintains this function rather for the convenience of the buyers, especially those from England, than for that of the sellers. It is, however, as a market for fatstock and meat of all kinds that Glasgow is really important. Some farmers market their own, but the trade in fatstock, originally bought by dealers in other markets, consigned to the Glasgow Abattoir and then sold in the Meat Market, is far more important. Thus, whilst about 11,000 cattle passed through the Cattle Market in 1955-56, no less than 115,000 passed through the Abattoir and almost all the latter were exposed for sale in the Meat Market. This probably represents at least a third of the fat cattle killed for home consumption in Scotland; fat sheep, lambs and pigs are handled on a similar scale. (See Table XXXVI.) In the case of fat pigs, the Glasgow

	Cattle Market		Abattoir
	1937–38	1955–56	1956–57
Cattle *	26,400	11,100	115,500
Calves	6,000	3,300	13,700
Sheep and lambs	324,300	89,600	421,100
Pigs	13,100	12,200	84,400

TABLE XXXVI. Glasgow's Stock Markets: throughput *per annum.*

* In addition, several thousand store cattle, mainly Irish, are sold annually at Merklands Wharf.

Source: Glasgow Corporation Markets Dept.

Abattoir and Meat Market probably handle more than half the Scottish trade. In addition, the Meat Market handles chilled and frozen meat imported via London or Liverpool. The home produce is obtained from every part of Scotland, particularly from the adjacent counties, Stirling, Perth, Angus Aberdeen, Fife, the Lothians, from south-east Scotland, from Ireland, and even from England, as far south as Norfolk, according to the season. It is said that prices in the Glasgow market affect those in many others—a mere whisper of an increase is sufficient to attract supplies from all other markets. The Western Isles and West Highland coast draw their supplies from Glasgow, and there is an 'export' trade to English markets, even to Smithfield (London) particularly for autumn-killed black-faced lambs. The black-faced lamb makes too small a joint for the Scottish table and consequently fetches a better price in Liverpool, Birmingham and London.

An interesting and important side-line in the Cattle Market is the sale of second-hand vehicles in the area formerly devoted to horses. It is by far the largest such market in Scotland and draws its supplies from all parts of the country. Similarly, dealers from all parts use this market to supply the requirements of their customers, and, at the seasonal peak of demand in early summer, English dealers also appear.

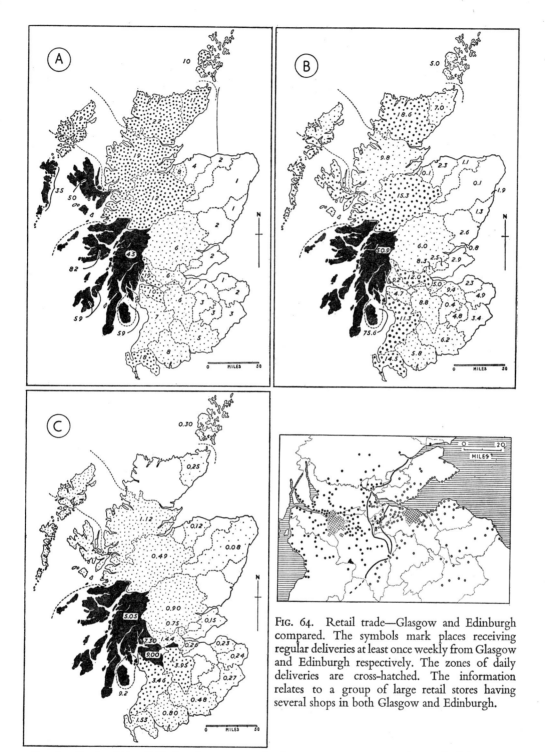

FIG. 64. Retail trade—Glasgow and Edinburgh compared. The symbols mark places receiving regular deliveries at least once weekly from Glasgow and Edinburgh respectively. The zones of daily deliveries are cross-hatched. The information relates to a group of large retail stores having several shops in both Glasgow and Edinburgh.

FIG. 63. Regional Retail Trade—three stores. The figures are customers per thousand of the total population of the counties and large islands. The three stores shown are selected to cover a range of types of goods; the data used are slightly different in each case, viz: A—All account customers (credit and mail-order); based on an analysis of five years' trading. B—Deliveries other than 'over the counter' (i.e. road, rail and postal, including mail orders); based on a 17 per cent sample of one year's trade. C—Credit account customers; based on a 17 per cent sample.

The fish, fruit and vegetable markets are only a little less important. The wholesale fish firms receive supplies from all Scottish ports according to landings. Some Glasgow firms operate their own trawlers, notably at Granton. Similarly, the fruit and vegetable firms draw supplies from all parts, according to season, and handle imports as well. The latter trade is not confined to the port of Glasgow; large supplies, notably of Dutch produce, are imported via Leith. Distribution, as in the case of meat, covers the whole of Scotland and sometimes extends into Northern Ireland and England. Finally, there is the cheese market, but this is relatively unimportant. In all groups of the wholesale trade there are some firms which operate outside the market—often from adjacent premises. About half the firms in the fruit and vegetable trade are thus situated and, the cheese market apart, the wholesale provision trade is not a formally organised market— most of the firms buying privately from other merchants or from importers. But, as in the case of the trades which have markets, Glasgow merchants and importers supply all parts of Scotland, their principal rivals being the importers and merchants of Leith. It is worth noting that Glasgow merchants often import through Leith and *vice versa*, according to the origin of the produce. Thus Danish and Dutch produce comes mainly through Leith, as does tea (by coastal shipment from London). South African, American and Australian dried and canned goods, on the other hand, enter mainly through Glasgow.

Area of Production				
	Ayrshire	Clyde Basin	East and Central Scotland *	South-west Scotland †
QUANTITY PRODUCED (thousand gallons)				
May	4,800	3,900	2,500	8,000
December	3,000	3,000	2,200	3,700
QUANTITY RECEIVED IN GLASGOW (thousand gallons)				
May	1,000	1,600	600	—
December	1,200	1,000	280	200

TABLE XXXVII. Glasgow's Milk Supply.

* Fife, Kinross, Perth, Angus, Stirling and Clackmannan.

† Dumfries, Kirkcudbright and Wigtown.

Source: Derived from data supplied by the Scottish Milk Marketing Board.

Milk supplies are in some ways comparable with those of meat, but whereas the south of Scotland, and in particular the Clyde Valley, is usually deficient in local supplies of fatstock, the opposite is true in the case of milk. (See Table XXXVII.)

Glasgow and its immediate suburbs constitute by far the largest single market for milk and dairy products in Scotland. It is singularly fortunate that the city lies in the heart of a region well suited to milk production. Natural conditions in west and south-west Scotland have encouraged the development of a dairy industry based on rotation grass. Even were no urban market locally available it is likely that milk would be one of the main products of agriculture in the Clyde Valley as it is in Ayrshire and the south-west. In fact, the area within a 25-mile radius of Glasgow, which contains about half the population of Scotland, manages to produce, over the year, more than enough liquid milk to supply the needs of that population. Milk, however, cannot be stored; consequently seasonal variations in production, which differ from district to district, affect supplies. Most of the manufacturing creameries are in Ayrshire and the south-western area; in spring and summer they are fully occupied with local supplies. The eastern areas, on the other hand, have insufficient manufacturing facilities to deal with all the milk, surplus to local liquid requirements, at this period of peak production. Consequently, milk from as far east as Fife and Angus may find its way to Glasgow. The Scottish Milk Marketing Board have a large creamery at Hogganfield, Glasgow, which acts as a 'balancing reservoir'. In winter a little milk from Wigtown and Dumfries may be sent to Glasgow, and at times a certain amount of milk, assembled in Glasgow, is subsequently consigned to other districts, as far afield as Edinburgh, to make up deficiencies.

THE PORT AND ITS HINTERLAND

In this connection it should be remembered that the Port of Glasgow, as defined by the area of jurisdiction of the Clyde Navigation Trust, is far more extensive than the city, and includes Paisley, Renfrew, Clydebank (with the mineral port of Rothesay Dock), Old Kilpatrick and Bowling (where there are oil and petrol installations), and Dumbarton (which still receives an occasional small coaster). The Customs port extends even farther downstream on the north bank, where the newly developed petroleum trade of the Gareloch and crude-oil traffic of Loch Long are supervised by Customs officials based on Glasgow. This is purely a matter of convenience of access. The Greenock Customs area, on the other hand, stretches from Dumfries northwards to Mull and includes Prestwick Airport and the Islay distilleries.

The trade of Glasgow, like that of any port, falls into several categories. In the foreign import trade, bulk cargoes such as oil, grain, ore and timber make up a large proportion of the total tonnage. In value, however, general cargoes including tinned and dried fruit, sugar, other foodstuffs, manufactured goods and such industrial raw materials as enter in small quantities, rank high. Such general cargoes are largely carried in 'liners', i.e. on regular services. Amongst the best known lines are, Clan (West, South and East Africa, Aden, India and Ceylon), City (The Mediterranean, Africa and India), Blue Funnel (The Far East and Australia), Donaldson (North America), Furness Line (North Pacific), Harrison (West Indies), Anchor Line (North America and India) and Moss, Hutchison (France and the Mediterranean). There are many others, especially in the European trade, maintaining frequencies up to once weekly to Antwerp and Ghent, and at least monthly to Rouen, Paris, Lisbon, and many other parts. The deep-water trade is carried on by vessels which generally include the

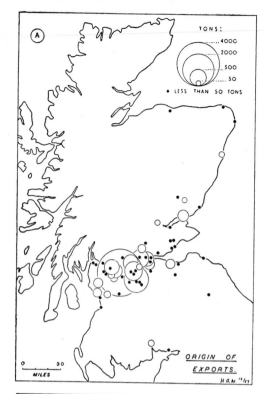

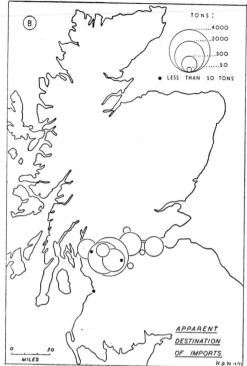

FIG. 65. The hinterland of the port. Maps A and B are based on analyses of the cargoes of a sample of twenty general cargo liners.

A. Exports: the origin of the cargoes of eight vessels leaving Glasgow during 1957.

B. Imports: the apparent destinations of the cargoes of twelve vessels reaching Glasgow during 1957. Note that a substantial proportion of the items apparently destined for Glasgow and Edinburgh (in fact, Leith) are for eventual distribution, from warehouse or quayside, to wholesalers and retailers in all parts of Scotland (see C).

C. The distribution of a sample (approximately 730 tons from about twenty vessels) of canned goods handled by a Glasgow importer: the large tonnages apparently destined for Glasgow and Leith are for subsequent redistribution by wholesalers. (To preserve the confidential nature of the figures, no scale is given).

Clyde as one of several European termini—often the last, after Birkenhead or Liverpool. Consequently the Clyde is also the earliest point of departure—a matter of some significance, as will be shown.

There is an important coastal and Irish trade, too, for Glasgow remains the source of the cargo services which are the life-lines of the Hebrides in spite of the extension of the railways to Oban, Mallaig and Kyle, which robbed her of much traffic—especially of passengers. Road transport, too, has led to a decline of coastal shipping to isolated mainland districts; it is interesting to note that David MacBrayne started business as a carter and subsequently extended his interests to shipping. His successors have inevitably replaced some of the shipping services by lorries and passenger coaches and have lost much island passenger traffic to the air service. In the Irish trade, as well as regular cargo services to several places, the Clyde has more passenger services than any other port—a reflection of the close connection still maintained between the populations of the West of Scotland and of Ireland. At one time Glasgow was the centre of a large fleet of small passenger and cargo vessels plying on the river and Firth of Clyde. The establishment of rail-heads on the coast, giving speedier connections with the city, whilst reducing the services on the river, encouraged the establishment of what were effectively 'outer suburbs' on the Clyde coast, including the Cowal peninsula. These were once served by a remarkable fleet of small steamers, now, alas, greatly reduced for a variety of reasons. Even the daily Ardrishaig (Kintyre) mail steamer *St Columba* no longer departs from Glasgow in the early hours, leaving Gourock, instead, after the arrival of a connecting train. In fact, of the coastal passenger services, Glasgow now only sees the departure of the summer pleasure steamers and of the Irish vessels. It is probably only their easy, overnight schedules, and their functions as fast cargo vessels, that have allowed these Irish services to continue the slow sail past Gourock and Greenock to and from Glasgow. Finally there are the 'puffers'—small coasters of about 100 tons, immortalised in the film *The Maggie*, and in the *Para Handy* series by Neil Munro. They, too, have lost ground, but still remain an essential link to many islands, taking out coal and other bulky materials unsuitable for Macbrayne's, and returning, sometimes, with dried, milled seaweed—the successor of the formerly important kelp cargoes. These tough little steamers were designed to pass through the Crinan and Forth and Clyde Canals, and have flat bottoms so that they may be beached for discharging on islands where there are no piers.

No port has a simple, definable hinterland except if it is the sole port of an island. Glasgow is no exception. The bulk cargoes—grain, oil and timber—are redistributed, with or without processing, all over Scotland. The iron ore is, of course, destined for the Clyde Valley, as are most of the less bulky raw materials. An analysis of the origins and destinations of a sample of general cargoes, outwards and inwards respectively, is shown on Figures 65A and 65B. That showing the destination of inward cargoes emphasises in a most striking manner the concentration of Scottish industry within thirty miles or so of Glasgow. The textile industries of Fife and Angus are the only major group that is not represented. However, the hinterland for inward cargoes is not so simple as this may seem to indicate. About a third of the tonnage shown as destined for Glasgow is in fact goods (mainly foodstuffs) warehoused for subsequent redistribution to wholesalers throughout the country. An example of this is shown in Figure 65C. Almost any cargo except ore and grain would show the same sort of pattern,

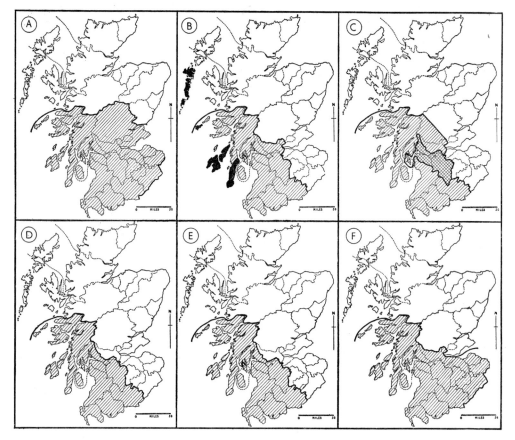

FIG. 66. Some Administrative Regions.

A. Scottish Milk Marketing Board.
B. Western Regional Hospital Board (areas served by Air Ambulance in black).
C. West of Scotland Agricultural Advisory Service and (cross-hatched) Department of Agriculture,
    Clyde Area.
D. Ministry of Works, South-western district.
E. National Assistance Board, Western region.
F. Fatstock Marketing Corporation.

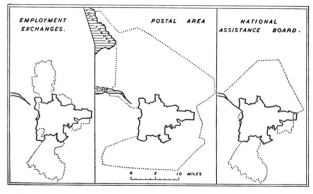

FIG. 67.   Some local administrative
areas.   The influence of the large
burghs, to the west and east, is clearly
seen in the north-south elongation of
many administrative or functional
districts such as these.

from importer to warehouse, from warehouse to wholesaler and so on, until it reached its final consumer. The origin of exports, which are of course mainly manufactured goods, is easier to ascertain. A sample of some cargoes has been analysed (Fig. 65A), and illustrates the function of Glasgow as a port for all Scotland.

'A port for all Scotland'—this statement might not please the inhabitants of Leith, Grangemouth and Dundee. Yet it is certainly true that Glasgow has something approaching a monopoly in many branches of Scottish overseas trade, particularly with more distant ports. No other Scottish port can rival the number of services to all parts of the world. Only in the north- and west-European trade does it meet serious competition from the east-coast ports. This enviable position has been reached as a result, partly, of its history and partly of its position; many of the lines serving Glasgow had their origins in the days of early steamers and even of sailing ships. Yet this position is singularly vulnerable. The many cargo lines which use Glasgow arrive, as has been mentioned, after calling in the Mersey and perhaps in Dublin, the Bristol Channel or a Continental port. Consequently the vessels arrive with only a small portion of their cargo space occupied. Correspondingly, most leave light, taking on perhaps three-fifths of their cargo at English ports, particularly Birkenhead (Clan, Anchor, Brockle-bank, etc.). Glasgow is thus at 'the end of the line'. The extension from the Mersey to the Clyde, although only one day's steaming, may add two weeks to a round voyage, allowing time for loading and unloading, and considerable extra dues. If trade becomes even a little less profitable, whether because of declining volume, increasing costs, slow turn-round, or for other reasons, operators are under strong pressure to cut out such marginal calls. There is a further adverse effect in that cargo from any specific ship may be up to several weeks later in discharging at Glasgow than at the Bristol Channel or the Mersey; correspondingly, cargoes must be loaded a week or ten days earlier in the Clyde. Consequently, urgent and high-value goods are often consigned through English ports, even though this involves road transport. Whisky and razor blades are two examples of Glasgow products commonly shipped from London, Southampton and Liverpool. Many of these factors can be improved by good management on the part of the port authority, the stevedores, the warehouse firms and others, but one factor remains at the present day: Glasgow's services were established when far more of Scotland's industries lay in the west. In recent years industrial developments in the east have been remarkable. There is now more attraction for cargo lines to establish new services at east-coast ports. In recent years, whilst there have been a few cases of lines ceasing to extend their normal voyages from the Mersey to the Clyde, there has also been the establishment in the east of new services, e.g. between Grangemouth and the Far East. This cannot but detract from the trade of Glasgow, and, so far as certain services are concerned, tend to reduce its hinterland.

GLASGOW AS A REGIONAL CAPITAL

Regional functions are never clearly separated from the more local, civic, or urban ones, save in respect of the area served. This is perhaps more true of Glasgow than of many British cities. As a regional *capital* in the strict sense, *i.e.* as an administrative centre, Glasgow loses by the proximity of Edinburgh. There is no official regional division of Scotland, and most government departments and many commercial under-

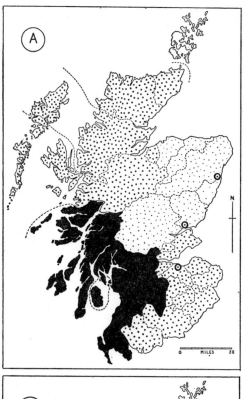

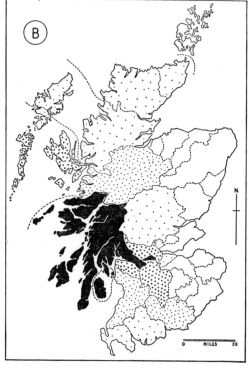

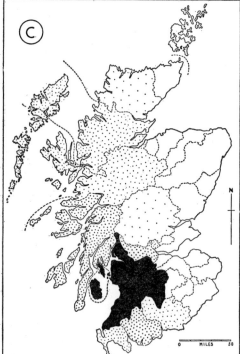

FIG. 68. Some regional functions of Glasgow.

A. As a centre of newspaper publication. Glasgow produces about 75 per cent of Scottish daily morning papers; the map shows the percentage of the total supply of Scottish morning papers supplied by Glasgow to each county. Other cities producing daily morning papers are marked.

B. As a centre of bread production and distribution. The map shows the percentage of total bread supplies to each county supplied by Glasgow. The data are estimates based on confidential statistics provided by four Glasgow bakeries; they include more than half the bread distributed from the city, but almost certainly underestimate the part played by Glasgow bakeries.

C. As a university city. The map shows the percentage of the student population of each county attending Glasgow University.

takings find it convenient, or pleasant, to operate from Edinburgh. Only the Board of Trade has its Scottish headquarters in Glasgow, for obvious reasons, though the Ministry of Works has a district office responsible for Argyll, the Clyde Valley and south-west Scotland. For certain purposes the Department of Agriculture recognises a similar 'West of Scotland' area, but including also west Perth and Stirling. The Western Regional Hospital Board, with its headquarters in Glasgow, includes the same area and Clackmannan. On a more mundane level the Fatstock Marketing Corporation, inheriting the Ministry of Food's regions, recognises two regional headquarters in Scotland: Glasgow and Aberdeen. Glasgow is responsible for Argyll, Stirling, Clackmannan and all counties to the south, an arrangement which is said to be unsatisfactory. The general pattern of trade suggests that Fife, Kinross and, possibly Perth should come within Glasgow's purview—a region which, it is interesting to note, would then be identical with that of the Scottish Milk Marketing Board. One might extend these examples, but the general pattern would remain: for purely administrative purposes, *sensu stricto*, Glasgow gives place to Edinburgh in almost every case, but in more practical matters Glasgow is often the leading centre, if not in all Scotland, then in the south at least, or in a substantial part of it. (See Fig. 66.)

From these precisely, and perhaps artificially, defined spheres of influence we may pass to some, not formally recognised, which, like Topsy, 'just growed'. Many of these are commercial. For example, Glasgow bakeries supply bread and confectionery to all parts of Scotland; confectionery is also widely distributed in England and some goes overseas. Confining ourselves to bread (Fig. 68B), which demands rapid, frequent and regular delivery, we find that Glasgow supplies by far the greater part of the demand in a region extending from the Outer Hebrides and West Highlands, south of the Great Glen, south to Ayrshire and Dumfries. Moreover, whilst there are about a dozen large bread bakeries in other parts of Scotland, many of them belong to Glasgow firms, and few compare in output with those in Glasgow. In general retail trading, too, Glasgow performs a regional function by means of mail-orders and credit accounts. Analysis of the records of several large stores (Figs. 63 and 64) demonstrates this point more clearly than any amount of descriptive writing. The ability of the Glasgow bakers and retail stores to supply such a large area is a result of several factors. Initially they are in a good position, having a very substantial local market to sustain them and carry their overheads (about a half of the population of Scotland lives within twenty-five miles of Glasgow Cross); and Glasgow's communications, particularly northwards, are better in some ways than those of Edinburgh. Because it is so dispersed, the population of the west coast from Kintyre to Wester Ross, and of the Islands from Islay to Lewis, cannot support a single substantial town. Consequently the population, many of them accustomed to seeking work in the Glasgow area, look to Glasgow as *their* town. The Highlanders may never have made up more than a minority of the immigrants to Glasgow, compared with the Irish, but it is nevertheless *the* town of the Highlands. Air services, not least the air-ambulance service, have increased this dependence. The very first journey of many a new-born Hebridean is a homeward flight from Glasgow, whence mother and baby have no doubt been seen off by fellow-islanders, resident temporarily in the city. Less happily, the injured and the sick are transported to the 'Southern General'—almost as quickly as those from the outer suburbs.

The circulation regions of daily newspapers are yet another illustration of these factors. There are two aspects—regional and national—to Glasgow's function in this respect. Regionally, Glaswegian papers such as *The Glasgow Herald*, *The Bulletin* and *Daily Record*, meet and compete in the east with daily morning papers published in Edinburgh, Dundee and Aberdeen. On the national level, the *Scottish Daily Express* is printed and published in Glasgow, whilst the *Scottish Daily Mail* originates in Edinburgh. Comparison of the published circulation figures reveals Glasgow's dominance in this field (Table XXXVIII). (See also Fig. 68A.)

Daily Morning Newspapers: Place of Publication	Circulation per day
GLASGOW:	
The Glasgow Herald	76,000
The Bulletin and Scots Pictorial	152,000
Daily Record	422,000
Scottish Daily Express	575,000
EDINBURGH:	
The Scotsman	56,000
Scottish Daily Mail	148,000
DUNDEE:	
The Dundee Courier and Advertiser	'over 112,000'
ABERDEEN:	
The Press and Journal	78,000

TABLE XXXVIII. Circulation of daily morning newspapers in Scotland.

Only in the north-east are Glasgow-published papers not in the majority; this is partly due to particularly active regional papers and partly to difficulties of daily distribution in this region. Naturally, in central and southern Scotland, *The Scotsman* and *The Glasgow Herald* are almost mutually exclusive. Unfortunately the confidential nature of the data supplied forbids publication of these interesting regions, but they are not dissimilar from those defined for other purposes.

Finally, investigation shows that Scotland is neatly regionalised—though quite informally—by the four Universities. Each draws the majority of its Scottish students from its local area and there is remarkably little interchange between most of the areas (Fig. 68c). With its enormous local population it is not surprising that Glasgow degree courses (of the University and Royal College of Science and Technology) are swamped by students from the nearby counties. There is a tendency for the student population of the Solway counties to be equally divided between Glasgow and Edinburgh, a regional influence which is seen also in newspaper circulation and other functions. The tendency for students from Inverness and the North-West Highlands and Islands to attend Aberdeen or Edinburgh, though not to the exclusion of Glasgow, may reflect better residential facilities as well as regional loyalties.

To summarise, then, one can only say that there is no one 'Glasgow region'. For some purposes Glasgow is undoubtedly the metropolis for a large part of Scotland and, certainly, for the majority of Scots. Being a commercial city, many of these purposes are commercial and reflect the economies of large-scale production (as of bread) and ease of distribution from the city. There is also an important regional loyalty, especially from Argyll and the Western Isles, reflecting close personal connections between that area and the city, and the lack of any alternative urban centre. In this respect Glasgow's 'monopoly' in the west contrasts with the marked division of loyalties in the east, where Edinburgh's influence, though it is the national capital, gives place northwards to that of the cities of Dundee and Aberdeen and, to some extent, of the large burghs of Inverness and Perth.

A very large number of organisations, commercial firms and individuals have supplied information and answered questions on the topics touched on in this essay. For their trouble and patience the writer is most grateful. To make individual acknowledgements here would be an immense task; it is hoped that all will appreciate the difficulty and will accept this general acknowledgement. The writer, alone, is responsible, needless to say, for any expressions of opinion based on information so supplied. The assistance of Miss Catherine Smith, M.A., in collecting and collating the information, has been invaluable.

THE UNIVERSITY OF GLASGOW

J. D. MACKIE, C.B.E.

Professor Emeritus of Scottish History and Literature, University of Glasgow

ALL visitors who come to Glasgow know that they are coming to a city of shipbuilders; and, though occasionally they seem to forget that Glasgow is also a great port and that she manufactures other things besides ships, they are prepared to find an industrial city. What surprises them sometimes is to discover that Glasgow is a historic city and that she has, in her midst, a historic university. Of the universities of the British Isles only Oxford, Cambridge and St Andrews are older than Glasgow, which was founded in the year 1451.

The reasons for this ignorance about our academic antiquity are two. In the first place Oxford (at least till Cowley developed), Cambridge and St Andrews are small places in which the universities occupy a conspicuous position, whereas the University of Glasgow exists in the midst of a population of over a million people which it can in no sense claim to dominate. Again the University has only recently—about eighty-five years ago—come to occupy its present home. The buildings which crown the heights of Gilmorehill are obviously mid-Victorian, and the circumjacent structures which have proliferated round the hill are plainly of modern design (Pl. XIII).

The original home of the University was in the High Street, near to the Cathedral; like all medieval universities the University of Glasgow was a child of the Church. Her real founder was William Turnbull, Bishop of Glasgow from 1447 to 1454, though the Bull of Foundation was obtained from Nicholas V, one of the Renaissance Popes. This explains that the papal privilege was accorded on the representations made by King James II; he was an Honorary Canon of Glasgow and did in fact follow up the papal action by granting, in 1453, a letter under his own Great Seal giving privileges of importance to the institution which he described as 'our most beloved daughter'. Yet though Glasgow may boast a Pope for its founder and a King for its patron, it owes its being to the resolute Bishop, a man well instructed both in the arts and in law and one who had rendered important practical services both to the Pope and to his own King. The motives of the Bishop have been variously estimated. Among them may be reckoned a desire to be not inferior to St Andrews; for the See of Glasgow always felt that it had a longer episcopal history than had St Andrews and that it had been the metropolitan Church of ancient Strathclyde. To St Andrews she granted the primacy, but throughout her history she always claimed second place and gave the impression somehow that the difference between the two was not really so very great. Her boundaries were immense—they extended into Roxburghshire—and the evidence of the papal taxations shows that Glasgow was a very good second indeed.

It would be wrong, however, to assume that Turnbull was actuated solely by a desire to magnify his office. It is safe to believe that like other good churchmen of the day he wished to defend the clergy from the shafts of criticism with the shield of learning; it is certain that from the very first the infant University was nurtured by the see and that a great part of its output of graduates went to serve in the see. The hand of the Bishop is to be seen everywhere; it was he really who made the first constitution of the University. This, as will readily be supposed, approximated to that of St Andrews, where Turnbull himself graduated, and so to the smaller French universities on the model of which St Andrews itself had been fashioned. The Bishop and his successors enjoyed pride of place as Chancellors, but the actual head of the University was to be the Rector, chosen annually by the indirect vote of the four nations—somewhat artificial nations—which represented generally the extent of the four western sees, Glasgow, Galloway, Argyll and the Isles. The teaching was to be done by Regents, each of whom took one year of students through the whole of the course, and before long the Faculty of Arts developed, inside the general framework of the University, an organisation of its own which soon came to be as important as the University itself.

By the terms of the Bull of Foundation the University was authorised to give degrees in every lawful faculty, but, as was also the case in St Andrews, it could for very many years do little more than give instruction in 'philosophy' (as we should say, 'arts'). Some teaching there was (given perhaps not continuously) in theology and in canon law, but this was largely in the hands of the clergy—the house of the Dominicans was very close to the first College. The College itself, built upon a site given by the first Lord Hamilton in 1460 and extended by an adjoining property presented by an alumnus, Thomas of Arthurlie, in 1467, was from the first the College of the Faculty of Arts. Thither, before long, came laymen as well as clerics, including representatives of some of the great families of the west, but the number of the students was always small and the revenue of the College itself microscopic. For the years 1484-85 the bursar had an income of £3, 5s. and expenses of £2, 15s.; what seems to have been a good period, 1488-90, produced the handsome balance of forty-seven shillings and fourpence. The Faculty of Arts, it is true, had finances of its own, but they too were very slender. The fact is that the teachers were paid by being given some living in the hands of the bishops, and that some of the early students held church livings too. If Turnbull had intended to make a permanent foundation by assigning definite parishes to his College, he died before he carried out the design, and the financial position of the University was precarious. The number of students soon tended to decline, and though there was a temporary recovery between 1518 and 1522 when the famous John Major, brought by Archbishop James Beaton, prelected, the decline continued rapidly as the old Church tottered towards its fall.

In the crash of that fall students and revenues alike disappeared; and though, in the scheme of education propounded by the reformers in the Book of Discipline of 1560, Glasgow was to be a University of two Colleges, there was, for some years after the Reformation, hardly a University at all. Small grants of local ecclesiastical revenues from Mary Queen of Scots and from the town of Glasgow barely kept things going, and it is not unfair to suppose that the University would have suffered extinction had it not been for the dynamic energy of Andrew Melville, who returned from Geneva to become Principal in 1574. Equipped with all the apparatus of European scholarship, Melville, with the aid of his nephew James and another able teacher, speedily made

Glasgow a place of the first repute in the academic world and moreover was instrumental in obtaining from the Regent Morton a grant of the revenues of the wealthy parish of Govan. These, though they were at first much diminished by a lease given from the previous holder, saved the University.

THE NOVA ERECTIO, 1577

Along with the grant the University received a new constitution, the *Nova Erectio*. This provided for a College to be governed by a Principal who was to teach theology and the sacred tongues, as well as to preach in Govan on Sundays, while three Regents were to provide the teaching in arts, each being now limited to a certain group of subjects instead of taking one year's entry through the whole curriculum. Arrangements were made for a simple economy and the sustenance of four poor students, and the continuance of the University (as opposed to the College) as a degree-giving institution was guaranteed by the retention of the old offices—the Chancellor, the Rector and the Dean of Faculty.

In 1580 Melville left for St Andrews, where he was soon embroiled in conflict with the Crown, and for the next decades the University suffered from the struggle between the supporters of Presbyterianism and the supporters of Episcopacy. None the less, partly because there was at this time a close connection between Glasgow and the Huguenots, at whose colleges distinguished scholars were taught, good learning flourished. Two famous Principals, Robert Boyd, 1615-22, and John Cameron, 1622-23, came to the College with great reputations which they had acquired in France.

THE BUILDING OF THE COLLEGE

Even good scholars could not keep clear from the ecclesiastical strife produced by the royal policy of imposing an episcopal settlement on the Scottish Church. The Presbyterian resistance bound itself together by the National Covenant, 1638, and the Bishops' Wars of 1639-40 proved to be the prelude of the great Civil Wars which involved all the British Isles and ended in the execution of the King by the English. The Scots, who at once proclaimed Charles II, were soundly beaten by Cromwell, and between 1651 and 1660 Scotland was ruled first by the Commonwealth and then by the Protector. The fortunes of the College reflected the ebb and flow of power. It was at one time Episcopalian, at another orthodox Presbyterian, and in the days of Principal Gillespie, 1653-60, under the control of an extreme Presbyterian who was yet an ally of sectarian Cromwell.

Yet it was in this troublous period that there arose, in place of the ramshackle buildings on the old site, a lovely College in the 'Scots baronial' style (Pl. Ib), with two quadrangles and graced with a great tower. When the scheme was started by the 'Episcopal' Principal Strang, money poured in from every side, and its completion by Gillespie owed much to the support of Cromwell, who, amongst others, produced the £200 sterling which Charles I had promised but forgotten to pay. After the Restoration the royal Arms were placed above the gate of the College, which once more passed under Episcopal control, while scions of the royalist noble families replaced the Presbyterian students (some of them also from great families) who had attended the College in the days when the Covenant had triumphed. During the rule of the restored Stuarts the University suffered from the perpetual religious *malaise*, and its reputation for learning somewhat declined; yet it still retained something of academic good manners, and when in 1689 the Glorious Revolution overthrew 'Prelacy' once more, the change was effected in the College of Glasgow with a conspicuous moderation. The last 'Episcopal' Principal, James Fall, on demitting office, received formal thanks for his services and half a year's salary.

Under the Revolution Settlement the University prospered well, partly because the fierce fires of religious dispute had died down and out of their embers a moderate Presbyterianism arose, and partly because Principal Dunlop, 1690-1701, was a cousin and brother-in-law of William Carstares, Principal of Edinburgh 1703-15, who was William III's man of business in Scotland.

It will be noted that from now on the power of the Principal definitely increases. The old 'Episcopal' Chancellor had disappeared; the Rector tended to become honorary. Both offices remained, and their holders promoted the interest of the College in high quarters, whilst the Rector's Court survived and might be used to bridle the independence of the Professors.

The use of the word 'Professors' serves to illustrate the great changes which took place in University teaching at this time. The three Regents of the *Nova Erectio* had at times been supported by a teacher of Humanity (Latin) during the seventeenth century, because it was realised that new students were not really able to understand the lectures which were given in Latin. A Chair of Mathematics was founded in 1691, a Chair of Greek in 1704, a Chair of Humanity in 1706, while in 1727 the three Regents were assigned to definite subjects—Logic, Moral Philosophy and Natural Philosophy. At the same time the Crown, to which the College was unflinchingly loyal, strengthened the Faculty of Theology by founding new Chairs in Oriental Languages and Ecclesiastical History, and laid the foundation for new faculties by the creation of Chairs in Medicine, Law, and Anatomy. In 1760 the establishment of a Chair of Astronomy raised the number of Professors to thirteen, and they, along with the Principal, collectively known as the 'Faculty', claimed the sole right of handling finance, on the ground that the *Nova Erectio* endowed not the University but the College. The rule of a close corporation of this kind was fraught with danger, but it is fair to say that the teaching was systematised—students normally did Greek in their first year and then the three philosophies in succession—logic, 'moral' and 'natural'.

At the same time some of the Professors gained great eminence by their writings on their own subjects. Simpson rediscovered Greek mathematics; Moor helped the Foulises to produce some wonderful editions of the classics; the lectures upon law given by Millar (the first man probably to use the term 'constitutional history') attracted universal admiration; in the realm of chemistry Cullen and Black made discoveries of far-reaching importance; Francis Hutcheson and Thomas Reid were in the very first rank of philosophers; James Watt, the mathematical instrument-maker to the University, experimented, not without the aid of some of the Professors, upon the Newcomen engine (still to be seen in our Museum) and produced the famous steam-engine of his own. Altogether the University seemed to be in a thriving way; the number of students increased; the emoluments of the Professors, who personally received the fees, increased too, and the value of the property rose with the rapid growth of the city.

U

There was, however, a reverse side of the picture which became more evident as the nineteenth century proceeded. As the scope of University teaching increased, the Crown founded new Chairs; but it did not provide adequate salaries, and very soon quarrels arose as to the status of the new Professors. The members of the old Faculty declined to admit the newcomers into their own body. They received them into the 'Senate' only, and kept the control of their 'College' revenues to themselves. The situation was absurd and invited interference from without, especially as, by this time, 'reform' was in the air. The position of the old universities was subject to attacks levied by burgh reformers, political reformers and ecclesiastical reformers which took issue in a series of Royal Commissions. The first of these, appointed in 1826, was due primarily to the complete breakdown of the finances of Edinburgh, which, as the 'Tounis College', had relied on burghal finance and this collapsed when the city went into bankruptcy. It is plain from the questions asked by the Commissioners that they expected to find great scandals in Glasgow, and it is plain also that no great scandals were unearthed. It is fair to say that the Commissioners made very sensible suggestions for improvement, but, although the Commission was renewed on the accession of William IV, none of its suggestions was carried into effect.

It was only by a Commission appointed in 1858 that radical changes in the government were made. Scotland was then convulsed not only by the movement for Parliamentary reform but by the consequences of the 'Disruption' of 1843 which cleft the Kirk of Scotland in twain, and the Act of 1858, though it was in its final form passed by a Tory Government, represented a general attack on the old conservatism. The old régime had something to say for itself. A teaching body which could command the services of Sandford and Lushington in Greek, Ramsay in Latin, William Thomson (later Lord Kelvin) in Natural Philosophy and Macquorn Rankine in Engineering, to mention no others, was not to be despised, and the contributions of the Glasgow Professors to medicine were considerable.

None the less, the day of the close corporation was done and the general effect of the Act of 1858 was to remove the control of the University from the old 'College' and divide its authority amongst several institutions. A General Council was created to represent the graduates, and the finances of the University were entrusted to the control of a University Court consisting of the Rector (still elected by the students), the Principal, the Dean of Faculties and four Assessors appointed by the Chancellor, Rector, General Council and *Senatus Academicus* respectively. The *Senatus* kept its power in teaching and discipline.

The constitution here invented, whose terms suggest rather a suspicion of Professors, was expanded rather than altered by the Act of Parliament of 1889 under which and under a series of ordinances dependent thereupon the University is still governed. On an enlarged University Court the Senate is now represented by four members, the General Council by four and the City of Glasgow by the Provost and one other; the Assessors of the Chancellor and Rector still keep their places, and of course the Rector himself.

While the constitution of the University has altered to keep pace with recent developments, the University has undergone great changes and a tremendous expansion. In 1870 the Old College in the High Street was abandoned and a new home was found at Gilmorehill. Regret at the destruction of the historic College is tempered by the knowledge that its original beauty had been greatly impaired by hand-to-mouth alterations (necessitated by the demands of 'practical' studies) and that the need for extra space was imperative. None the less, not as regards building alone, the breach with the past was regrettable; the University lost something of its personality.

On the commanding site of Gilmorehill, however, it has developed enormously. There are now some seventy-five Professors as well as many lecturers of great eminence; the number of students, which rose to undesirable dimensions immediately after the last war, is now over 6,000. The great buildings which crown the hill have been expanded by the erection of new laboratories and new departments until the site occupied in 1870, which seemed too big at the time, is now fully occupied, and it has been found necessary to occupy land outside the original precinct. So, still expanding, both physically and in its intellectual content, and still retaining the proud tradition of the past, the University of Glasgow is setting forth upon its second five hundred years.

THE ROYAL COLLEGE OF SCIENCE AND TECHNOLOGY

CHARLES G. WOOD

The Librarian of the Andersonian Library, The Royal College of Science and Technology

THE Royal College of Science and Technology was founded in 1796, and has vigorously sustained throughout the 162 years of its existence a record of development which few institutions can parallel. Its founder, John Anderson, Professor of Natural Philosophy in the University of Glasgow at that period, was a remarkable man; but even so, the success of his idea, a University of Applied Science, owed much to the fortunate conjunction of the man, the time and the place. His personality was typical of the liberal spirit of enquiry which, at the end of the eighteenth century, was ready to recognise Applied Science not only as an academic study but also as an important factor in industrial development. And this new outlook took shape in Glasgow, so soon to be the centre of an industrial expansion which spread throughout the Clyde Valley and extended across Scotland. Against this historical perspective, of more than usual significance, the growth of John Anderson's highly individual idea is recounted.

John Anderson was born in 1726, the son of a minister. He was successively a soldier in the 'Forty-Five', a student at Glasgow University, a private tutor, and then Professor of Natural Philosophy in the University. He occupied the Chair for thirty-nine years, until his death in 1796. During that time he achieved no particular fame by reason of original research; instead, his real impress stemmed from his keen interest in the applications of science and from his clear vision of science as a social influence and an aid to production.

At that time there was no means, either in Scotland or in any other part of the country, by which a craftsman or machine repairer might acquire a rational knowledge of the scientific principles underlying his work. Recognising that something should be done to meet this need, Anderson took the initiative in organising courses of lectures in the University suited to the needs of mechanics and artisans and framed specifically to deal with problems which cropped up in their everyday experience. This was the positive expression of his belief in the utility of science. The lectures, on three days of the week, relied intentionally on experimental method and were designed to meet a situation containing a novel challenge. He wrote a special text-book for this new type of student in which he dealt with such very practical subjects as 'methods of making houses less subject to being burnt'; 'how to save timber and gain strength in erecting machines and building ships'; 'of instruments and machines for architecture and manufacture', and so on. Here indeed was science turned to practical purposes.

It is recorded that he was familiar with the masters and men in the small workshops of the town, and there is evidence that Anderson knew how to appeal to his working-class audience for whom his lectures were devised. On the other hand, his relationship

308

with academic colleagues and the University body was marred by quarrels and indiscretions. The period was not, perhaps, a particularly happy one for University affairs, but some of the quarrels were due to a clash of personalities, and some to his role as an innovator. The garb and bearing of the artisan students who came to his well-attended lectures must have been disturbing to the conservative University authorities.

Anderson had no illusions that the experiment would be continued by anyone in the University after his death, and he decided to do what he could towards establishing another institution where his ideas could be freely developed. Accordingly, he made a will bequeathing the bulk of his property 'to the public for the good of mankind and the improvement of science, in an Institution to be denominated '*Anderson's University*'. The intention of the founder was to provide opportunities for liberal and scientific education suitable for all classes, but he had particularly in mind the scientific education of skilled artisans for whom at that time no provision was made.

At Anderson's death in January 1796, the Trustees charged with fulfilling the instructions of his will found themselves with few assets, but they were determined that the project should succeed. Having managed to raise money, they obtained, in June of the same year, a Charter of Incorporation from the city magistrates, and thus *Anderson's Institution* was constituted.

Through succeeding changes of name, which have been mainly associated with phases in the development and growth of the original foundation, the present College is in direct succession to *Anderson's Institution* of 1796. In 1828, *Anderson's Institution* became *Anderson's University*, a name which was maintained until 1877, when the variant of *Anderson's College* was adopted. Of major significance was the date 1886, when other institutions in Glasgow concerned with technical education were regrouped with Anderson's College to form *The Glasgow and West of Scotland Technical College*. In 1912, H.M. King George V honoured the College by directing that it should be known as *The Royal Technical College, Glasgow*. A scheme of affiliation with the University of Glasgow was approved by His Majesty in Council on the 7th of March 1913; and in 1919, recognition as a University College brought the College within the financial provisions of the University Grants Committee. In 1956 the name was changed to *The Royal College of Science and Technology, Glasgow*. This retrospect to 1796 covers more than a century and a half of growth and development which has stemmed from the imaginative educational plan of the founder.

The inadequacy of funds dictated but a modest beginning to this chronicle, and when, in 1796, a single Chair was established, Dr Thomas Garnett, an Edinburgh graduate, was appointed Professor of Natural Philosophy and Chemistry. The success of his lectures justified the hopes of the Trustees. Garnett resigned in 1799 to become the first Professor of Experimental Philosophy, Mechanics and Chemistry at the Royal Institution in London. He was succeeded by Dr George Birkbeck whose experience and achievements with enthusiastic audiences in Glasgow remained with him when he removed to London in 1804. The name of Birkbeck is well remembered as the founder of the London Mechanics' Institution (formed in 1824 on the same lines as Anderson's Institution), which now, as Birkbeck College, is a constituent College of the University of London. Birkbeck was succeeded in 1804 by Dr Andrew Ure, an able applied scientist. At his resignation in 1830, separate Chairs of Natural Philosophy and Chemistry were established.

Thomas Graham, as first Professor of Chemistry and occupant of the Chair for seven years, gained eminent distinction amongst his European contemporaries by his work on the diffusion of gases and on the constitution of hydrated salts. He established a laboratory for the experimental teaching of chemistry, and for the first time in the United Kingdom systematic laboratory instruction was provided for students. He was appointed Master of the Mint in 1855, and Glasgow honours his memory by the statue in George Square. Sir Thomas Thorpe and Professor William Dittmar were also outstanding successors to the Chair of Chemistry and were responsible, along with others, for the evolution of a strong Chemical School having close connections with the industries of the time.

By the mid-century, other Departments of the College had also prospered. A Chair of Mathematics established in 1825 contributed to the widening horizon of activity. The Medical School of *Anderson's Institution* which had commenced with a Chair of Surgery in 1800 had been strengthened by the creation of additional Chairs, and at the reorganisation in 1886, opportunity was taken to establish the Medical School as a separate institution with its own governing body. *The Anderson College of Medicine*, as it was known, continued in existence until 1947, at which date it was absorbed, in all honour, in the Medical School of Glasgow University.

By the time the effects of the Industrial Revolution had brought a fresh stimulus to scientific and technical enquiry, the College was providing not only a structure of technical education but a purposeful liaison with industry. A notable example is afforded by the establishment of the first Chair of Applied Chemistry in Britain when, in 1870, James Young endowed the Chair of Technical Chemistry. Dr James Young was a conspicuously successful man of his time. A capable pupil of Thomas Graham, he had elected to follow an industrial career. His investigations into the production of oil by the low-temperature distillation of shale had culminated in the promotion of the Scottish shale oil industry; his patent rights earned for him a considerable fortune and the College benefited from his philanthropy.

In 1899, the Agricultural Department of the College, which had been created at the reconstitution of the College in 1886, was amalgamated with the Scottish Dairy Institute, Kilmarnock, and henceforth known as *The West of Scotland Agricultural College*.

The administrative reorganisation of 1886, referred to above, is an instance of the way in which the College matched itself to the needs of the community then experiencing rapid industrial developments. During the remainder of the century the major developments were in the field of engineering. The Chair of Applied Mechanics had already been founded in 1876 and foreshadowed other Chairs in Motive Power (later Mechanical), Mining, Civil, and Electrical Engineering, whilst a Chair of Metallurgy reflected the growing importance of materials of construction in the engineering world.

In the early part of the century and in the period between the world wars the College made substantial progress, and the range and standard of its technological studies steadily advanced. Today, the scope of the Applied Sciences taught in the College is shown by its present organisation. The Departments include Mathematics, Natural Philosophy, Chemistry, Chemical Technology, Metallurgy, Mechanical, Civil and Chemical Engineering, Electrical Engineering, Mining Engineering, Naval Architecture, Pharmacy, Food Science, Textile Technology, Navigation, and Industrial

Administration. The Department of Industrial Administration is one of the most recent developments and most of the courses are conducted in a residential establishment at 'Chesters', Bearsden. Architecture is another subject of study. The College, with the co-operation of the School of Art, maintains the Glasgow School of Architecture. In addition to undergraduate courses in the subjects listed, there is a large volume of post-graduate study and research; in particular, there are numerous special researches conducted for industry and in co-operation with the Research Associations.

After World War II, the number of students in the College greatly increased to the extent of about two-and-a-half times the pre-war total. This commitment caused serious overcrowding in all Departments, and the Governors realised that, if the College was to maintain its position of eminence in applied science and technology, major extensions would be required. At the same time the Government was seriously concerned that the supply of scientists and technologists for service in industry was so inadequate; it decided that there must be a large increase in the facilities for higher technological education. The College was selected as one of the centres for major expansion, and the Governors worked out a long-term plan of development. Priority was given to Engineering, and an extension was recently completed for Mechanical, Civil, Chemical and Mining Engineering at a cost of nearly a million pounds: towards this sum, industry and private individuals generously contributed more than £350,000. The John Street extension, now approaching completion at a cost of about £250,000, represents the latest phase of the programme. It is a multi-storey structure and will be a new Students' Union. Another building of about the same magnitude as the Engineering extension, to be devoted mainly to Chemistry and Chemical Technology, has been planned for the coming quinquennium. Although situated in the centre of the city, the College is fortunate in having land for still further extensions either already in its possession or earmarked for it by the Planning Authority. With its future development thus assured, the College looks forward with confidence to contributing to the scientific and industrial needs of the future in ways as notable as those of the past.

GLASGOW AND THE FINE ARTS

A. McLaren Young

Senior Lecturer in the History of Fine Art, University of Glasgow

During the past two hundred years Glasgow has shown an awareness of the visual arts equalled by few other British cities. Its architects have produced work both distinctive and original, and one of them, Charles Rennie Mackintosh, is a figure of international reputation; its patrons and collectors of art have been enthusiastic and, on occasion, far-sighted; and though its painters have been of comparatively minor importance, the Glasgow School of the late nineteenth century did for a time receive a recognition which was more than local. It is therefore relevant that, in any survey of Glasgow and its achievements, some attention should be given to fine arts and the reasons why, in an industrial centre, they should so unexpectedly flourish.

The growth which accompanied the commercial prosperity of modern Glasgow swept away all but a few traces of the little medieval city with its post-Reformation additions. The buildings that remain—the Cathedral, a house or two, and a few dismembered steeples—are, now that they no longer get in anyone's way, preserved like archaeological specimens. Of these, by far the most important is the Cathedral, the best surviving Scottish example of medieval church architecture. It stands impressively, on the site of earlier foundations, on the bank of the Molendinar Burn. Except for the somewhat abrupt western façade, the result of the amputation of a tower and consistory house, it is remarkably well preserved—and this damage was at the hands, not of the Reformers, but Victorian 'improvers' with ideas of Gothic correctness. Nearly all the building dates from the thirteenth century (the chapter house and spire were added some two hundred years later) and is in the Gothic style known as First Pointed. Among its most distinguished features are the well-proportioned nave and the remarkable lower church which owes its form and spaciousness to the slope of the ground beneath the choir. Modest in comparison with its great English contemporaries such as Salisbury and Lincoln, it is nonetheless much more than a provincial imitation (Pl. II).

Apart from a few pious reconstructions, nothing remains of the next major monument of Glasgow architecture, the Old College of the University. In 1870 it was sold to a railway company who wished to use its site as a goods yard. To judge, however, from the many existing drawings, plans and descriptions, it was a good example of a seventeenth-century Scottish style which owed much to Netherlandish influences and nothing to what was being done in England. It was built between 1632 and 1659, probably from the designs of John Mylne, a follower of William Wallace, the best-known of Scotland's seventeenth-century architects. It lacked the dignified symmetricality of Wallace's masterpiece, George Heriot's Hospital in Edinburgh, but its two quadrangles, with their picturesque stair towers, and the well-proportioned great tower, which rose from one side of the central block, produced a friendlier and more intimate atmosphere (Pl. Ib).

Little else of the architecture of old Glasgow could have compared with the Cathedral and the Old College. Nor is there evidence of anything of more than local importance in the other arts. Painting was late in coming to Scotland; it was well into the eighteenth century before any serious thought was given to it in Glasgow.

The first half of the eighteenth century brought trade and wealth to Glasgow; it also brought a period of intellectual activity whose greatest manifestation was Adam Smith's *Wealth of Nations*. From 1729 to 1746 Francis Hutcheson was Professor of Moral Philosophy in the University. He was an adherent and upholder of the principles of Shaftesbury and his contributions to the theory of aesthetics are of no less importance than his purely ethical writings. His liberal and humanistic outlook sweetened the whole of Scottish thought and helped to bring about a state of affairs where patronage of art, artists and architects was not regarded as an eccentricity. The stimulus he provided long outlived him; it accounts for much of Glasgow's artistic enterprise during the next hundred years.

It was within the University that this new spirit first showed itself. During the period of Hutcheson's professorship, Robert Foulis, later to be joined by his brother Andrew, became College printer. He was a man of little formal education, but moving in academic surroundings he was soon able to meet the Professors as an equal. Beginning, tactfully enough, with the publication of the writings of the Principal, William Leechman, he produced over three decades a series of editions of classical and modern authors, many of which are landmarks in the history of fine printing and book production. In 1752 he decided to extend his activities by the establishment of an academy of fine arts, thus anticipating by more than fifteen years the school of the Royal Academy in London. He persuaded the University, if not to incorporate this venture, at least to tolerate it, and the largest room in the College was given over to its use. Teachers of painting, engraving and sculpture were brought from abroad and pictures of all schools were imported to serve as models of the highest excellence. Foulis's catalogue lists thirty-eight Raphaels, thirty-five Rubenses, twenty-one Titians, eight Rembrandts and among other names Leonardo, Michelangelo, Correggio, Veronese, Tintoretto Dürer, Poussin, Claude, Van Dyck and Bruegel. Alas, virtually none of these attributions was correct. When, after the collapse of the Academy, the collection was sold at Christie's in 1776 it fetched, Raphaels, Rembrandts and all, only £398, 5s. od.

Few of the pupils of the Foulis Academy achieved more than local recognition. David Allan, with exaggeration sometimes called the 'Scottish Hogarth', produced a number of genre pictures; and James Tassie had a wide reputation for his attractive, if repetitious, medallion portraits. One aspect, however, of the Academy's training is worthy of notice. Foulis insisted that his best pupils should travel abroad to make a study of the great Italian masters. With them they carried introductions to Gavin Hamilton, a West of Scotland artist, who was for many years an unofficial leader of the British colony in Rome.

Hamilton, the son of a Lanarkshire laird, had been a student in the University during the time of Francis Hutcheson. Early in the seventeen-forties he set up in Rome as a painter. He made an intensive study of Italian art and Roman antiquities and was soon able to supplement his earnings with a profitable trade in old masters and classical

313

sculpture. His large history pictures foreshadow, in kind if not in performance, the art of the greatest French painter of the late eighteenth century, Jacques-Louis David. Hamilton's works may well, as his contemporary Reynolds was ready to point out, have lacked the poetry of great painting; they did, however, contain a theoretical basis of neo-classicism which other, and greater, artists were to turn to good account.

Another student in the University of Hutcheson's time was the famous anatomist and obstetrician, William Hunter. His association with the arts—his purchase of works by Rembrandt, Rubens and Chardin and his professorship of Anatomy in the newly founded Royal Academy—belongs to London rather than Glasgow; but his bequest of the Hunterian Museum to his old University implies a conscious recognition of the liberal nature of his early education.

If Hunter, in his relationship to Glasgow, was something of the Anglo-Scot, so was William Buchanan, the most active British art dealer of the early nineteenth century. By about 1802, within a few years of graduating in Glasgow, he had established himself in London and, with agents all over Europe, was making a series of spectacular purchases. Among his importations were several of the great masterpieces now in the National Gallery; in Genoa he bought Rubens's *Horrors of War*, in Rome Titian's *Bacchus and Ariadne*, and his agent, G. A. Wallis, following close behind Wellington's Peninsular Army, secured Velazquez's *Rokeby Venus*. In his later life Buchanan returned to Glasgow, where he died in 1864. It is possible (though there are no records to prove it) that he knew and influenced Alexander McLellan, who, more than anyone else, set the pattern of Glasgow as an art-collecting centre.

McLellan was very much the product of a great commercial city, a coach-builder who became Deacon-Convener of the Trades House and a city magistrate. About 1823, at the age of twenty-seven, he started to buy pictures 'illustrative of the characteristics and progress of Italy, Germany, Spain, the Low Countries and France'. He spent enormous sums on his collection which he intended to leave as the nucleus of a municipal art gallery. This wish was not carried out quite as he meant it. When he died in 1854 he was deeply in debt and the Corporation had to buy for £15,000 what under happier circumstances it would have received as a gift. There is no question, however, that the McLellan Collection was a great bargain, containing as it does pictures which must rank with the greatest—to name but two, Giorgione's *Christ and the Adulteress* and *St Victor and a Donor* by the Maître de Moulins. It is perhaps symptomatic of the relationship that existed between the town and its college that McLellan's secondary benefaction, which the circumstances of his death made impossible, was the endowment of a Chair of Fine Art in the University.

Thanks largely to McLellan, Glasgow still possesses the finest municipal art museum in Great Britain. Another early benefactor was the portrait painter, John Graham-Gilbert, whose smaller but choice collection contained the magnificent Rembrandt, *A Man in Armour*. In the late eighteenth and earlier nineteenth centuries Glasgow was in the main more remarkable for its artistic patronage than creative effort. Indeed—and this applies also to architecture where the foregoing generalisation is less true—it tended to be old-fashioned. In the era of Constable, Turner, Raeburn and Lawrence, Glasgow artists worked in an idiom which belonged essentially to the eighteenth century. In the sound, if somewhat unimaginative, portraiture of Graham-Gilbert we find the mood and patterns of the age of Reynolds applied to nineteenth-century

314

material. Other Glasgow painters, who lacked Graham-Gilbert's intellectual qualities, produced little of artistic significance.

As might be expected, the period of Foulis's and McLellan's patronage of painting also encouraged the sister art of architecture. Allan Dreghorn's St Andrew's Parish Church, 1739, freely modelled on St Martin's-in-the-Fields, was the first major example of a succession of notable Georgian and Regency buildings. Later, the Adam brothers, whose father had designed the country house of Pollok which (with its splendid collection of pictures) is now within the city boundary, were among the distinguished outside architects whose services were called on. Hard-headed vandalism has replaced the graceful façade of the Royal Infirmary by a towering block of architectural bad manners, but the Trades House in Glassford Street survives as a reminder of other buildings which have gone. The Greek Revival, presaged by the Adams, was to find worthy exponents among the architects of the next generation. Of these, the deservedly most-recognised is David Hamilton whose Royal Exchange, 1829-30, now the municipal Stirling Library, compares favourably with the best work in this style done in other parts of the country. Up to 1850 or so, decent, classically proportioned streets and terraces—the best preserved is Blythswood Square—were being built in what had become the centre of the city; if surpassed in scale and importance by those of London, Edinburgh and Dublin, they nonetheless show an awareness of architectural values far in advance of any other industrial town in the Kingdom.

The immediately pre-Victorian architecture followed, in general, a classical style which had been developed elsewhere; in the later nineteenth century much of it was to acquire an almost perverse individuality. It is not so much that there was any revolutionary change—that was to come later—as that there was not. While in England the Gothic Revival, heralded by Pugin, developed by Butterfield and made fashionable by Gilbert Scott, was winning its triumphal successes, the great majority of the Glasgow architectural profession remained resolutely conservative. In 1866 Alexander Thomson, whose views had earned for him the nickname of 'Greek Thomson', read a paper to his fellow-architects on Gilbert Scott's design for the new University building, one of the few really big neo-Gothic incursions. He was, needless to say, against it; and his opinions may reasonably be taken as representing those of his audience. As a statement of the dogma of those most violently opposed to the Gothic Revival, Thomson's paper is an important document in the history of taste. It was not only the revived style that he attacked; the original he considered nearly as objectionable—an architecture of ignorance with forms derived from its builders' lack of skill. Of the proposed University building, he concluded, 'I think the less the professors say about artistic merits the better; and certainly the local architects have nothing to fear from this invasion from the South.'

Gilbert Scott's new University was built more or less as designed, but, apart from churches, the Southern invasion was kept reasonably at bay. There are in Glasgow few public buildings in the neo-Gothic style, and hardly any terraces or private houses. For this resistance Thomson's own example may well have been a deciding factor. His architecture was not just a kind of Georgian, freakish in a mid-Victorian context, but a logical and at times somewhat eclectic development of it. Moray Place, Strathbungo, 1862, and Great Western Terrace, 1870, combine all the solidity and certainty of their age with a grace and sense of proportion which was almost everywhere being discarded.

Both are respectably Greek, but, despite his nickname, Thomson could break the rules when it suited him; in St Vincent Street Church, 1859, there are Egyptian elements, and Caledonia Road Church, 1856-57, shows an awareness of contemporary German ideas. All, however, add up to something highly individual which is now beginning to receive the attention of students of architecture.

The face of Glasgow as it appears today is largely the creation of the later nineteenth century. Park Circus and its surroundings, the massive terraces by the Botanic Gardens and further west, and most of the big banks and commercial houses belong to this period. None of his contemporaries and immediate successors quite possessed Thomson's originality. But there were among them men of talent and good sense such as Charles Wilson, James Sellars, T. L. Watson and John Burnet and his son Sir John J. Burnet. For the most part they remained faithful to the classical style. When in 1905 the most prolific of them, the younger Burnet, received the commission for the King Edward VII Galleries of the British Museum he had, unlike his English rivals who were returning to classicism, the inheritance of a century's development behind him. To this tradition also belonged the townscapes of Muirhead Bone, the distinguished draughtsman and engraver of a generation later.

The well-to-do inhabitants of the large houses and terraces of Victorian Glasgow had developed a taste in painting different from that of any other British city. Glasgow, which had looked askance at the Gothic Revival, never took whole-heartedly to the Pre-Raphaelites, the favourites of most of the English provinces; nor did it accept unquestioningly the successes of the Royal Academy. With perhaps the same perversity, which at an earlier period had shown itself in a kind of independent conservatism, it supported the unofficial artist rather than currently admired masters of the Academies and Salons. Whistler, an enemy of the artistic establishment, was characteristically the only London artist to be held in general regard. (It is significant that the first Whistler in any public gallery was bought by the Corporation of Glasgow; and the University gave honorary degrees to Whistler and Rodin, not Millais and Alma-Tadema). This is not to say that Glasgow in any sense favoured the *avant-garde*; in the 'eighties and 'nineties that would have meant an appreciation of the French Impressionists. What the local art collectors liked was painting of an advanced but less revolutionary kind. Corot and the Barbizon group, Boudin, Monticelli, Fantin-Latour, Mauve and the Maris brothers—these were the artists whose works were brought to Glasgow in ever-increasing numbers.

The man most responsible for this state of affairs was Alexander Reid. The son of a partner in a firm of carvers and gilders who, during the 'eighties, had branched into picture dealing, Reid was sent to Paris in 1886 to form his taste and learn the business of the art trade. There he met and became the friend of the van Gogh brothers. When, however, Vincent suggested that he should set up as a dealer in Impressionism, Reid's Scottish canniness compelled him to reject the idea. He preferred to work on safer ground, and on his return to Glasgow his persuasive powers were employed on the sale of works by artists whose reputations were already established. Other dealers, notably Craibe Angus, soon followed his example, and so great was their success that there are pictures by Monticelli, who never came to Britain, now categorised as belonging to his 'Glasgow period'.

At much the same time as Reid's activity, and in many ways complementary to it, there came into being the movement known as the Glasgow School of Painting. Dissatisfied with what they considered the pedestrian competence of Victorian painting, several young artists came together with the aim of producing something more original. Their chief influences were from the art which was delighting the Glasgow connoisseurs, Whistler, the Barbizon painters, Bastien-Lepage, the Hague School and the increasingly fashionable Japanese print. W. Y. Macgregor, somewhat older than the others, made his studio the meeting-place for the group. To it came E. A. Walton, George Henry, E. A. Hornel, the sculptor Pittendrigh Macgillivray and a number of others. The 'Glasgow boys', as they were to be called, soon received reinforcements. Joseph Crawhall, a Northumberland squire, joined them on their painting expeditions to Cockburnspath and Brig o' Turk; Arthur Melville from Edinburgh associated himself with them; the amateur John Quinton Pringle worked unobtrusively on the fringes of their circle; and the slightly younger D. Y. Cameron was, till his death in 1945, their last active survivor. They achieved immediate success, not only at home but on the Continent and in America. From exhibitions in Paris, Munich, Antwerp and Pittsburg they carried away gold, silver and bronze medals; and they constituted a large contingent in the International Society of Sculptors, Painters and Gravers, which, under Whistler's presidency, held its first exhibition in 1899.

It must be admitted that, in spite of its felicities and its triumphs, something very much went wrong with the Glasgow School. George Henry, perhaps the most talented of them all, raised hopes that were not to be realised; his *Galloway Landscape* of 1889, which in many ways paralleled what Gauguin was doing at Pont-Aven, is an exception among the trite decorative graces that constitute the bulk of his work. The things that have lasted best are the less ambitious contributions of the group—Pringle's modest landscapes and Crawhall's water-colours of animals and hunting scenes rather than the grander efforts of Hornel and Macgregor.

Charles Rennie Mackintosh, the greatest and most influential of all Glasgow architects, grew up at a time when the Glasgow School was at its most coherent; his first student success, however, was for the design of a highly classical public hall, 1890, which, appropriately, won for him an Alexander Thomson Travelling Scholarship. He might therefore be described as the product of all the local artistic movements of the late nineteenth century; that he was very much more than this is accounted for by the unusual originality of his genius. Today Mackintosh is regarded as one of the pioneers of modern architecture, an international figure who, despite the shortness of his career, can be associated with Frank Lloyd Wright and Walter Gropius.

The conservatism of the late Victorian Glasgow architects did not prevent them from making use of new methods of construction. Thomson had designed a cast-iron warehouse employing his material functionally and not, like Gilbert Scott, as a camouflaged substitute for something more expensive. Mackintosh went further. In 1894 he wrote, 'We must clothe modern ideas with modern dress—adorn our designs with living fancy.' For him the conventional trappings of the Greek and Gothic Revivals had no relevance in an age neither Greek nor Gothic. He was, however, willing to learn from the past. The vertical emphasis of so much of his work has much in common with the vernacular architecture which he called, without derision, Scotch Baronial. Mackintosh had made a thorough study of this, 'the only style we can claim as being in whole or part our own'. This concern for tradition ensured that his architecture was something more than merely functional; and he gave to it, scarcely less than to the furniture and craftwork which he also designed, an embellishment evolved from such diverse sources as Celtic and Egyptian decoration. The note-books of his tours of Scotland, England and Italy are full of observations and sketches, many of which he was to use for his own purposes. But his was the curiosity of the artist, not the pasticheur; what he took from the past he translated into the language of his own time.

Two or three private houses, a few tea-rooms (none of which remains intact), two council schools, one church and, above all, the building of the Glasgow School of Art—these were Mackintosh's principal works. His style, and more so the style of his closest associates, was not to everyone's taste or comprehension. But there were a few loyal patrons, among them William Davidson, W. W. Blackie and Miss Catherine Cranston; and in the Art Nouveau exhibitions of Vienna and Turin his new 'Glasgow style' became a term of international currency. Unlike the decent arts and crafts of William Morris and his circle, with which it has something in common, his decoration is often extravagant. But any impartial examination of his architecture, the towering Library wing of the School of Art for example, shows that his reputation, now higher than in his lifetime, is well deserved.

Mackintosh did not die till 1928, but his later years were largely unproductive. In our own day Glasgow has produced no artist who can be set beside him. In architecture, where its greatest creative contributions have been made, there has been sound if unadventurous work; in painting, Leslie Hunter and others still active have not disgraced the past. But the best traditions have been upheld by the patrons of art. The late Sir William Burrell spent a lifetime in acquiring an encyclopaedic collection which ranges from prehistoric pottery to modern painting; and others, despite the discouragements of modern taxation, have bought Impressionist and contemporary pictures of good quality. The enthusiasm of the past is perhaps less evident; but in a state of affairs where art is not ignored there is always hope for artists.

RESEARCH INSTITUTIONS IN THE WEST OF SCOTLAND

compiled by

CATHERINE B. SMITH

Research Assistant, Department of Geography, University of Glasgow

THE research institutions listed below are all public organisations supported, partially or wholly, by Government grants. While many of them are concerned with the problems, both agricultural and industrial, peculiar to the West of Scotland, several, particularly the industrial institutions, serve the whole of Scotland. Many of these also co-operate closely with the Universities and Technical Colleges and private, commercial and industrial concerns—and, in fact, often apply lines of research initiated by these bodies. The inclusion of one private concern—that of South Cathkin Farm—merits mention as being the only farm of its type in the West of Scotland to be run by a commercial concern.

The Scottish Marine Biological Association has its headquarters at the Marine Station, Millport, Isle of Cumbrae. The Association originated as a small committee, formed in 1894, to take over the use of Sir John Murray's famous floating laboratory, *The Ark*, as the *The Millport Marine Station*, pending the erection of a permanent building. The first buildings on the present site at Keppel, about a mile from Millport, were opened in May 1897, and in subsequent years they were to be considerably extended, but the present name was not adopted until 1914, when the Association was incorporated as a non-profit-making Company.

Early history and achievements are set out in the British Association, General Handbook, Glasgow Meeting, 1928. In 1950 the Association, which had hitherto carried on its work solely at Millport, assumed the additional responsibility of the Oceanographic Laboratory, Edinburgh, with a staff to investigate the biology and distribution of plankton, using sampling equipment towed by commercial vessels and weather ships. This work, initiated by Professor Sir Alister Hardy, had been formerly carried on at the Department of Zoology and Oceanography, University College, Hull. One of the aims of this research is to apply knowledge of the plankton to the study of fluctuations in commercial fisheries. At Millport, work at sea is undertaken by two research vessels (M.F.V. *Calanus*, length 75 feet, crew of six; M.V. *Mizpah*, crew of three) which are equipped for hydrographic work and for the collection of specimens and material for research and training purposes. In addition, facilities are offered to visiting research workers from home and overseas, whether as independent investigators or under the auspices of a university or other institution. Classes of instruction in marine biology are held for students from universities, colleges and schools; and facilities are also available to parties accompanied by their teachers. A classroom and lecture hall, built and equipped in 1956, by means of a grant from the Carnegie Trust for Scottish Universities, is used for this purpose. The Robertson Museum and an Aquarium, enlarged and reconstructed by the aid of grants from the above Trust, are open to the public.

Under the guidance of an independent Council of elected members, representing Scottish Universities, marine fishery laboratories and other institutions, the Association's work is carried out by a qualified research staff—fifteen at Millport, twelve at Edinburgh, with a total staff of sixty-one—under the supervision of a Director at the Marine Station and an Officer-in-Charge at the Edinburgh Laboratory. Both laboratories are well equipped to prosecute marine research on a comprehensive scale. Membership of the Association is open to any private person or public body wishing to further the work, but in recent years maintenance of the Laboratory and of the research programme has increasingly depended upon Government grants from the Development Fund. Enquiries concerning research facilities, membership, publications, etc., should be addressed to Dr C. H. Mortimer, D.Sc., F.R.S.E., Director and Secretary,

Marine Station, Millport, Isle of Cumbrae, Scotland. Correspondence concerning the Edinburgh Laboratory should be addressed to Mr R. S. Glover, B.Sc., Officer-in-Charge, Oceanographic Laboratory, 78 Craighall Road, Edinburgh, 5.

The West of Scotland Agricultural College was formally constituted in 1899 (one year before its sister College in Edinburgh, five years before its counterpart in Aberdeen but 109 years after Edinburgh University had instituted its Chair of Agriculture) from two main roots. The first of these was advisory work among cheese-making farmers in South-West Scotland dating from about 1860, and the second was certain systematic classes in agriculture carried on in Glasgow at technical college level, from 1886. The College is an independent body, under a representative Board of Governors, which nevertheless has nowadays to look to the Treasury for at least 75 per cent of its income. Grant-aid is channelled through the Department of Agriculture for Scotland (neither U.G.C. nor A.R.C. being directly involved). The College's physical resources include a main centre for teaching and administration in Blythswood Square (which was acquired in 1900), County offices throughout its allotted territory and the 660-acre estate at Auchincruive, near Ayr. The latter is mainly devoted to farming (400 acres), poultry husbandry (40 acres), horticulture (20 acres) and estate forestry (114 acres). There are also residential facilities for students.

The work of the College lies in the three fields of teaching, advisory work and research—an integration which, in Great Britain, is peculiar to Scottish Agricultural Colleges and similar to the system operating in the United States. In the sphere of teaching, studies are carried on at Diploma and Short Course levels apart from the provision, by formal agreement, of the subject of Agriculture within the Course for the Degree of B.Sc. in Agriculture in the University of Glasgow. (The Principal of the College is at present the Professor of Agriculture in the University.) Diplomas are granted in Agriculture, Dairying, Poultry Husbandry and Horticulture, and in the case of Dairying and Poultry Husbandry the facilities serve all Scotland. Short courses, varying in duration from a few days to six months, are provided in a variety of applied agricultural and related subjects. In addition, the College gives assistance to Local Education Authorities in providing systematic instruction at local evening classes in Agriculture, Agricultural Engineering and Horticulture.

The advisory functions are performed by providing a free service of technical advice to farmers, market-gardeners, landowners, bee-keepers, veterinary surgeons, agricultural architects and milk technologists in the counties of Ayr, Argyll, Bute, Clackmannan, Dumfries, Dunbarton, Kirkcudbright, Lanark, Renfrew, Stirling, Wigtown and West Perth. The work is carried out by advisory officers stationed in the field and is supported by scientific and economic specialists in Glasgow and at Auchincruive and by applied research carried on at these centres. The territory covered includes some 15,000 farms.

While not a 'research institute', the College undertakes research (on an applied basis) designed particularly to deal with the problems of farmers, market-gardeners, poultry farmers, crofters, milk depots and dairy factories, bee-keepers and veterinary surgeons. This, in turn, leads to an appreciable amount of more fundamental work. Projects are at present in progress (some ninety-four) in the fields of animal husbandry, bacteriology, botany, soil chemistry, crop husbandry, economics, grassland husbandry, horticulture, milk utilisation, plant pathology, poultry husbandry, veterinary medicine and zoology. The results of the work are published partly by the College and partly as papers in the appropriate scientific journals.

The College's work is organised on the basis of nineteen departments, Agriculture, Bacteriology, Botany, Chemistry, Dairying, Milk Utilisation, Agricultural Engineering, Economics, Zoology, Bee-keeping, Horticulture, Poultry Husbandry, Crop, Animal and Grass Husbandry, Farm Buildings, Veterinary Science, Plant Pathology and Extension Services. There is a large agricultural Library. The professional staff of the College numbers about 150, of whom fifty are engaged in county extension work.

The Scottish Horticultural Research Institute runs a West of Scotland Unit at Auchincruive, in Ayrshire. It is concerned mainly with strawberry breeding, work which was started about twenty-five to thirty years ago as a joint effort by the Department of Agriculture for Scotland and the West of Scotland Agricultural College. This strawberry breeding unit was incorporated into the Scottish Horticultural Research Institute when the latter was established in 1951, the Institute's headquarters and main research staff and facilities being at Mylnefield, near Invergowrie, under the control of a Director.

The breeding work at Auchincruive is aimed at developing varieties of strawberry resistant to a soil-borne fungus—*Phytophthora fragariae*, which is very common in the West of Scotland, several parts of England and of the United States, and elsewhere. More recently it has been shown that we now have a number of physiologic races of the fungus, some of which attack some varieties, but not others, so that the problem of developing resistant varieties is becoming increasingly complex and increasingly difficult. Up till recently, the pool of resistant genes has been very small, but a concerted effort is now under way to find new and unrelated gene sources of resistance, based mainly on seed of wild strawberries from Chile. The Unit maintains a number of glasshouses and laboratory facilities where the work is carried out. Field work is done in a field which is heavily infected with all the known races of the fungus, so that the varieties or selections which will grow in this particular field are almost certain to be successful in any other condition where the races of the fungus, found in Great Britain, occur. There is, however, some indication that the races of the fungus which are prevalent in other parts of the world are not the same as we have here. New selections developed at Auchincruive are sent to Mylnefield at an early stage for individual assessment by the staff there. The three new varieties introduced to commerce, namely, Climax, Talisman and Redgauntlet, have all proved highly successful and commercially acceptable.

The Hannah Dairy Research Institute at Kirkhill, three miles inland from the town of Ayr, was founded in 1928. The previous year, the Secretary of State for Scotland, acting on recommendations made by the Development Commissioners, had appointed a Committee of Management to establish an institute for dairy research in Scotland and a year later the Hannah Institute was founded. The original buildings were opened in 1931 on a site which became available when the late J. M. Hannah, Esq., of Girvan Mains, Ayrshire, presented the estate of Auchincruive to the Nation for purposes of agricultural education and research. By the terms of that gift the larger part of the estate was set aside for the West of Scotland Agricultural College, and the farm of Kirkhill, which now extends to about 135 acres, was reserved for the research institute.

By establishing the Institute near the town of Ayr on the south-west coast of Scotland the founders ensured that it would have the advantage of being reasonably near to both the University of Glasgow, where it would have contact with those engaged on fundamental research in pure science, biology and medicine, and to the West of Scotland Agricultural College, where it would be able to keep in touch with those engaged in the teaching and practice of agriculture. At the same time it was situated also in the heart of one of the best-known dairy districts in the world, a district that is the original home of the well-known Ayrshire breed of dairy cattle.

The Institute is largely financed by a Government grant received mainly through the Department of Agriculture for Scotland. Its control however, is in the hands of the Council of the Institute—its governing body—which is nominated by the University of Glasgow, the West of Scotland Agricultural College and the Secretary of State for Scotland. The Chairman of the Council is the Principal of the University. The research programme is arrived at in agreement with the Agricultural Research Council and the Department of Agriculture for Scotland. In all, the staff at the Institute includes some thirty graduates and about thirty technical assistants, with a Director in charge.

The original buildings were greatly extended in 1951. They contain laboratories for research work in chemistry, biochemistry, physiology, nutrition, pathology and bacteriology. Some of the main subjects of research are as follows: problems associated with intensive production of feeding-stuffs for dairy stock and with self-sufficiency in feeding-stuffs on the dairy farm; problems having a direct bearing on the animals themselves: the relative value of different feeding-stuffs for the rearing of young stock and for milk production: environmental physiology of cattle: factors affecting milk yield and persistency in lactation: rumen digestion: nutrition of the very young calf: energy metabolism of ruminants and the efficiency of utilisation of feeding-stuffs by cattle: the prevention and control of mastitis; factors affecting the composition and bacteriological quality of milk and milk products; problems associated with the keeping quality and stability of milk and of milk products such as condensed and dried milks.

South Cathkin Farm, Rutherglen, was purchased by The British Oil & Cake Mills, Ltd, as an experimental and demonstration farm in 1945. For the first few years it was run mainly as a commercial dairy farm. It is 250 acres in extent, of which 200 are useful arable land, the balance being woodland and scrub. It is an entirely livestock farm; any cropping done is purely for feeding livestock. Cropping generally amounts to some 30-35 acres, with the remainder of the farm under temporary grass, for the production of hay and silage.

Since 1954 the farm has been used mainly for *experimental* purposes; to demonstrate what other research workers have discovered, and to show farmers the results. In that year The British Oil & Cake Mills, who own the farm, started Progeny Testing with Ayrshire bulls in conjunction with the Scottish Milk Marketing Board and the Ayrshire Cattle Herd Book Society. Since that date three Progeny Tests, involving four Ayrshire bulls in each Test, have been carried out and at the moment the fourth one is running. The Test involves taking in at South Cathkin Farm thirteen daughters from each of four bulls chosen by the Scottish Milk Marketing Board for testing. These fifty-two heifers arrive at the farm some six weeks before calving and are on the farm for an average of 270 days of their first lactation. Annual Reports are published by The British Oil & Cake Mills, Ltd, and are available to all interested parties.

In addition to the Ayrshire Bull Progeny Testing, considerable work has been done in recent years on the oral administration of hormones to fattening cattle. This work is done purely by The British Oil & Cake Mills and, again, all the information gained is available to anyone interested.

Finally, over this same period there has been considerable investigational work done on the early weaning of calves. During this particular period, the Fourth Progeny Test is running, further experimental work with rations containing hormones is being done and further investigational work on early weaning of calves.

The Mechanical Engineering Research Laboratory is one of the fourteen research stations of the Department of Scientific and Industrial Research. It was set up in 1947 to carry out an extensive programme of fundamental and applied research complementary to, and in liaison with, that carried out in industry. The laboratory is on a site of about seventy acres at East Kilbride, the new town some eight miles south-east of Glasgow city centre. Part of the work is carried out in temporary accommodation at Thorntonhall, about four miles from East Kilbride.

The Laboratory is organised in seven divisions—Properties of Materials; Mechanics of Solids; Fluid Mechanics; Lubrication and Wear (at Thorntonhall); Mechanisms and Metrology; Plasticity (partly at Thorntonhall); Heat Transfer and Thermodynamic Tables. Work on the properties of materials ranges from fundamental research on the physics of solids to testing engineering components which have failed in service. The programme includes the examination of metals under various types and conditions of loading, such as tension, torsion, impact, combined stress, fatigue and creep. Materials are tested at temperatures between $-200°$ C and $+900°$ C, but most of the work is at room temperature. In the Mechanics of Solids Division, new and improved methods are being developed to determine stress distributions in structures and components so that they can be designed more exactly. Problems ranging from low-speed aerodynamics and hydraulics to complex fluid flow are dealt with in the Fluid Mechanics Division. The facilities available in the Hydraulic Machinery building include open and closed circuits for research on pumps, turbines and associated equipment such as valves, pipes and ducts; calibrating lines for flow-measuring instruments; an oil-and-special fluids laboratory; and an aerodynamics laboratory. At Thorntonhall, the Division dealing with Lubrication and Wear conducts research into the fundamental mechanical, physical and chemical reactions which occur when two loaded surfaces slide over one another. Work covers experimental and theoretical studies of hydrodynamic lubrication, fundamental investigations into the nature of structures produced in the deformation of surfaces and modes of lubrication and occurrence of wear in machine parts. In the Mechanisms and Metrology Division, the characteristics and functioning of mechanisms and mechanical devices used in engineering practice are being investigated. Precise methods and equipment are being developed to measure the elements of mechanisms and machines. At present, particular attention is being paid to the measurement and performance of gears. The elimination and suppression of noise are also the concern of this Division.

In the past, commercial formation and cutting processes were developed largely by trial and error methods based on earlier production experience. The Plasticity Division, which is located partly at Thorntonhall, is making a detailed theoretical and experimental study of the plastic deformation of metals to provide a fuller understanding of the laws governing the flow of metals in commercial processes such as forging, extrusion and machining. Lastly, the Heat Transfer laboratory contains facilities for measuring thermal conductivities, investigating under controlled conditions such processes as convection and radiation, and testing full-scale and semi-scale heat exchange equipment. Tables of physical properties of technically useful substances are being prepared, comprising thermodynamic properties, viscosity and thermal conductivity.

At the time when it was decided to establish a new Research organisation of the Department of

Scientific and Industrial Research—the Mechanical Engineering Research Laboratory—in the new town of East Kilbride, it was also decided to set up in the same district small branch laboratories or out-stations of the existing Building, Road and Fuel Research Stations. These are accommodated temporarily at Thorntonhall until permanent quarters are provided at East Kilbride.

The Building Research Station (Scottish Laboratory) is such an out-station of the D.S.I.R. Building Research Station, the headquarters of which are at Garston, Watford, Hertfordshire. The Scottish Laboratory was established in 1949 to strengthen the liaison between this Station and the building industry in Scotland and the North of England and it has at present a total staff of fourteen.

The functions of the Laboratory include both advisory and experimental work. In the former, it provides a close link with the Government departments and other authorities responsible for building in Scotland, especially the Departments of Agriculture and Health and the Scottish Education Department. The technical problems of the construction and maintenance of dwellings and schools figure largely in this work. There is similar collaboration with those concerned with the development of Scottish resources of building materials, particularly the Scottish Council (Development and Industry), the Ministry of Works and individual manufacturers. For this reason, much of the experimental research at the Laboratory relates to the study of materials such as concrete, stone and bricks. Special attention is paid to the effects of climate on building materials and structures and, for this purpose, an exposure site and meteorological station have been established.

Numerous field experiments and observations are also undertaken, of which the following examples may be mentioned—site studies of Scottish building procedure and craft techniques; comparison of the efficiency of electrical and other space-heating systems in various buildings; a study of driving rain conditions on high buildings and measurement of temperature rise in mass concrete. The work thus supplements in many directions the researches in progress at the main Station at Garston, with which close contact is maintained throughout. An enquiry service is available and publicity is given to the results of the Station's work through the medium of lectures, films and exhibitions throughout Scotland.

The Road Research Laboratory, at Thorntonhall, is the Scottish Branch of the D.S.I.R. Road Research Laboratory, whose Head Office, Materials and Construction Division and Colonial Section are located at Harmondsworth, Middlesex, and the Traffic and Safety Division at Langley, Bucks. It was set up in 1949 in order to make the results of work carried out at the main Laboratories more readily available to road engineers in Scotland and to investigate any road problems peculiar to Scotland, which may arise from, for example, its topography, climate or subsoil conditions.

In its advisory capacity, the Laboratory meets requests for advice from road engineers and others responsible for building and maintaining roads and for making them safe and convenient for road users. It also brings to the notice of road engineers the results of research which are of special value in Scotland. In its experimental work, the Laboratory carries out research into the development of cheap forms of road construction for use in the Highland areas, such as the use of morainic gravels in cement-stabilised road bases and bituminous surfacings. Study is also being made of the engineering properties of peat and the problems of constructing roads over compressible subsoils and of traffic conditions in the principal Scottish cities and on the single-track roads of the Highlands. The Scottish Laboratory serves many different interests—the Scottish Home Department (Roads Division); the police and local highway authorities, their engineers and road safety officers; civil engineering consultants and contractors; and the quarrying industry and producers of coated macadam and asphaltic surfacing materials.

The Scottish Branch of the Fuel Research Station was projected in the early post-war years and opened at Thorntonhall in the summer of 1949. The main Fuel Research Station of the Department of Scientific and Industrial Research is at Greenwich. Consideration had originally been given to having the Branch at or near Falkirk, but the planning of a combined D.S.I.R. site at Thorntonhall made it possible for Building Research, Road Research, Fuel Research and part of the Mechanical Engineering Research Laboratory to enjoy common facilities within one site. The primary object of the Branch was the testing of solid fuel-fired domestic appliances such as stoves, fires and cookers, and in its location at Thorntonhall, it enjoyed the advantages of being near the light castings industry of Falkirk, Bonnybridge and Glasgow.

This is a testing rather than research laboratory and investigations are mainly concerned with the techniques of testing and analysis. The need for appliance testing had become evident as a result of the extent of the post-war housing programme and the Government undertook to see that there would be available to Local Authorities appliances which reached certain prescribed standards of construction and performance and which would be able to burn coke or other smokeless fuels as well as coal. It was the task of the Fuel Research Station to carry out the test programme, and work has been carried on since then at the main station at Greenwich and at the Branch at Thorntonhall. In general, appliances of English manufacture are tested at Greenwich and Scottish ones at Thorntonhall, but this is a matter of convenience, not of principle, and there is no hard and fast rule.

The Branch has also a chemistry and fuel analysis laboratory. Among other duties, this laboratory analyses samples of fuel obtained in the course of their regular surveys by the National Industrial Fuel Efficiency Service, and also peat samples collected by the Peat Survey of the Department of Agriculture for Scotland. Another sphere of activity at Thorntonhall is the measurement and investigation of atmospheric pollution, work which has grown steadily since the Branch started. Advantage has been taken of the proximity of the new town of East Kilbride to measure changing pollution as an industrial and urban area develops in rural surroundings. With the coming of the Clean Air Act there has been increasing interest in pollution measurement on the part of Local Authorities and advice is being given on the operation and siting of instruments for this purpose.

The British Cast Iron Research Association opened, in 1950, its Scottish laboratories at Blantyre, some nine miles south-east of Glasgow. Previously they had been located at Falkirk, where they were first inaugurated in 1925. These Falkirk laboratories had originally been formed in 1918 by the National Light Castings Association—now known as the British Ironfounders Association—under the name of the Foundry Technical Institute, for the purpose of furthering the study of cast iron and the application of control methods in foundry practice, and to provide technical training for foundry apprentices. The educational activities of the Institute were later transferred to the Education Authority and the laboratories were taken over by the British Cast Iron Research Association to provide services for its Scottish ironfounding members. By 1948, however, the increase in membership and the increasing demands on the Scottish laboratories necessitated a move to larger premises and in 1950 the present laboratories at Blantyre were officially opened by Lord Bilsland. The headquarters of the Association are at Alvechurch, Birmingham.

In common with all research associations, the British Cast Iron Research Association derives its income from the industry it serves and from H.M. Government through the Department of Scientific and Industrial Research. Since its industrial income is provided nowadays through the agency of the Joint Iron Council by means of a levy on foundry pig-iron, membership of the British Cast Iron Research Association is freely available to every iron foundry in the United Kingdom, the only formality being that each foundry must complete an application form and agree to conform to the Articles of Association.

The Association seeks to promote the scientific and technical advancement of the ironfounding industry by: conducting independent and co-operative research; giving practical advice on individual foundry problems; and centralising and co-ordinating information. It also endeavours to assist in more efficient production and increased productivity of iron castings; to help the industry to meet competition from other materials and processes and to enlarge the range of applications of cast and malleable cast iron; and to assist the promotion of foundry education at all levels.

Broadly speaking, it functions through four main divisions—the Research Department, the Development Department, the Intelligence Department and the Operational Research Team. The first, the Research Department, carries out an extensive programme of both long- and short-term research. The Development Department, whose principal function is to give practical advice and help to foundries on individual problems, includes the Foundry Atmosphere Section, concerned with the control of dust and fume inside and outside the foundry. The responsibility of the Intelligence Department is to look after all aspects of documentation and published information, including library services and to edit the Association's own publications. It is also responsible for the organisation of technical conferences. Lastly, the function of the Operational Research Team is to advise on means of improving production efficiency and productivity with reference to operations and equipment, quality of product, output, costs and correct deployment of manpower.

Many of these services are available on a reduced scale at the Blantyre laboratories, particularly those which come within the purview of the Development Department. A close liaison is maintained between Blantyre and the Association's headquarters at Alvechurch. The Scottish laboratories are, moreover, equipped to make all the routine tests and examinations required by the foundry: analytical, metallo-

324

graphic and mechanical. It has machine-shop facilities and can also undertake the usual physical tests of moulding materials and the analysis and calorific value determination of fuels.

The British Shipbuilding Research Association runs a Ship Structure Research Establishment at Glengarnock in Ayrshire. The establishment is operated for the British Shipbuilding Research Association by the staff of Lloyd's Register of Shipping. This co-operation between the Association and Classification Society is regarded as of particular importance as it is through modifications to the Rules of the Society that advances in knowledge of ships' structures receive their practical application.

The full-scale testing of ships' structural members was instigated in 1938 by the Research Committee of the Institute of Welding, subsequently known as the Welding Research Council. The primary object was to compare the relative merits of riveted and welded stiffening, in view of the extended application of welding in shipbuilding which was then taking place. Choice of site for the establishment was largely determined by the obvious advantages to be gained from having a constructional company—Colville's, Ltd—near at hand where all specimens could be fabricated. With the transfer of the research activities of the Institute of Welding to the British Welding Research Association towards the end of the war, this work also was carried on by that Association for a short time, but it was transferred to the British Shipbuilding Research Association in 1945, since when the scope of the work has been extended to include a wide variety of types of rolled and built-up sections and different forms of end-connexions.

When this work was taken over by the British Shipbuilding Research Association, the equipment consisted of a single testing machine capable of applying lateral loads only to the specimens, most of which were stiffened areas of plating. The total load could reach an equivalent of 180 tons distributed over a twenty-four-foot span. At the beginning of 1952, a new machine was put into operation which broadens the field of investigation considerably and enables tests to be carried out on full-scale components of ships, such as sections of deck and shell which are stressed in tension or compression by the bending of the main hull girder in addition to the locally applied lateral loads. Loads of up to 300 tons laterally and 600 tons axially can be applied.

The British Shipbuilding Research Association Committee, concerned with the programme of work, includes representatives of the shipbuilding industry, Lloyd's Register of Shipping, the Marine Division of the Ministry of Transport and the Admiralty. In planning the programme of tests, the immediate needs of the industry, together with possible new developments likely to lead to structural economies, are kept constantly in mind.

The Admiralty Hydro-Ballistic Research Establishment is situated in lonely country near the head of Glen Fruin, a mile or two from Garelochhead. It was originally set up by the Air Ministry but was taken over by the Admiralty in 1947 and is now controlled by the Director of Physical Research, through the Admiralty Research Laboratory. This Establishment carries out fundamental investigations into the problems arising on the entry of high-speed weapons into water—problems which are of great importance as long as there is a Service interest in attacking, from the air, vessels on or beneath the surface. In general, the work is carried out on fairly large-scale models of the weapons under investigation, though full-sized missiles have been launched on occasion. For this work two glass-sided tanks are available, of which the larger is 150 feet long, 40 feet deep and 30 feet wide. Both are equipped with launching gear which can produce the highest-scale speeds at a wide range of angles of entry. These tanks are fully instrumented, to enable the behaviour of the weapon, at entry and shortly thereafter, to be recorded and photographed. A special filtration plant is operated to produce the high degree of clarity necessary in the water in the tanks. In this connection it is noteworthy that, through the 150-foot length of the larger tank, the smallest print normally visible at that distance can be read with ease.

The co-operation of Directors and Officers-in-Charge of the various organisations, in supplying information, is gratefully acknowledged.